name the 4 nasal sinuses

Synovial tissue = excretes fluid

Contrast - KV
Density - MAS

all nerves outside brain & spinal cord = peripheral

Cancer
Papilloma; epithelium
Adenoma; glands
Lipoma; connective tissue - adipose
Osteoma; bones
Myoma; muscle
Angioma; sml blood or lymph vessels
Nevus; moles - birthmarks

Carcinoma; originating in epithelium (spread by lymph)
Sarcoma; connective tissue. (Spread by blood)

Serous membrane;
  1. pleurae - lungs
  2. pericardium - heart
  3. peritoneum - Abd

epithelium which covers serous membrane = mesothelium.

Parietal = wall
Visceral = means organs (viscera)

A HANDBOOK OF

ANATOMY

AND

PHYSIOLOGY

FOR

STUDENT X-RAY TECHNICIANS

COMPILED BY:

M. MALLETT, M.D.

RADIOLOGIST, EDMONTON, ALBERTA, CANADA

FOURTH EDITION

This Handbook is again respectfully dedicated to an older generation of Radiological Technicians, deceased and living, who by individual incentive and perseverance, and without the help of training programs, lectures, and adequate text books have helped to develop the art of Radiography, and who through the formation of American and Canadian Societies of Radiological Technicians have advanced radiographers to a professional status.

ACKNOWLEDGMENTS

The author wishes to thank Mrs. G. V. Cashman, Mr. Ross Smith, R. T., and Mr. Robert Taylor for the preparation of the drawings included in this book.

THE AUTHOR OF THIS HANDBOOK HAS NO FINANCIAL INTEREST IN THE PUBLICATION OF THE TEXT, AND WILL RECEIVE NO ROYALTY FROM ITS SALE.

Published in the United States by

THE AMERICAN SOCIETY OF RADIOLOGIC TECHNOLOGISTS

645 North Michigan Avenue, Chicago, Illinois 60611

Copyright 1962 by the Canadian Society of Radiological Technicians (Alberta Division) in Canada, Great Britain, and the United States of America, and printed in the United States by permission of the copyright owners.

PREFACE TO THE FOURTH EDITION OF THE HANDBOOK

The reception which was accorded to the first edition of this Handbook indicated that it had served the purpose for which it was published. The object was to supply information in Anatomy and Physiology of the human body to meet the specific needs of student x-ray technicians.

In the second edition an attempt was made to correct errors in composition and spelling. The entire text was rewritten. The separation between paragraphs was improved to facilitate quick reference. Some new sections were added, and others expanded.

In the third edition the size of type was enlarged to facilitate the use of the reference with more ease.

In the fourth edition an attempt has been made to correct errors in the composition and spelling. The text has not been rewritten.

For the sake of brevity and clarity the definition method has again been utilized when possible. The Handbook has been divided into chapters to correspond to the various systems of the body. The skeletal system has been further divided with a chapter for each of the main subdivisions. Each chapter has been further separated into many sections which have been numbered. Each section deals with one subject only. It is to be hoped that by reference to the table of contents or index the student may readily find, with no waste of time, the section desired. Further, instructors may rapidly assign by number certain sections for study or review.

While the text is primarily a reference book for student technicians, it has been considered advisable to add some further sections to supply information that may be of value to the fully trained x-ray technician. These sections should not be included in any course of studies. The teacher may indicate by number those sections that are outside of the prescribed course, and exclude these from requirements for examination.

The skeletal system has again been covered in detail because so much radiography is concerned with bones and joints. The information on the other systems of the body has been limited to a brief description of the various organs concerned, together with their location and function.

The illustrations present the radiographic appearance rather than the post-mortem. An attempt has been made to draw and label those parts of structures which are frequently called for on requisitions to the department; also those that are used as landmarks in radiography. The number has been increased as it is felt that a visual image is very valuable. When possible, the drawings have been placed opposite the written descriptions for easy reference.

Some of the commonly used pathological terms have been included and defined in each chapter. This information is necessary as many requests to the x-ray department specifically ask for films to demonstrate or exclude some pathological condition. A knowledge of these terms will therefore help in interpreting requisitions correctly. The key to most of these terms may be found in the ending: appendicitis - itis, an inflammation (of the appendix); or osteoma - oma, a tumor (of bone).

It is hoped that medical stenographers may find this book useful in their work. It is felt that a medical stenographer, receptionist, or accountant may derive considerable help from attending a course in Anatomy and Physiology with student radiographic technicians.

The American Society of Radiologic Technologists deeply appreciates the generosity and cooperation of Dr. M. Mallett in granting us permission to make this fourth edition readily available to students and technicians in the United States.

208 bones in body

- TABLE OF CONTENTS -

	INTRODUCTION TO THE HANDBOOK, 6	XIII	THE BLOOD, 104
I	ANATOMICAL NAMES - NOMENCLATURE, 9	XIV	THE CIRCULATORY SYSTEM, 107
II	CELLS - TISSUES - ORGANS - SYSTEMS, 16	XV	THE RESPIRATORY SYSTEM, 121
III	TISSUE DENSITY IN RADIOGRAPHY, 22	XVI	THE DIGESTIVE SYSTEM, 125
IV	THE SKIN - NAILS - HAIR, 25	XVII	THE URINARY SYSTEM, 139
V	BONES: CLASSIFICATION, STRUCTURE, DEVELOPMENT, 29	XVIII	THE FEMALE REPRODUCTIVE SYSTEM, 142
VI	THE SHOULDER GIRDLE AND UPPER EXTREMITY, 34	XIX	THE MALE REPRODUCTIVE SYSTEM, 146
		XX	THE ENDOCRINE OR DUCTLESS GLANDS, 149
VII	THE PELVIS AND LOWER EXTREMITY, 45	XXI	THE NERVOUS SYSTEM, 154
VIII	THE VERTEBRAL COLUMN, 60	XXII	THE SPECIAL SENSE ORGANS, 165
IX	THE THORAX, 67	XXIII	CONTENTS OF THE BODY CAVITIES, 172
X	THE BONES AND JOINTS OF THE SKULL, 72	XXIV	INSTRUCTIONS FOR WRITING EXAMINATIONS, 175
XI	JOINTS - ARTICULATIONS, 92	XXV	REVIEW OF ANATOMY AND PHYSIOLOGY, 177
XII	THE MUSCULAR SYSTEM, 94		

LIST OF ILLUSTRATIONS - "F." -

The illustrations, diagrams, and drawings are indicated by the letter F. (figure), and are numbered consecutively, e.g., F. 1, F. 2, F. 3, etc.; while the explanatory sections are indicated by the letter S. (section) and are also numbered consecutively, e.g., S. 1, S. 2, S. 3, etc.

F. 1 Anatomical position and median line, 10	F. 18 Structure of a long bone, 30	F. 39 Bones of lower extremity, 45
F. 2 Lateral position, 10	F. 19 Growing bone, 31	F. 40 Bones of pelvis, 47
F. 3 Supine position, 10	F. 20 Epiphyses upper extremity, 33	F. 41 Innominate bone, 47
F. 4 Prone position, 10	F. 21 Epiphyses of tibia, fibula, 33	F. 42 Femur, frontal, lateral, 49
F. 5 Cell structure, 15	F. 22 Epiphyses of hand, 33	F. 43 Tibia and fibula, 49
F. 6 Cell division, 15	F. 23 Epiphyses of hips, 33	F. 44 Knee joint, 49
F. 7 Types of tissues, 15		F. 45 Ankle joint, medial, 49
F. 8 Divisions of the body, 18	F. 24 Bones of upper extremity, 34	F. 46 Ankle joint, frontal, 49
F. 9 Ovary and ovum, 20	F. 25 Scapula and clavicle, 36	F. 47 Foot, dorsal view, 52
F. 10 Development of embryo, 20	F. 26 Humerus, frontal view, 38	F. 48 Foot, lateral view, 52
	F. 27 Radius and ulna, 38	F. 49 Foot, medial view, 52
F. 11 Radiographic centering, 23	F. 28 Elbow joint from behind, 38	F. 50 Tibia, fibula, lower ends, 53
F. 12 Magnification of image, 23	F. 29 Elbow joint, lateral view, 38	F. 51 Sacroiliac, hip joints, 55
	F. 30 Shoulder joint, 38	F. 52 Knee joint, frontal, lateral, 55
	F. 31 Bones of the hand, 39	F. 53 Ankle joint, frontal, lateral, 55
F. 13 Skin - diagram, 25	F. 32 Wrist, lateral view, 39	F. 54 Joints of forefoot, 55
F. 14 Epidermis, magnified, 25	F. 33 Ulna, upper end, 40	
F. 15 Finger nail, 26	F. 34 Ulna, lower end, 40	F. 55 Vertebral column, lateral, 58
F. 16 Hair, sebaceous, sweat gland, 27	F. 35 Shoulder joint, 41	F. 56 Atlas, 59
	F. 36 Elbow, frontal, lateral, 41	F. 57 Axis, 59
	F. 37 Joints of wrist, finger, 41	F. 58 Typical cervical vertebra, 59
F. 17 Parts of a long bone, 30	F. 38 Middle finger, thumb, 44	F. 59 Thoracic, dorsal vertebra, 59
		F. 60 Lumbar vertebra, 59

LIST OF ILLUSTRATIONS - continued -

F. 61 Dorsal vertebrae, lateral, 59
F. 62 Sacrum, superior surface, 61
F. 63 Sacrum, frontal view, 61
F. 64 Sacrum, lateral view, 61
F. 65 Coccyx, 61
F. 66 Joints upper cervical, 62
F. 67 Interarticular joints, 62
F. 68 Intervertebral joints, 62
F. 69 Lumbo-sacral joint, 62

F. 70 Sternum, ribs, cartilages, 66
F. 71 Sternum, frontal view, 66
F. 72 Sternum, lateral view, 66
F. 73 Ribs, 66

F. 74 Skull - vertex, 70
F. 75 Skull - frontal, 70
F. 76 Skull - occipital view, 70
F. 77 Skull - lateral view, 70
F. 78 Skull - basal view, 70
F. 79 Skull - lateral, DETAILED, 71
F. 80 Skull - frontal, DETAILED, 71
F. 81 Frontal bone, 74
F. 82 Parietal bone, 74
F. 83 Occipital bone, 74
F. 84 Left facial bones, 74
F. 85 Temporal bone, 77
F. 86 Temporal, inner surface, 77
F. 87 Sphenoid bone, 77
F. 88 Ethmoid bone, 77
F. 89 Maxilla, 79
F. 90 Zygomatic bone, 79
F. 91 Palate, hard or bony, 79
F. 92 Palatine bone, 79
F. 93 Nasal septum, 79
F. 94 Lateral wall nasal fossa, 79
F. 95 Mandible, lateral view, 80
F. 96 Mandible, medial view, 80
F. 97 Teeth, upper and lower, 80
F. 98 Hyoid bone, 80
F. 99 Structure of a tooth, 82
F. 100 Fontanels, 88
F. 101 Landmarks of skull, 88
F. 102 Venous sinuses of skull, 88
F. 103 Venous sinuses from above, 88
F. 104 Paranasal sinuses, 88

F. 105 Immovable joints, skull, 91
F. 106 Slightly movable, symphysis, 91
F. 107 Movable joint, example, 91
F. 108 Intervertebral joints, 91
F. 109 Interarticular joints, 91
F. 110 Ball & socket joint, hip, 91
F. 111 Hinge joint, knee, 91
F. 112 Metacarpo-phalangeal jt., 91

F. 113 Skeletal muscle fibers, 94
F. 114 Levers at joints, 94
F. 115 Tendons of back of hand, 94
F. 116 Bursae at knee, 94

F. 117 Muscles of body, frontal, 98
F. 118 Muscles of body, posterior, 98
F. 119 Sternomastoid, pectoralis, major, deltoid muscles, 99
F. 120 Intercostal muscles, 99
F. 121 Diaphragm, from below, 99
F. 122 Diaphragm, frontal view, 99
F. 123 Sacrospinalis muscle, 101
F. 124 Psoas major muscles, 101
F. 125 Deltoid, biceps, brachialis, 101
F. 126 Quadriceps muscle, 101

F. 127 Blood cells, 106

F. 128 Heart & great vessels, 108
F. 129 Radiographic appearance, 108
F. 130 Heart, chambers, 108
F. 131 Heart, frontal view, 108
F. 132 Heart, cross section, 108
F. 133 Portal vein & branches, 108
F. 134 Heart, openings, septa, 110
F. 135 Pulmonary arteries, veins, 110
F. 136 Aorta and venae cavae, 110
F. 137 Lymphatic duct, 113
F. 138 Pulmonary, systemic, portal circulations, 113
F. 139 Patent foramen ovale, 116
F. 140 Patent ductus arteriosus, 116
F. 141 Thrombus, 116
F. 142 Embolus, 116
F. 143 Larger systemic arteries, 118
F. 144 Larger systemic veins, 118

F. 145 Respiratory passages, 120
F. 146 Trachea and lungs, 120
F. 147 Respiratory bronchiole, 120
F. 148 The larger bronchi, 120
F. 149 Pulmonary blood vessels, 120
F. 150 The larynx, 121
F. 151 Quadrants, regions, abdomen, 125

F. 152 Parts digestive tract, 127
F. 153 Peritoneum, lateral view, 127
F. 154 Peritoneum, cross section, 127
F. 155 Nose, mouth, pharynx, 129
F. 156 Contents of abdomen, 129
F. 157 Salivary glands, 129
F. 158 The esophagus, 129
F. 159 The stomach, 129
F. 160 Layers of small bowel, 131

F. 161 Small bowel, longitudinal, 131
F. 162 The colon, 131
F. 163 Cecum and appendix, 131
F. 164 The liver, 131
F. 165 The pancreas, 131
F. 166 Gall bladder, bile ducts, 132
F. 167 Cholangiogram - T tube, 135

F. 168 Urinary tract, 138
F. 169 Kidney in urogram, 138
F. 170 Female bladder, urethra, 138
F. 171 Male bladder, urethra, 138
F. 172 Kidney, vertical section, 138
F. 173 Renal corpuscle, 138

F. 174 Female reproductive organs, frontal view, 143
F. 175 Female pelvis, lateral, 143
F. 176 Section of ovary, 143
F. 177 The female breast, 144
F. 178 Testis, lateral view, 146
F. 179 Male reproductive organs, lateral view, 146
F. 180 Descent of testis, 147

F. 181 Pituitary gland, 150
F. 182 Thyroid gland, 150
F. 183 Parathyroid glands, 150
F. 184 Thymus gland, 150

F. 185 Brain, lateral view, 155
F. 186 Brain, sagittal section, 155
F. 187 Brain, from above, 155
F. 188 Brain, basal view, 155
F. 189 Ventricles & meninges, 157
F. 190 Spinal cord, 157
F. 191 Spinal cord, section, 157
F. 192 Cross section cord, 157
F. 193 Lateral ventricle, 163
F. 194 Lateral ventricles, frontal view, 163
F. 195 Myelogram, 163

F. 196 Eyeball, from above, 165
F. 197 Eyeball, lateral view, 165
F. 198 Pupil, frontal view, 165
F. 199 Optic nerves, crossing, 167
F. 200 Muscles of eyeball, 167
F. 201 Tear glands and ducts, 167
F. 202 Ear, external, middle, inner, 170
F. 203 Optic and olfactory nerves at base of brain, 170
F. 204 Nerves of smell, 170
F. 205 Taste buds of tongue, 170
F. 206 Organs in anterior chest and abdomen, 173
F. 207 Blank outlines, 174

TABLES OF CONTENTS - Listed under sections -

INTRODUCTION

Definitions, 6
Objectives, 6
Student's use of Handbook, 6
Suggestions for Instructors, 7
Reference books, 8
Teaching material, 8

CHAPTER I. ANATOMICAL NAMES - NOMENCLATURE

S. 1 Origin of anatomical names and plural forms, 9
S. 2 Prefixes and suffixes, 9
S. 3 Descriptive anatomical terms, 11
S. 4 Terms used to describe opposites, 12
S. 5 Terms describing movement, 13
S. 6 Spelling, 13
S. 7 List of terms used in Chapter I., 13

CHAPTER II. CELLS, TISSUES, ORGANS, SYSTEMS

S. 8 Cells, 16
S. 9 Structure of cells, 16
S. 10 Cell division, 16
S. 11 Tissues, 17
S. 12 Organs, 17
S. 13 Systems, 19
S. 14 Divisions of the body, 19
S. 15 Body cavities, 19
S. 16 Embryology, 19
S. 17 Congenital or developmental anomalies, 20

CHAPTER III. TISSUE DENSITY

S. 18 Density, 22
S. 19 Tissue and organ density, 22
S. 20 Tissue density and radiography, 22
S. 21 Body thickness and radiography, 22
S. 22 Contrast media, 23
S. 23 Surface markings and bony prominences, 24
S. 24 Applications of anatomy to radiography, 24

CHAPTER IV. THE SKIN AND APPENDAGES

S. 25 The layers of the skin, 25
S. 26 The structure of the skin, 25
S. 27 Subcutaneous tissue, 26
S. 28 The nails, 26
S. 29 The hair, 26
S. 30 Sebaceous glands, 27
S. 31 Sweat or sudoriferous glands, 27
S. 32 Functions of the skin, 27
S. 33 Radiological applications, 27
S. 34 Terms used in Chapter IV., 28

CHAPTER V. BONES: CLASSIFICATION: STRUCTURE: DEVELOPMENT

S. 35 Terms for bony prominences, depressions, 29
S. 36 Functions of bones, 30
S. 37 Classification of bones, 30
S. 38 Structure of bones, 31
S. 39 Development of bones, 32
S. 40 Congenital anomalies, 32
S. 41 Radiographic appearance of growing bones, 32
S. 42 Terms used in Chapter V., 33

CHAPTER VI. THE SHOULDER GIRDLE AND UPPER EXTREMITY

S. 43 List of bones, 34
S. 44 List of joints, 34
S. 45 Important parts and prominences, 35
S. 46 Detailed study of bones, 35
S. 47 Joints - detailed study, 41
S. 48 Anomalies of upper extremities, 42
S. 49 Landmarks, bony prominences, upper extremity, 42
S. 50 Application to radiography, 42
S. 51 Terms used in Chapter VI., 43

CHAPTER VII. THE PELVIS AND LOWER EXTREMITY

S. 52 List of bones, 45
S. 53 Important parts and prominences, 45
S. 54 Detailed study of bones of pelvis, 46
S. 55 Detailed study of bones lower extremity, 50
S. 56 Detailed study of joints, 53
S. 57 Congenital anomalies, 54
S. 58 Landmarks and bony prominences, 54
S. 59 Application to radiography, 55
S. 60 Terms used in Chapter VII., 56

CHAPTER VIII. THE VERTEBRAL COLUMN

S. 61 List of bones - vertebral column, 60
S. 62 List of joints, 60
S. 63 Parts of a vertebra, special vertebrae, 60
S. 64 Detailed study of vertebrae, 60
S. 65 Joints of vertebral column, 63
S. 66 Congenital anomalies, 63
S. 67 Landmarks, bony prominences, 63
S. 68 Application to radiography, 64
S. 69 Terms used in Chapter VIII., 64

CHAPTER IX. THE THORAX

S. 70 Bones of the thorax, 67
S. 71 List of joints, 67
S. 72 Important details, bones of thorax, 67
S. 73 Detailed study bones of thorax, 67
S. 74 Detailed study of joints, 68
S. 75 Congenital anomalies, 68
S. 76 Landmarks, prominences, bones of thorax, 69
S. 77 Application to radiography, 69
S. 78 Terms used in Chapter IX., 69

CHAPTER X. THE BONES AND JOINTS OF THE SKULL

S. 79 List of bones of cranium, 72
S. 80 Parts, prominences, bones of skull, 72
S. 81 Detailed study, bones of skull, 73
S. 82 The teeth, 81
S. 83 Parts, structure of a tooth, 82
S. 84 The cranial fossae, 82
S. 85 The basal foramina, 82
S. 86 Intracranial grooves, 83
S. 87 Joints of the skull, 83
S. 88 Development of cranial bones, 83
S. 89 Congenital anomalies, 83
S. 90 Summary of structures and landmarks, 84
S. 91 Application to radiography, 89
S. 92 Terms used in Chapter X., 89

CHAPTER XI. JOINTS - ARTICULATIONS

S. 93 Classification of joints, 92
S. 94 Application to radiography, 93

CHAPTER XII. THE MUSCULAR SYSTEM

S. 95   Classification of muscles, 94
S. 96   Muscles important to the technician, 94
S. 97   Skeletal muscles defined, 94
S. 98   Structure of skeletal muscles, 95
S. 99   Functions of muscles, 95
S. 100 Muscle spasm, 96
S. 101 Paralysis of muscles, 96
S. 102 Distribution of muscles, 96
S. 103 Muscle grouping by location, 97
S. 104 Detailed study of muscles, 100
S. 105 Terms used in Chapter XII., 103

CHAPTER XIII. THE BLOOD

S. 106 Constituents of the blood, 104
S. 107 The blood plasma, 104
S. 108 The blood cells, 105
S. 109 Some pathological terms, 106
S. 110 Terms used in Chapter XIII., 106

CHAPTER XIV. THE CIRCULATORY SYSTEM

S. 111 Contents of the chest or thorax, 107
S. 112 Parts of the circulatory system, 107
S. 113 Detailed study of circulatory system, 107
S. 114 Structure of a blood vessel, 112
S. 115 Functions of the circulatory system, 112
S. 116 Circulatory system in the fetus, 114
S. 117 Anomalies of heart and blood vessels, 114
S. 118 Some pathological conditions, 115
S. 119 Application to radiography, 115
S. 120 Terms used in Chapter XIV., 116
S. 121 Larger systemic arteries, 116
S. 122 The pulse, 117
S. 123 Pressure points to arrest hemorrhage, 117
S. 124 Larger systemic veins, 117
S. 125 The portal system of veins, 119

CHAPTER XV. THE RESPIRATORY SYSTEM

S. 126 Parts of the respiratory system, 121
S. 127 Detailed study of respiratory passages, 121
S. 128 Detailed study of the lungs, 122
S. 129 Physiology of respiration, 123
S. 130 Some pathological terms defined, 123
S. 131 Application to radiography, 124
S. 132 Terms used in Chapter XV., 124

CHAPTER XVI. THE DIGESTIVE SYSTEM

S. 133 Divisions of the abdomen, 125
S. 134 Structure of walls of digestive tract, 126
S. 135 Definitions of some terms used, 126
S. 136 Development of digestive system, 126
S. 137 Parts of the digestive system, 126
S. 138 Detailed study of digestive system, 127
S. 139 Functions of the digestive system, 132
S. 140 Some congenital anomalies, 133
S. 141 Some pathological conditions, 134
S. 142 Terms used to describe operations, 134
S. 143 Application to radiography, 134
S. 144 Terms used in Chapter XVI., 136

CHAPTER XVII. THE URINARY SYSTEM

S. 145 Parts of the urinary system, 139
S. 146 Detailed study of urinary system, 139
S. 147 Physiology of the kidney, 140
S. 148 Functions of the kidney, 140
S. 149 Some congenital anomalies, 140
S. 150 Some pathological conditions, 140
S. 151 Application to radiography, 140
S. 152 Terms used in Chapter XVII., 141

CHAPTER XVIII. THE FEMALE REPRODUCTIVE SYSTEM

S. 153 Parts of female reproductive system, 142
S. 154 Detailed study, 142
S. 155 Some pathological terms, 144
S. 156 Some operative procedures, 145
S. 157 Application to radiography, 145
S. 158 List of terms used in Chapter XVIII., 145

CHAPTER XIX. THE MALE REPRODUCTIVE SYSTEM

S. 159 Parts of the male reproductive system, 146
S. 160 Pathological conditions and operations, 147
S. 161 Descent of the testes, 148
S. 162 List of terms used in Chapter XIX., 148

CHAPTER XX. THE ENDOCRINE OR DUCTLESS GLANDS

S. 163 List of ductless glands, 149
S. 164 Detailed study of the ductless glands, 149
S. 165 Some pathological conditions, 152
S. 166 Application to radiography, 152
S. 167 Terms used in Chapter XX., 153

CHAPTER XXI. THE NERVOUS SYSTEM

S. 168 Parts of the nervous system, 154
S. 169 Definitions of some terms, 154
S. 170 Detailed study - central nervous system, 155
S. 171 The meninges or coverings, 158
S. 172 Ventricles or cavities of brain, 158
S. 173 The autonomic nervous system, 159
S. 174 Some anomalies of the nervous system, 160
S. 175 Some pathological conditions, 160
S. 176 Summary for technicians, 161
S. 177 Blood supply to the brain, 162
S. 178 Application to radiography, 162
S. 179 Terms used in Chapter XXI., 163

CHAPTER XXII. THE SPECIAL SENSE ORGANS

S. 180 Parts of the eyeball, 165
S. 181 Detailed study of the eyeball, 165
S. 182 Application to radiography, 166
S. 183 Application to fluoroscopy, 167
S. 184 The ear - important parts, 169
S. 185 Study of the parts of the ear, 169
S. 186 The end organs of smell, 171
S. 187 The end organs of taste, 171

CHAPTER XXIII. CONTENTS OF THE BODY CAVITIES

S. 188 Contents of the various cavities listed, 172

CHAPTER XXIV. ANSWERING OF EXAMINATION PAPERS

S. 189 List of instructions, 175

CHAPTER XXV. REVIEW OF ANATOMY AND PHYSIOLOGY

S. 190 to S. 210, 177

INTRODUCTION TO THE HANDBOOK

DEFINITIONS.

ANATOMY is the study of the structure and form of an organism, and human anatomy deals with the structure and form of the various parts of the human body.

PHYSIOLOGY is the study of the function or behavior of the various organs and structures of the body.

PATHOLOGY is the study of disease, its causes and its effects, upon the body, structures and organs.

POSITIONING is a term used in radiography to denote the correct placing of the part to be filmed. This includes the centering or placing of the part to be filmed in the center of a holder containing an x-ray film and the positioning of the x-ray tube so that the central ray will pass through this part.

OBJECTIVES.

Having completed a course in Anatomy and Physiology, the student technician should have acquired sufficient knowledge to accomplish:
(a) the correct interpretation of requisitions sent to the x-ray department;
(b) the correct interpretation of instructions regarding positioning as outlined in standard books on x-ray technic;
(c) the accurate positioning of a patient for any examination, using landmarks studied in anatomy;
(d) the recognition of the various structures in the processed film in order to decide if what was requested has been obtained;
(e) an interest in the work in the department rather than indifference;
(f) the positioning of a patient for therapy so that the central ray will pass through the part to be treated, as well as an interest in accomplishing the desired effect from the therapy.

THE STUDENT'S USE OF THE HANDBOOK.

The arrangement of the material contained in this Handbook has been designed with a definite purpose in mind. The aim has been to make it as easy as possible for the student to acquire the necessary knowledge for the practical work in the department as well as for examination purposes.

Most chapters begin with a list of the structures or organs to be discussed. Following this the important parts of each structure are listed. Finally each structure is studied in detail. The student may therefore first get a bird's eye view of the subject matter. After completing the study, the student may use the lists to check his knowledge.

Each student must acquire a good working knowledge of the parts of the skeletal system, and familiarity with the names of the various parts of each bone and joint. Many of these are used as landmarks for positioning in radiography. These are often asked for, specifically, on the requisition; and the technician must know their location in order to obtain what is required, e.g., the tibial tuberosity. The student should also learn the names of the organs and structures of the other body systems. Their position in the body is important in order to be able to center the patient properly. It is necessary to have some knowledge of the normal function and behavior of these organs. Some radiographic procedures depend upon the function of the part. For instance, the normal behavior of the gall bladder is important in outlining the diet, the time of taking the gall bladder dye, and the time when films should be taken for a gall bladder examination.

Anatomy is largely a memory course. There are a great many names to be remembered. Many of these are as new to the student as the words of some foreign language. There are about five hundred terms relating to the skeletal system alone. These names should be pronounced over and over. Their spellings should be learned. Some students seem to learn best by writing the names repeatedly. In any event the student must make a practice of using them in conversation in the department when possible.

The student who takes time to learn the prefixes and suffixes listed will find this a great help in learning the new terms. In addition, an attempt should be made to break down words and analyze them, e.g., peri-ostitis, supra-condylar, etc.

The method of study must vary with the individual. Some students learn best by studying alone, while others prefer to study in a group using the question or quiz method. It is extremely doubtful if satisfactory results can be obtained in a room in which there is a radio or television set in operation, or other people engaging in conversation. Some students who cannot get privacy have solved this problem by purchasing ear plugs, and inserting them into the ears during the study period.

In studying anatomy there is a distinct advantage in obtaining a visual picture of the part studied. Therefore, anatomical diagrams, drawings, charts, photographs, x-ray films, and especially the bones of the skeleton, should be looked at repeatedly.

The student must follow some orderly system in studying any part, using suitable headings. For example, in studying the heart, the various structures should be mastered in some such order as: the coverings, the chambers, the partitions, the openings, and the valves. A further step would be to learn the coverings from the outside to the inside or vice versa. The parts of a vertebra must be learned in orderly fashion: all the parts of the body, then the parts making up the arch, and finally all the processes. In describing a bone, one should begin at one end and proceed systematically towards the other end. In naming the glands of internal secretion, one should begin at the head end and name each in order to the tail end. The student must acquire this habit in the beginning. Things should not be mixed up helter skelter. Jumping back and forth from one thing to another will result in the leaving out of some parts.

The student should not attempt to memorize word for word lists of the parts of any structure as they appear in the text, but should rather form in mind a picture of the structure or organ. In this way the various parts can be pictured and more readily recalled. No student knows a subject until that student can close the textbook and describe the object to some second person, or aloud to himself.

Anatomy is a most fascinating subject. Most students are anxious to learn something about their bodies. It is fortunate that each student has at hand in his or her body an example of the parts studied. In studying this subject one should refer to these parts. For example, when studying the bones and joints of the upper limb, the student should refer to his own upper extremity. One should attempt to form a mental picture through the skin, fat, muscles, etc., of the bones and joints and their relative positions.

Unfortunately there is no short cut to the study of Anatomy. Medical students, student nurses, and student technicians must spend hours in acquiring the necessary information. There is also such a large volume of material to be studied that it must be mastered in small doses. After each lecture, and as soon as possible, the subject matter must be absorbed. If left to be crammed at the end of the course, such a mass of material will have accumulated that the student will be hopelessly bogged down and lost.

SOME SUGGESTIONS FOR INSTRUCTORS.

Elimination of unnecessary detail. Teachers of Anatomy must keep constantly in mind the objectives of the course as outlined above. The greatest error will be a tendency to teach more than the student can absorb or use in his or her work. Anatomy is so intensely interesting that an instructor who knows his subject well will be tempted to include many interesting details. This may confuse the student and obscure the main points. Any student will remember what he or she uses in everyday procedure.

Introduction of new material. As each part of the body is studied, specimens, pictures, charts or models should be presented. To the student a visual picture is worth much more than verbal or written descriptions.

Review of subject matter. No lecture should be considered completed until a review of the material covered is given in the lecture following. Student technicians are actually senior high school graduates, not university undergraduates. A review will serve to impress the subject as well as to correct false impressions. A question and answer period may be used.

New anatomical names and descriptive terms. Because these words are entirely new, they must be pronounced and explained carefully and even written on a blackboard. Having been introduced, they must be used over and over in subsequent lectures in order that they may become familiar to the student, e.g., medial; anterior; proximal; superior; cephalic; etc.

Radiographs in teaching. No study should be considered complete until radiographs demonstrating the part have been exhibited and explained.

Landmarks and surface markings. As technicians are concerned with the positioning of patients for x-ray examinations, landmarks denoting the position of organs, as well as bony prominences, must be pointed out and emphasized.

Review by graduate technician in the department. This should be the responsibility of the chief technician in every x-ray department, and must be done regularly. It would seem unwise for this senior to present material that has not yet been covered in the lectures. The student may get misconceptions that will be difficult to correct.

If arrangements can be made to do so, each lecture in Anatomy might be followed immediately by a further demonstration of x-ray films, etc. If the lecturer is too busy, this task might be given to a graduate technician, who should be required to sit in on the lecture.

The class might be broken up into small groups for the further study of bones and joints. A senior technician should sit with each group and go over again each point covered in the lecture. (In a large class the students cannot possibly see the bone structures on a skeleton at the front of the room.) If this cannot be done, slides of the bones and joints might be used so that the structures discussed are enlarged and visible to students.

With a very large class it would be advisable for the lecturer to have slides made of all structures to use instead of the skeleton.

Combining classes of student technicians and nurses for Anatomy lectures. The practice of having student technicians take the same classes as student nurses should be condemned. While the student nurse needs a general knowledge of anatomy, the student technician must have a more detailed one. As radiography of bones and joints plays such an important part in the technician's work, about one-half of the lectures should be devoted to the skeletal system. Anatomy courses for nurses do not demand this instruction.

Study methods. The instructor might profitably spend a lecture period suggesting methods of study. Students should be repeatedly urged to approach any subject with some system in mind. As each topic is discussed, the arrangement of the list of parts preceding the study in each chapter should be pointed out. The orderly manner in which the detailed study is carried out should be emphasized.

Some time should be spent in instructing the students how to write answer papers. Demonstrations to show how to write examinations will save the teacher time and mental anguish when he corrects papers. Periodic tests should be given during the course. See Chapter XXIV.

REFERENCE BOOKS.

Testbook in Anatomy and Physiology (for student nurses) Kimber, Grey and Stackpole, MacMillan Co.
Cunningham's Anatomy - for medical students.
Grey's Anatomy - for medical students.
Human Anatomy - Morris - for medical students.
The colored plates in these texts should prove valuable for visual instruction if used with discrimination.

TEACHING MATERIAL.

1. The human skeleton, mounted and unmounted bones.
2. Models of the torso and organs.
3. Postmortem and pathological specimens.
4. Anatomical charts.
5. Photographs, cuts, drawings - projected.
6. Blackboard drawings.
7. Slides for projection illustrating parts studied; - especially valuable with a large class.

CHAPTER I. ANATOMICAL NAMES (NOMENCLATURE)

S.1 THE ORIGIN OF ANATOMICAL NAMES.

1. Latin (L) and Greek (G) words are used as names for many parts of the body. In all countries wherein these terms are adopted the names will be the same; for example, from Latin: scapula, the shoulder blade; femur, the thigh bone; radius and ulna, the forearm; from Greek, kephal (cephale), the head; karpos (carpus), the wrist; and trachea, the windpipe.

2. Names derived from Latin, Greek, French, Anglo-Saxon from which English words have been formed, e.g., clavicle, from clavicula (L), the collar bone; condyle, from kondylos (G), a knuckle or knob; shaft, from scaeft, (Anglo-Saxon).

3. Both Latin and Greek names have been retained, e.g., ren (L) and nephros (G) for kidney, from which the adjectives renal and nephritic emerge.

DESCRIPTIVE NAMES.

The ancient anatomists often named a part of the body after something it resembled,
e.g., clavicula, the clavicle or collar bone, as this bone resembles a key, and clavicula means a key;
pelvis, a basin, from the resemblance to a basin.

PLURAL FORMS.

In English the plural form of many words is formed by adding "s" or "es" to the singular form. In Latin the plural form varies with the ending of the singular form.

1. Words ending in "a" change the "a" to "ae", e.g., ulna, ulnae; fibula, fibulae; tibia, tibiae.

2. Words ending in "us" change the "us" to "i", e.g., radius, radii; humerus, humeri; etc.

3. Words ending in "um" change the "um" to "a", e.g., ilium, ilia; ischium, ischia; ovum, ova.

4. Unusual plurals: femur, femora; cornu, cornua.

5. One group of words ending in "us" has the same plural form as the singular, e.g., fetus, manus, meatus. There is a tendency to give these words an English plural form, e.g., fetus, fetuses.

ADJECTIVES.

Adjectives are formed from nouns, e.g., ulna, ulnar; radius, radial; femur, femoral; clavicle, clavicular.

S.2 PREFIXES AND SUFFIXES

Words are built up from a root or stem, and a syllable or syllables placed before or after the stem, e.g., ducere (L) to lead or bring; from the stem "duc" are formed many words, such as abduct, adduct, circumduct, ductless.

A PREFIX is a syllable placed before a stem. This changes the meaning somewhat. A knowledge of the more common prefixes will help to explain the change in meaning of many words, e.g., the adjective of clavicle is clavicular; supraclavicular means - above the clavicle; infraclavicular means below this bone. From sternum the adjective sternal is formed. Substernal means below the sternum; retrosternal means behind the sternum. (See list next column).

A SUFFIX is a syllable or syllables added to the end of a stem to modify the meaning. (See list).

PREFIXES USED IN ANATOMICAL AND MEDICAL WORDS.

a, or ab	- away from: abduct, to draw away from.
a, or an	- without: anuria, without urine.
ad	- towards: adduct, to bring towards or across the midline.
ante	- before, in front of: antebrachium, forearm. lying before the brachium or arm.
anti	- against: antiseptic, against sepsis.
bi, bis	- two or twice: bipartite, two parts.
contra	- against: contralateral, the opposite side.
de	- away, take away: decapitate, to take off the head or top.
di, dis	- two: dicephalic, two heads.
dia	- through: diameter, the measurement through.
dys	- difficult: dysphagia, difficult swallowing.
ecto	- outer: ectoderm, the outer skin.
en, endo	- inside: endothelium, a lining membrane.
ento	- inside: entoderm, inner layer of skin.
epi	- upon: epicondyle, upon a condyle.

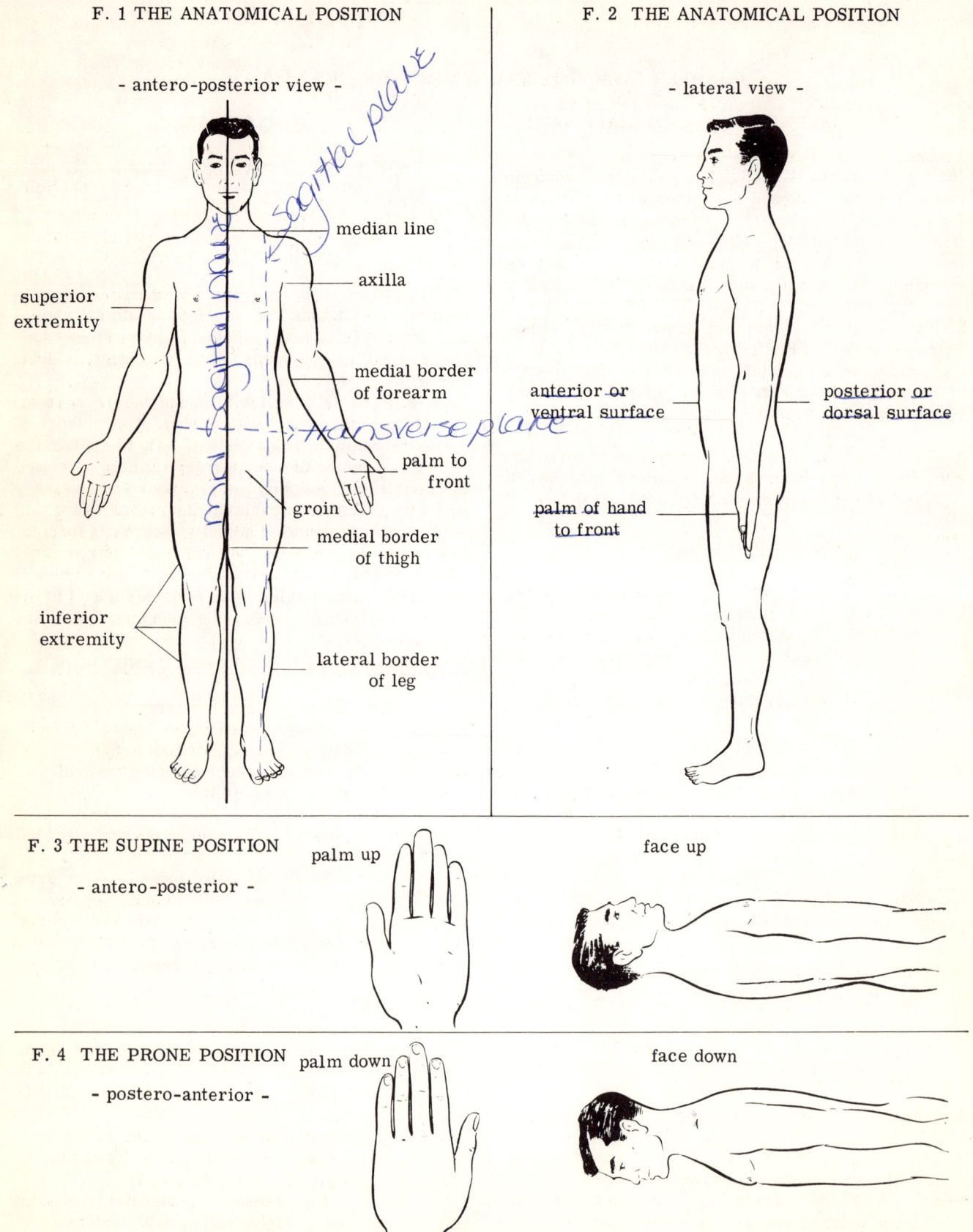

F. 1 THE ANATOMICAL POSITION
- antero-posterior view -

F. 2 THE ANATOMICAL POSITION
- lateral view -

F. 3 THE SUPINE POSITION
- antero-posterior -

F. 4 THE PRONE POSITION
- postero-anterior -

e, or ex	- out of, or outside: evert, to turn out.	centesis	- a tapping or puncture, paracentesis, a tapping with hollow needle to remove fluid from the abdomen, etc.
extra	- outside or beyond: extracellular, outside a cell.	ectomy	- to cut out: appendectomy, to cut out the appendix; or gastrectomy, nephrectomy.
hemi	- half: hemithorax, half of the thorax.		
hydro	- water: hydrocephalus, water in the head.	iasis	- a condition or state, the presence of: cholelithiasis, presence of gall stones.
hyper	- above: hypertension, high blood pressure.	itis	- an inflammation: tonsillitis, appendicitis.
hypo	- under: hypodermic, under the skin.	less	- without: ductless, without a duct.
in	- not: inoperable, cannot be operated upon.	lith	- a stone: phlebolith, a stone in a vein.
in, intra	- inside of: intravenous, inside a vein.	logia	- changed to logy, the science or study of: zoology, the study of animals.
infra	- below: infra-orbital, below the orbit.	oid, oides	- like, resembling: condyloid, like a condyle.
inter	- among or between: intercostal, between ribs.	oma	- a tumor: lipoma, a fatty tumor; osteoma, a bone tumor; chondroma, cartilage tumor.
macro	- large: macrocephalic, a large head.		
meta	- beyond: metacarpals, beyond the carpals.	osis	- a condition or state like "iasis": diverticulosis, having diverticula.
micro	- small: microcephalic, a small head.	ostomy	- a mouth or opening: cholecystostomy, an opening in the gall bladder to drain.
ortho	- straight or correct: orthopedics, the correction of deformities of children.	otomy	- an incision or cut: cholecystotomy, to cut into the gall bladder.
pan	- all: pansinusitis, inflammation of all the paranasal sinuses.	pathy	- disease: adenopathy, disease of glands.
para	- beside: parathyroid, beside the thyroid.	ptosis	- a falling down: nephroptosis, the falling down of the kidney.
peri	- around: pericardium, around the heart.	ulus, olus, culus	- small: malleolus, a little hammer.
poly	- too much or many: polyuria, too much urine.	uria	- referring to urine: dysuria, difficulty in voiding or passing urine.
post	- after: postmortem, after death.		
pre	- before or anterior to: premolar, in front of the molar.		

§ 3 DESCRIPTIVE ANATOMICAL TERMS

pseudo	- false: pseudoarthrosis, false joint.
re	- again or back: reduce, to put back.
retro	- behind: retrosternal, behind the sternum.
semi	- half: semilunar, like a half-moon.
sub	- under: submental, under the chin.
super	- above: superficial, close to the skin.
supra	- above: supra-orbital, above the orbit.
syn	- together or joined: syndactylia, fingers or toes joined together.
trans	- across: transposition, on the opposite side of the body to the normal.
ultra	- beyond: ultraviolet, beyond the violet.
un	- not: unhealthy, not healthy.
uni	- one form or the same: uniform, all alike.

THE ANATOMICAL POSITION: the standing position, facing the front, with the palms of the hands turned to the front. In any description of a part of the body it is assumed that the body is in this position.

MEDIAN LINE OF THE BODY: a line drawn perpendicularly through the center of the forehead, nose, chin, chest, abdomen, and pelvis, and between the legs, dividing the body into two equal parts.

PLANE: from planus (L) for flat; a real or imaginary flat surface, such as might be made by taking a saw and cutting through the body or a part of it, then turning this so as to view it from the cut or flat surface. Many anatomical photographs, drawings, and diagrams are labeled according to the plane or flat surface they represent. See below.

SUFFIXES USED IN ANATOMICAL AND MEDICAL WORDS.

algia	- pain: cephalalgia, a headache.
cele	- swelling or hernia: meningocele, hernia of the membranes of the brain or cord.

1. Median or mid-sagittal plane: a plane through the median line of the body cutting from front to back through the sagittal suture of the skull and continued

down through the body in the same direction, dividing it into equal parts, then turning one half to view it from its cut surface.

2. <u>Sagittal plane</u>: any plane parallel to, or in the same direction as, the mid-sagittal plane and to one or the other side of the median line.

3. <u>Frontal or coronal plane</u>: a plane made by cutting across the body from side to side and therefore parallel to the coronal suture of the skull.

4. <u>Transverse or horizontal plane</u>: a plane made by cutting across the body or part of it at right angles to the long axis. If the body or part is upright, the cut would be parallel to the horizon.

5. <u>Longitudinal plane</u>: a plane along the length or long axis of the body or a part of it, which would be in a vertical direction if the subject is in the anatomical position.

A SECTION is a slice cut from the body or a part of it similar to a slice of bread, and viewed from the cut surface. A section may be cut in any plane. Sections are named according to the plane through which the cuts are made.

1. Mid-sagittal or median section.
2. Sagittal section.
3. Frontal or coronal section.
4. Transverse or horizontal section.
5. Longitudinal section.

S. 4   TERMS USED TO DESCRIBE OPPOSITES

<u>Medial or mesial</u>: that part of a structure or organ which lies nearest to the median line of the body, e.g., the medial malleolus of the tibia.
<u>Lateral</u>: that part of a structure or organ which lies farthest away from the median line of the body, e.g., the lateral malleolus of the fibula.

<u>Anterior</u>: towards the front or in the front part of the body, structure or organ,
e.g., anterior fontanel (fontanelle) of the skull.
<u>Posterior</u>: towards the back or in the back part of the body, structure or organ,
e.g., posterior fontanel.

<u>Ventral</u>: in human anatomy refers to the front, like anterior,
e.g., ventral surface of the abdomen.
<u>Dorsal</u>: refers to the back, like posterior,
e.g., the dorsal surface of the forearm.

<u>Superior</u>: refers to the upper, or that part nearer to the head end,
e.g., superior or upper lobe of a lung.
<u>Inferior</u>: refers to the lower part, or that part farther away from the head end of the body,
e.g., the inferior or lower lobe of a lung.

<u>Internal</u>: on the inside of the body, or a part of, i.e., the inner, e.g., internal auditory meatus.
<u>External</u>: on the outer side, the outer, e.g., external auditory meatus.

<u>Proximal</u>: that part of a structure close to the source, or origin, e.g., proximal phalanx of a finger.
<u>Distal or terminal</u>: that part farther away from the source or origin, e.g., a distal phalanx.

<u>Visceral</u>: adjective of viscus, i.e., relating to an organ itself, e.g., visceral pleura or pericardium.
<u>Parietal</u>: adjective of paries, a wall; relating to the wall of a structure, e.g., parietal pleura.

<u>Intrinsic</u>: part of an organ or structure itself, e.g., an intrinsic growth of the stomach.
<u>Extrinsic</u>: originating outside an organ, e.g., pressure on the stomach by an extrinsic mass.

<u>Cephalic</u>: adjective from cephalon, the head; refers to the head, e.g., cephalic presentation of a fetus.
<u>Cephalad</u>: towards the head or head end.

<u>Caudal</u>: adjective from cauda, the tail; refers to the tail or tail end, e.g., caudal fin of a fish.
<u>Caudad</u>: towards the tail end.

<u>Palmar</u>: refers to the front or palm of the hand, e.g., palmar wart, a wart on the palm.
<u>Plantar</u>: refers to the sole of the foot, e.g., plantar wart, one on the sole of the foot.
<u>Volar</u>: refers to the palm of the hand or sole of the foot.

<u>Supine</u>: position assumed when lying on the back with the face up; or referring to the hands, the palms up.
<u>Prone</u>: lying face down, or if referring to the hands, with the palms down.

<u>Longitudinal</u>: lengthwise or along the long axis.
<u>Transverse</u>: across or at right angles to the long axis, e.g., transverse section of the arm.

<u>Vertical</u>: perpendicular to the horizon.
<u>Horizontal</u>: parallel to the horizon.

<u>Greater or major</u>: the larger, e.g., greater trochanter of femur; greater tubercle of the humerus.
<u>Lesser or minor</u>: the smaller, e.g., lesser trochanter of the femur; lesser tubercle of the humerus.

S. 5 TERMS DESCRIBING MOVEMENTS.

Adduct: to lead, draw or bring across or towards the median line (ad - towards, and ducere - to lead). To adduct the arm would mean to bring it towards or across the median line. (adductor, adduction)

Abduct: to draw away from the median line of the body (ab - away from). To abduct the arm would mean to draw it away from the median line. (abduction)

Circumduct: to move in a circular direction. (circum - around). To circumduct the arm would mean to move it in a circular manner.

Flex: to bend. To flex the elbow would mean to bend it. Other terms: flexor, flexion.

Extend: to straighten or stretch out. To extend the elbow would mean to straighten it. (extension)

Invert: to turn in or inwards, (in, and vertere, to turn). Invert the foot, to turn it in. (inversion)

Evert: to turn out (e - out, and vertere). To evert the foot would mean to turn it out.

Pronate: to turn the hand palm down, or lie with the face down. (pronator, pronation, prone)

Supinate: to place the hand with the palm up, or lie face up. (supinator, supination, supine)

Rotate: to turn along one axis, e.g., to rotate the arm, to turn it. Internal rotation - to turn inwards, or external rotation - to turn outwards.

S. 6 SPELLING.

Many anatomical words have two spellings, the American and the British. Because the American spellings are more simplified, they have been used in the Handbook.

American	-	British
anemia	-	anaemia
cecum	-	caecum
fetus	-	foetus
hemorrhage	-	haemorrhage
sulfate	-	sulphate

Prefixes are usually joined directly to a word without a hyphen. When there is apt to be an awkward piling up of letters, or a mispronunciation, a hyphen is used. The present tendency appears to be to omit a hyphen even when two vowels come together, e.g., intrauterine. In the Handbook a hyphen has been used with such words as supra-orbital, etc. Possibly the most important thing to remember is that the one spelling should be used throughout.

In the Handbook compound words are usually spelled with a hyphen. If these compound words are divided, the division should take place at the hyphen. Many anatomical words are compounded. In anatomy and in radiography the order of the words often indicates direction. In radiography the direction of the x-ray beam is from the first mentioned towards the last, e.g., supero-inferior; from above downwards; infero-superior; from below upwards.

Many of these compound words are used with reference to the skull, as

occipito-frontal; fronto-occipital
submento-vertical; vertico-submental.

Most students have certain words which they are apt to misspell. Sometimes it is due to ignorance of the correct spelling. Often it is due to carelessness or failure to give any thought to the spelling.

The following list illustrates the above statements.

attachment	- not attachement
cartilaginous	- not cartilagenous
dilatation	- not dilitation
eponychium	- not epionychium
flaccid	- not flacid
foreshorten	- not forshorten
inflammation	- not inflamation
indispensable	- not indispensible
instillation	- not installation, if putting inside
labeled	- not labelled
laity	- not laiety
lumborum	- not lumbrorum
movable	- not moveable
oculomotor	- not occulomotor
plural	- not pleural, referring to several
pulposus	- not polyposus
preceding	- not preceeding
procedure	- not proceedure
protuberance	- not protruberance
radiopaque	- not radioopaque
temporal	- not temperal, re temporal bone

S. 7 A LIST OF WORDS USED IN CHAPTER I.

1. SING. - PL.

ulna	- ulnae	radius	- radii	ischium	- ischia	femur	- femora
fibula	- fibulae	humerus	- humeri	ilium	- ilia	cornu	- cornua
tibia	- tibiae	fetus		ovum	- ova		
		manus					
		meatus					

2. ADJECTIVES.

Ulna - ulnar   radius - radial   femur - femoral   clavicle - clavicular

3. PREFIXES.

a, ab - away	en, endo - inside	inter - among	re - again
a, an - without	ento - inside	macro - large	retro - behind
ad - towards	epi - upon	meta - beyond	semi - half
ante - before	e, ex - out	micro - small	sub - under
anti - against	extra - beyond	ortho - straight	super - above
bi, bis - two	hemi - half	pan - all	supra - above
contra - against	hydro - water	para - beside	syn - together
de - away	hyper - above	peri - around	trans - across
di, dis - two	hypo - under	poly - too much	ultra - beyond
dia - through	in - not	post - after	un - not
dys - difficult	intra - inside of	pre - before	uni - same form
ecto - outer	infra - below	pseudo - false	

4. SUFFIXES.

algia - pain	itis - inflammation	oma - tumor	ptosis - falling down
cele - hernia	less - without	osis - condition	ulus, olus - small
centesis - puncture	lith - stone	ostomy - mouth	culus - small
ectomy - cut out	logia, logy - body	otomy - cut, incision	uria - urine
iasis - condition	oid, oides - like	pathy - disease	

5. DESCRIPTIVE ANATOMICAL TERMS.

anatomical position	median plane	transverse or	section
median line of body	mid-sagittal plane	horizontal plane	sections as above
plane	frontal, coronal plane	longitudinal plane	for planes

6. TERMS DESCRIBING OPPOSITES.

medial, mesial	internal	cephalic	supine
lateral	external	cephalad	prone
anterior	proximal	caudal	longitudinal
posterior	distal, terminal	caudad	horizontal
ventral	visceral	palmar	transverse
dorsal	parietal	plantar	greater, major
superior	intrinsic	volar	lesser, minor
inferior	extrinsic		

7. TERMS DESCRIBING MOVEMENT.

abduct	dorsiflex	flex	rotate
abduction	dorsiflexion	flexion	rotation
abductor	extend	flexor	rotator
adduct	extension	prone	supine
adduction	extensor	pronate	supinate
adductor	evert	pronation	supination
circumduct	eversion	pronator	supinator
circumduction	evertor		

Edema; too much fluid in tissue
dehydration = too little fluid

!! I know !!

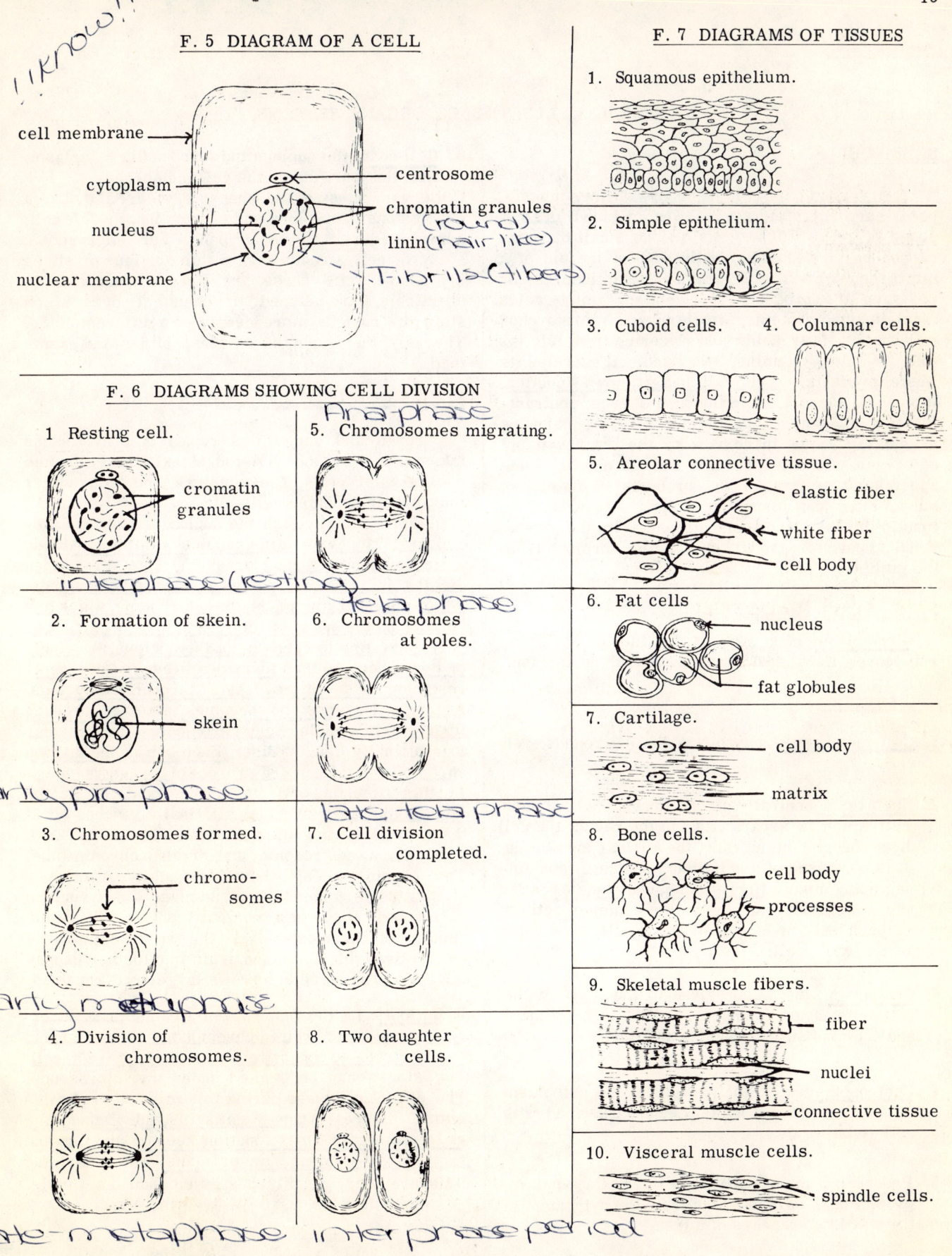

CHAPTER II. CELLS, TISSUES, ORGANS, SYSTEMS.

S. 8 CELLS.

Every single part of the body, whether muscle, bone, cartilage, fat, nerve, skin, or blood, is composed of cells. These cells are so small that they cannot be viewed individually without the aid of a microscope. Each cell breathes, and absorbs, or takes up the products of digestion: amino acids from digested proteins, simple sugars from starches and sugars, fatty acids and glycerine from fats, as well as salts, vitamins, etc. Each cell excretes its waste products. Each cell has its own function. It may be support, as in the case of bone; contraction and movement, as in muscles; the carrying of messages, as in nerves; or the transportaton of oxygen, as in the case of red blood cells. Some specialized cells take the products of digestion, salts, etc., and manufacture new substances, as insulin in the pancreas, adrenalin in the suprarenal glands, or growth-stimulating hormone from the pituitary gland.

S. 9 STRUCTURE OF CELLS.

Protoplasm is a word used to include any living substance. Each cell is made up of protoplasm.

Cell structure.

1. Cell membrane: a covering that surrounds each cell.

2. Nucleus: a centrally placed rounded part of each cell which is separated from the rest of the cell by a covering membrane, the nuclear membrane. It is composed of a semiliquid substance containing many minute fibrils, linin, and granules called chromatin. The nucleus is the center of activity of each cell, and its destruction will cause death of the whole cell.

3. Cytoplasm: the name given to that part of the cell outside of the nucleus. This is semiliquid and contains small granules and fibrils.

4. Centrosome: a small granule in the cytoplasm lying close to the nucleus, and concerned with cell division.

5. Processes: many cells have fibers (long narrow projections) spreading out from the cytoplasm of the cell like branches of a tree.

6. Cell body: the nucleus and surrounding cytoplasm, i.e., that part inside the cell membrane.

Cells vary in size and shape; some are flat, like a cobblestone; some long and narrow, as a muscle cell; some spider-like, as in bone. For microscopic study of cell structure very thin sections or slices are shaved off. These are fixed or hardened in chemicals, are dipped in chemical dyes which stain the nucleus more deeply or a different color. They are then mounted on glass slides and examined.

S. 10 CELL DIVISION. (Genetics)

Growth and sometimes repair of body tissues takes place by the division of existing cells into two daughter cells. These mature, and each divides into further daughter cells, etc.

Before cell division the nuclear membrane disappears. The chromatin granules within the nucleus unite to form a thread or skein. This thread then divides into several pieces, called chromosomes. While this is taking place, the centrosome, which lies outside of the nucleus, divides into two parts, one part migrating to each end of the nucleus. A spindle of new fibers is then formed between the new centrosomes, these fibers passing through the nucleus. A single chromosome becomes attached to each fiber of this spindle. Each chromosome then divides longitudinally (length-wise). Each half of the divided chromosome is then drawn to one of the centrosomes. At this time the cell membrane constricts in the middle like an hour glass. It finally pinches off at the center dividing the spindle into two parts. Each part has a centrosome and divided chromosome. The chromosomes become granules. A nuclear membrane is formed about them so a new nucleus is formed. Each new nucleus contains the same number of chromosomes as the parent cell. These new cells divide again and again into further daughter cells. The structure grows larger or is repaired.

Mitosis is the name given to this process of cell division in which chromosomes are formed and migrate to opposite poles of the parent cell. The stages can be studied under the microscope. The different figures during this process are called mitotic figures. Cancer cells instead of maturing and assuming normal function keep on dividing and redividing to form a tumor mass. These dividing cells are more readily destroyed than adult cells. This principle is used in treating cancer by x radiation.

Stroma – connective; binding around cell or tissue

S. 11 TISSUES.

If this is destroyed tissue will not grow

A Tissue is a group of cells similar in form and function. Four types are described: 1. epithelium, 2. connective, 3. muscular, 4. nerve tissues.

1. Epithelium includes membranes covering surfaces such as the skin, and lining cavities and tubes, such as the digestive tract, heart, blood vessels, uterus, bladder, etc. The cells are bound together to form a continuous membrane. Many of these membranes consist of a single layer of cells like cobblestones cemented together. Others, instead of being flat, are shaped like cubes or cylinders like the lining membrane of the bowel. Others consist of several layers of cells on top of each other like bricks in a wall. The skin has this pattern.

Endothelium is a word used in connection with the epithelium forming the lining membrane of the heart and blood vessels. Endo – in or inside.

Mesothelium is used as a name for the lining membrane of body cavities, and comes from mesoderm.

Mucous membranes have this name because they secrete mucus, a sticky, stringy fluid.

Serous membranes secrete a thin watery fluid. These membranes form the pleura of the chest, peritoneum of the abdomen, and pericardium of the heart.

Synovial membranes line joint cavities and bursae, and secrete a fluid to lubricate the joint.

2. Connective or areolar tissues are the supporting and binding tissues of the body. Their function is to support and hold together other more important tissues, and to fill in spaces. They are found between layers of muscles, under the skin and under other lining membranes, as well as between organs. If a piece of raw beefsteak be pulled apart, white glistening fibers will be seen between the layers of lean meat. This is connective tissue. The cells vary in shape and are often separated from each other with fibers between cells. These fibers may be elastic or fibrous (non-elastic). Blood vessels and nerves pass through the connective tissue to reach the structures they supply. Some connective tissues are modified to fulfill a definite function:

(a) Adipose or fat tissue is modified connective tissue. The cell nucleus is pushed to one side of the cell body, which is filled with fat. A layer of fat lies under the skin. Some fat is found wherever connective tissue is located. There are more fat cells in every organ and structure of the obese or fat person than in the thin one.

(b) Cartilage or gristle consists of oval shaped cells with a cement substance between and holding them together. This cement or matrix may be clear (hyaline) or may contain fibers radiating out from the cell bodies into the matrix (fibro-cartilage).

(c) Bone or osseous tissue is composed of cells having many processes extending out from the cell bodies like the legs of a spider. The spaces about the processes and between the cells are impregnated with calcium phosphate. The bone cells and processes form a pattern with channels for blood vessels.

3. Muscular tissue is composed of elongated spindle shaped cells, which contain many fibers running lengthwise in the cytoplasm. These fibers, by their contraction, shorten the muscle cells, and the muscle contracts. The cells are joined together by connective tissue to form little bundles. The bundles are also bound together by connective tissue.

Types of muscles.

(a) Skeletal, voluntary or striated muscle is found attached to bones and ligaments. It has cross markings; hence striated. It is supplied by sensory and motor nerves. It will contract in response to messages along the motor nerves from the brain; hence called voluntary.

(b) Visceral, involuntary or smooth muscle is found in the walls of many organs; hence visceral. It cannot be made to contract at will; hence involuntary. It has no cross markings and is called smooth muscle. Usually there are two layers in the wall of an organ, a circular layer with fibers encircling the organ, and a longitudinal layer in which the fibers run lengthwise, e.g., the wall of the intestine.

(c) Cardiac muscle is found only in the heart. It is a special type of striated muscle.

4. Nerve tissue: see nervous system.

S. 12 ORGANS.

An organ is a group of tissues forming a single unit, and concerned with some particular function, e.g., kidney, liver, heart, lung, etc.

The parenchyma is the active tissue in an organ, and performs the function of that organ.

F. 8 DIVISIONS OF THE BODY - BODY CAVITIES

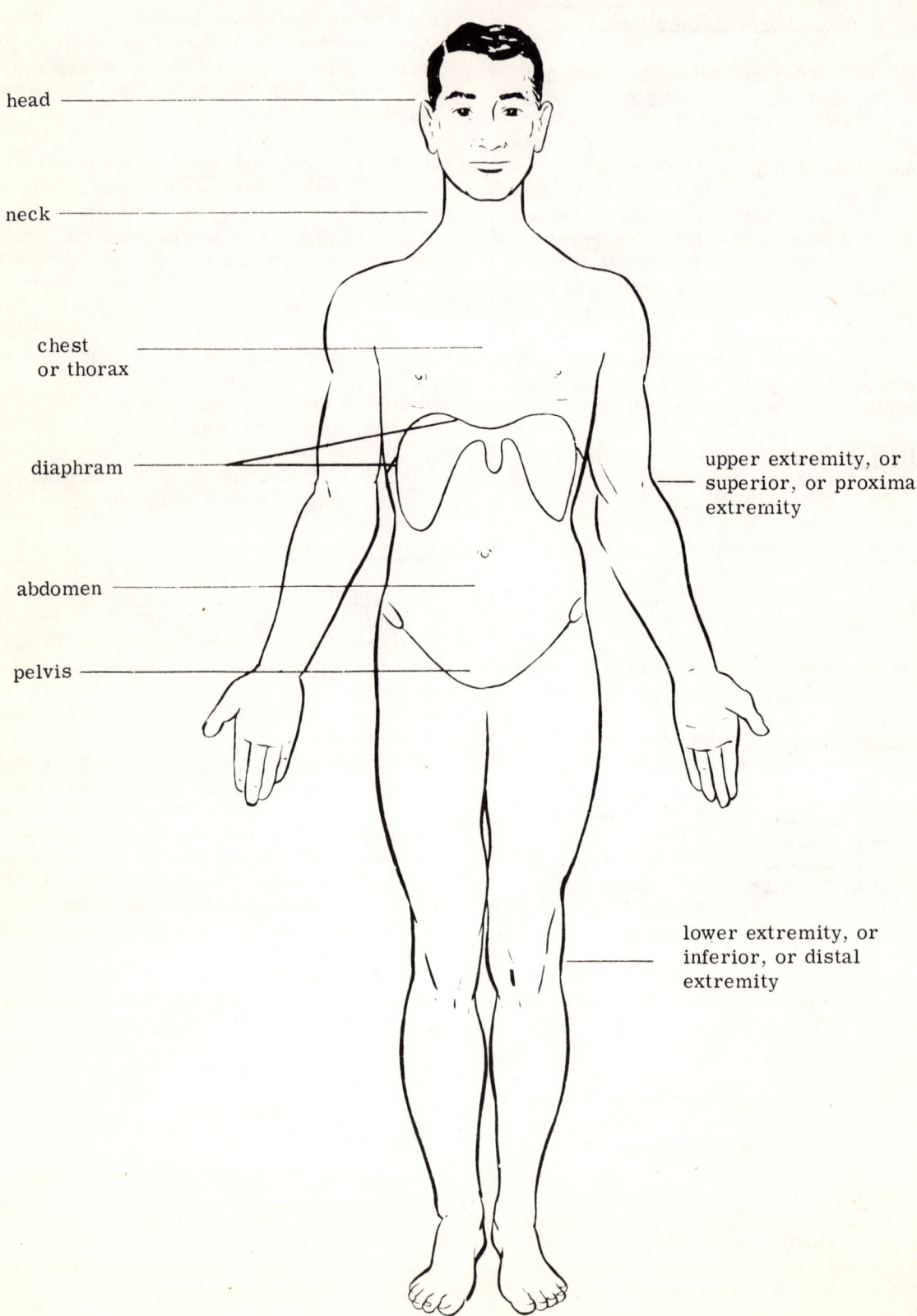

The stroma is the supporting and binding tissue about the active cells, the connective tissue. Blood vessels and nerves pass through this tissue.

S. 13 SYSTEMS.

A system is a group of organs and tissues concerned with some particular body function. Nine systems, commonly recognized, are given below.

1. THE CIRCULATORY or cardio-vascular system includes the heart, blood vessels and lymphatics. Usually the reticuloendothelial elements, such as the spleen, and bone marrow and blood cells are included.
Occasionally the lymphatics are referred to as the lymphatic system.

2. THE DIGESTIVE SYSTEM or alimentary tract includes the mouth, throat, esophagus, stomach, small bowel, and colon, as well as the accessory organs, the liver, gall bladder, and pancreas.

3. THE ENDOCRINE SYSTEM includes the ductless glands, namely the pituitary, pineal, thyroid, parathyroid, thymus and adrenal glands as well as parts of the testes, ovaries and pancreas.

4. THE MUSCULAR SYSTEM includes all the skeletal or voluntary muscles.

5. THE NERVOUS SYSTEM includes the brain, spinal cord, peripheral nerves, and the autonomic nervous system, i.e., the sympathetic and parasympathetic.

6. THE REPRODUCTIVE or genital system includes the female and male organs of reproduction.
 (a) Female organs: ovaries, uterine tubes, uterus, vagina, and external genitals.
 (b) Male organs: testis, spermatic cords, seminal vesicles, prostate, and penis.

7. THE RESPIRATORY SYSTEM includes all the air passages and the lungs.

8. THE SKELETAL SYSTEM, the osseous system, includes the bones and joints.

9. THE URINARY SYSTEM includes the kidneys, ureters, bladder, and urethra. Because some of these structures are common to both the reproductive and the urinary systems, they are grouped as the genito-urinary system. Actually the kidneys are excretory organs and along with the skin, lungs and intestines are called the excretory organs.

S. 14 DIVISIONS OF THE BODY.

1. The head.

2. The neck.

3. The trunk: thorax or chest, abdomen and pelvis.

4. The extremities:
 (a) Upper, proximal or superior extremities or limbs.
 (b) Lower, inferior or distal extremities or limbs.

S. 15 THE BODY CAVITIES.

The body cavity or coelom lies in front of the vertebral column or backbone. It is divided into: the chest or thorax, abdomen and pelvis.

1. The chest or thoracic cavity occupies the upper part and is enclosed by the chest wall. Between it and the abdomen is the dome-shaped muscular partition, the diaphragm. This is attached along its margin to the inner surface of the chest wall, as a bell tent is pegged to the ground.

2. The abdomen or abdominal cavity extends from the under surface of the diaphragm to the pelvic bones. Here a ridge of bone passes around the inner surface of these bones to mark its lower limit, at the pelvic inlet.

3. The pelvis or pelvic cavity is encircled by the bones of the pelvis and extends from the inlet or ridge described above to the floor of the pelvis.
Actually the abdominal and pelvic cavities are not separated but are a continuous cavity. Some of the bowel lies in the abdomen, some in the pelvis, and the position of one coil will vary from time to time.
The term "false pelvis" is misleading. It is applied to the lower part of the abdomen. This part is protected behind by the upper parts of the pelvic bones, above the true pelvis.
The contents of each body cavity will be found listed at the end of the Handbook. These should be reviewed after the various structures have been studied. Their position is important in positioning in radiography.

S. 16 EMBRYOLOGY.

Embryology is the study of the fertilized ovum from fertilization to birth. Embryon (G) and logy (science).

The ovum (pl. ova) is the female reproductive cell, and is formed in the ovary.

The spermatozoon (pl. spermatozoa) is the male reproductive cell and is developed in the testes. Many thousands of them are expelled into the female vagina during intercourse.

Embryo, in human beings refers to the developing, fertilized ovum to the end of the third month.

Fetus, in human beings refers to the unborn young, i.e., the fertilized ovum from the end of the third month until birth.

Fertilization is the penetration of the ovum by a spermatozoon, and the union of their nuclei.

An ovum is expelled from an ovary about every twenty-eight days. This varies with the individual. It finds its way into the uterine tube. Here it may be met by a spermatozoon and fertilized. The spermatozoon, to reach the ovum, must swim up through the vagina, uterus, and out into the uterine tube. If an ovum is not fertilized, it passes along the uterine tube into the uterus and out through the vagina; and menstration begins. If fertilized, the ovum passes into the uterus and becomes imbedded in the uterine wall. It develops by a process of cell division similar to that described above. Here, however, each chromosome must consist of a female and a male part. The ovum divides into two daughter cells. These again divide making four, then eight, sixteen, etc. These cells become arranged into a ball-like structure resembling a raspberry. Later the center becomes filled with fluid, with the cells in one layer surrounding this. In one area in this ball the cells multiply rapidly, forming at first two, then three, layers. These layers of cells are termed the ectoderm, mesoderm and entoderm. (See 1., 2., 3. below) All the tissues and organs of the body develop from these layers of cells. Each layer forms certain definite structures, similar in all embryos.

1. The ectoderm, or outer layer, grows around to encircle the other layers, and forms:
   (a) the skin, hair, nails; (b) the nervous system.

2. The entoderm, or inner layer, becomes a hollow tube, and forms the lining membrane of:
   (a) digestive tract; (b) trachea, bronchi, lungs, liver and pancreas.

3. The mesoderm, or middle layer, lies between the ectoderm and entoderm. It forms two distinct layers:
   (a) one under the ectoderm; (b) one surrounding the tube-like entoderm.

The mesoderm forms:
   (a) all connective and modified connective tissues including cartilage, bone and fat;
   (b) muscles, skeletal, visceral, and cardiac;
   (c) blood vessels, and their endothelial linings, lymphatic vessels, glands and blood cells;
   (d) some parts of the urinary system.

S. 17 CONGENITAL or DEVELOPMENTAL ANOMALIES.

Occasionally normal development does not occur, and unusual appearing structures are formed:

spina bifida, in which the arch of one or more vertebrae may be incomplete behind;

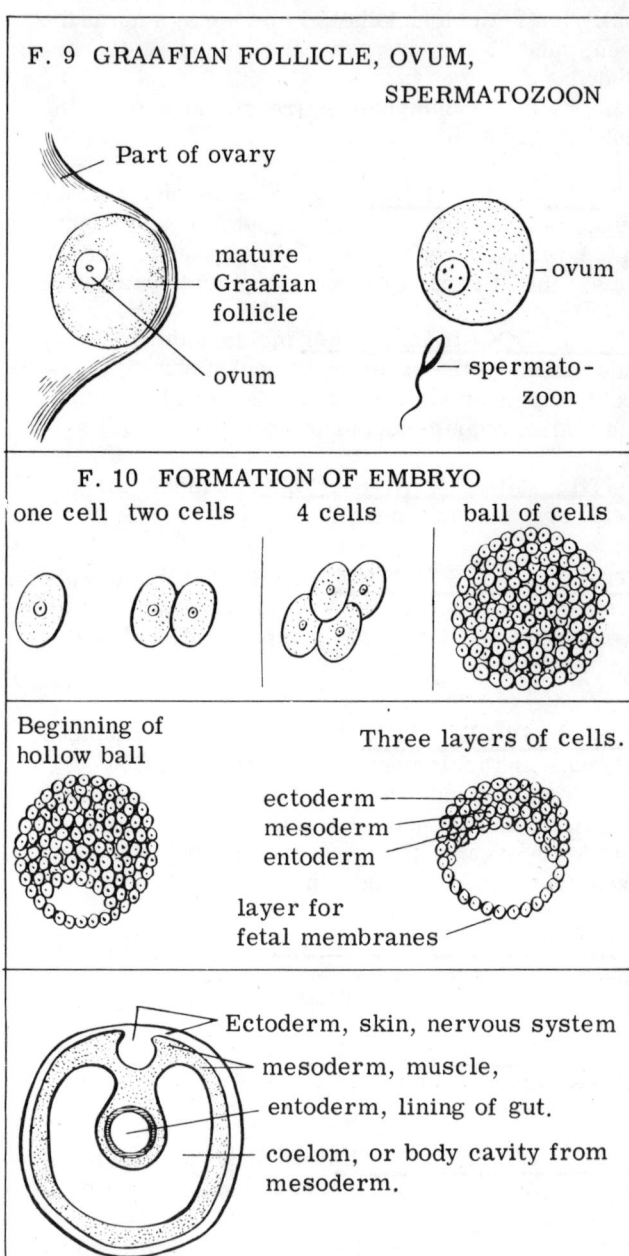

F. 9 GRAAFIAN FOLLICLE, OVUM, SPERMATOZOON

F. 10 FORMATION OF EMBRYO

atresia, or failure of a tube to become hollow as in atresia of the esophagus;

supernumerary digits, wherein the subject has more than the normal number of fingers or toes;

imperforate anus, in which the anus is closed, and the contents of the bowel cannot be expelled.

undescended testicle, in which the testicle remains in the abdomen or above the scrotum;

transposition, in which an organ normally found on one side of the body is on the opposite side.

Many other anomalies may occur. It is remarkable that in such a complicated structure that they do not occur more frequently.

heart can be transposed opposite side from normal

fetus: when you can tell what it's going to be — human, chicken, etc. cow

CHAPTER III. TISSUE DENSITY IN RADIOGRAPHY.

S. 18 DENSITY.

The density of any substance is its weight (mass) per unit volume. This varies with the substance. For example, a quart of water weighs more than a quart of feathers. To compare the density of two substances, the same units of volume and weight must be used. The unit of volume may be the pint, quart, a cubic foot, or the metric unit, the cubic centimeter (cc). The unit of weight may be an ounce, a pound, or the metric unit, a gram (gm).

1 cc. of water weighs 1 gram.
1 cc. of lead weighs 11.34 grams.
1 cc. of gold weighs 19.34 grams.

S. 19 TISSUE AND ORGAN DENSITY.

The density of the various tissues and organs of the body varies considerably and depends upon:
(a) the composition of the cells of the organ;
(b) whether these cells are closely packed together, or widely separated;
(c) the composition of the material filling in the spaces between the cells;
(d) in hollow organs, whether they are empty, filled with air or other gas, some liquid or solid.

Examples follow.

Fat is light or of low density; so much so that it will float on water, i.e., it is lighter than water.

Cartilage is relatively light.

Bone, because of the calcium phosphate between its cells, is quite dense in comparison.

The liver and kidney, being solid organs with closely packed cells, are dense.

The heart, although it is hollow, contains blood, so it is dense.

The stomach, if empty, is light; if filled with air, is still light; but if filled with a meal consisting of liquids and solids, is dense.

S. 20 TISSUE DENSITY AND RADIOGRAPHY.

To understand the importance of tissue density in radiography the student should review the principles which underlie x-ray exposure and processing. The x-ray film is coated on both sides with an emulsion containing silver bromide. When exposed to x-rays some change occurs in the silver bromide. This change is apparent only in the processed film. The silver bromide affected by x-rays becomes converted to black silver. The film turns black. The silver bromide, not affected, is washed off. A part of the body, with organs and structures of different densities, is placed upon an x-ray film. An x-ray exposure is made. The various organs absorb x-rays in proportion to their densities. Solid organs absorb most of the x-rays. Very few rays will reach the film under them. Their images will appear light grey. Parts of lesser density, such as fat, muscle, and cartilage, will not absorb many rays, so more of these rays will pass through them to affect the underlying film. Their images will appear dark, as more silver will be affected. The degree of blackness will vary with the density of the part exposed, varying from grey to black. The technician's first problem will be to select a technic which will demonstrate all of these parts of different densities.

Fortunately, no one structure will have the same density throughout. Bone, because it has an outer dense layer, an inner less dense layer, and often a central cavity, will vary in density. These parts will absorb x-rays to a different degree and will therefore show an image of different degrees of greyness. The internal structure may be made apparent with proper technic.

S. 21 BODY THICKNESS AND RADIOGRAPHY.

In addition to the relative density of an organ as compared to that of adjacent structures, its thickness and size are also important in radiography. The larger and thicker an organ, the more x-rays will be absorbed by it. Consequently, the lighter the image will be. Large individuals have large organs, muscles, and bones, etc. To get comparable views of their organs, it is necessary to adjust the technic to compensate for the additional thickness. Thickness due to fat will not obstruct the rays to such a degree as will large well-developed muscles.

A thickness voltage technic has been developed to improve the radiography of thin and thicker patients. The thickness of the part is measured, and the voltage is then adjusted according to a table which has been compiled.

S. 22 CONTRAST MEDIA.

CONTRAST MEDIA (sing. - contrast medium) are substances used in radiography to outline hollow organs. They must be of lesser or greater density than the walls of the organ they fill, as well as that of the surrounding structures. They will fill the hollow organ, assume its shape, show any irregularity in outline or filling defect. If the organ moves, they will show changes due to motion. They may be very light, as air or gas; or may be quite dense, as barium sulphate and iodine.

As stated above, hollow organs with thin walls will not show as separate images on the processed film. The stomach, bowel, gall bladder, bronchi, ureters, urinary bladder and uterus are examples.

Other organs with thick walls will show an image of their outline only. Cavities within them will not be visible. The kidneys are of this class.

The heart, when radiographed, will either be filled with blood or will be in a contraction phase. The chambers will not be outlined.

Barium sulphate (sulfate) is a dense, insoluble compound. It is mixed with water and given by mouth or rectum to outline the digestive tract. Thin or thick mixtures are used. Barium should be thoroughly mixed with water in one vessel, and poured into a glass or enema can immediately before using. It settles rapidly. In a constipated patient water from it will be absorbed in the colon, and the barium may form hard lumps and cause obstruction. The bowels must be kept active by drinking water and taking laxatives.

Iodine is a relatively dense chemical. Many compounds are used as contrast media. In order to be of value, the compound used must be absorbed by the organ to be filmed. One group of compounds is used to outline the gall bladder. These are taken by mouth. Another group is given intravenously to outline the bile ducts. A third group is injected intravenously to outline the urinary tract. Each drug company has its own compounds. Each firm uses trade names for their products, but they all contain some iodine. Some

---

F. 11 RADIOGRAPHIC CENTERING

1. Tube centered at right angles to knee joint.
2. Tube poorly centered to knee joint.

F. 12 MAGNIFICATION OF IMAGE

1. Object at a distance from film.
2. Object close to film.

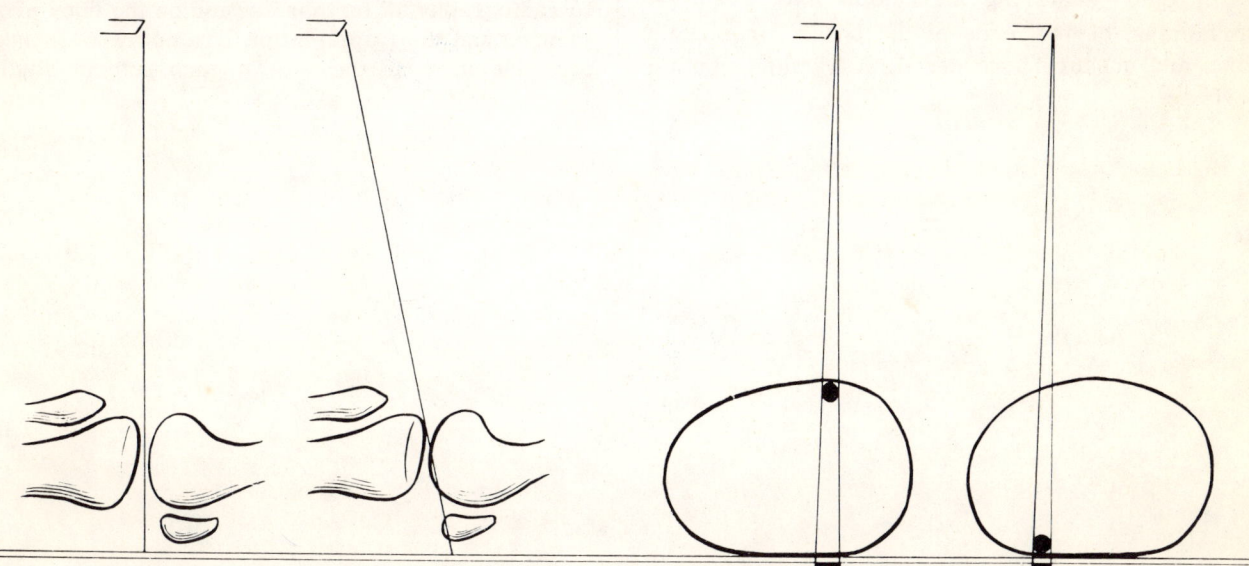

In 2 above the joint surfaces overlap, due to poor centering.

In 1 above the image is magnified as it lies at some distance from the film.

patients are sensitive to iodine. If the subject is sensitive, or has a history of asthma or eczema, caution must be used. The patient may die.

S. 23 VALUE OF SURFACE MARKINGS AND BONY PROMINENCES.

Many bones have prominences that can either be seen or palpated (felt) through the skin. In radiography these are used as guides for centering in order to obtain satisfactory films of the underlying bones and joints.

They are also used as landmarks in centering for various structures and organs within the body. In thin subjects they can often be seen or felt. In thicker patients it is sometimes impossible even to palpate them. The iliac crests provide an example.

When there is much swelling, as usually happens following an injury, it is often impossible to locate them. When there is much tenderness resulting from the injury, it is unwise to attempt to find them. Under these conditions the technician must guess at their location. A knowledge of the normal will be of considerable help. The technician may then form a mental picture of where they should be.

S. 24 SOME APPLICATIONS OF ANATOMY TO RADIOGRAPHY.

In radiography correct centering of the part to be filmed, and correct centering of the x-ray tube so that the central rays will pass through the part desired, is very important.

Improper centering at a joint may result in overlapping of the ends of the bones forming the joint, and obscure bone detail. A fracture or other bone abnormality might be missed. Correct centering will depend upon a knowledge of the bony prominences at the joint and the application of this information to correct centering.

The closer an organ or other structure is to the x-ray film the less distortion and magnification there will be. It is necessary to know whether an organ lies in the anterior (front) or posterior (back) part of the body in order to determine whether an antero-posterior or postero-anterior view should be taken. Anatomy furnishes this information.

To overcome some of the difficulties, standard or routine positions have been adopted for the various parts of the body. These standard positions usually provide for positioning to obtain two views at right angles to each other. An antero-posterior or a postero-anterior view is taken, depending upon the position in the body of the part to be filmed. A further lateral view is also taken.

Following injury it may be impossible to obtain these routine views. First, there is danger of causing further damage by moving the injured part. Second, there is often so much pain that the patient cannot move the part himself, nor can he permit the technician to do so. Technicians can often obtain two views at right angles to each other by rotating the whole body along with the injured part. These may not be routine views, but if at right angles to each other, will be very valuable.

In order to obtain these routine or emergency views when necessary, the technician must have a mental picture of each part of the body.

As each part of the body is studied, peculiarities of the anatomy of that part will be outlined and applied to radiography. A further section on the bony prominences and their application to radiography is therefore included at the end of each subject studied.

CHAPTER IV. THE SKIN AND APPENDAGES.

S. 25 THE LAYERS OF THE SKIN.

1. Epidermis:
   - (a) horny layer - stratum corneum,
   - (b) translucent, clear layer - stratum lucidum,
   - (c) granular layer - stratum granulosum,
   - (d) germinal layer - stratum germinativum.

2. Dermis, true skin or corium:
   - (a) papillary layer,
   - (b) reticular layer.

S. 26 THE STRUCTURE OF THE SKIN.

The term "layer" is a confusing one. One speaks of a layer of cloth, meaning a single thickness of cloth. As used above, with reference to the skin, a layer consists of several thicknesses, tiers, or rows of cells placed one on top of the other. The cells of any one layer are similar.

The skin consists of two distinct layers, the epidermis or cuticle, and beneath this the dermis or true skin.

The epidermis (epi, upon) or outer layer is a membrane of epithelium. It is made up of many tiers of cells placed one on top of the other. It is often called stratified epithelium (stratum, a layer). The epidermis is formed from the ectoderm or outer layer of the embryo. See Section 16.

In this epidermis four layers of cells can be identified. Each layer is several cells thick. The cells of one layer are similar. From the outside these layers are named: the horny layer, the translucent or clear layer, the granular layer, and the germinal layer.

The horny or outer layer is composed of several thicknesses of degenerating cells which actually become scales.

Directly under the horny layer are several tiers of clear cells; hence the name translucent or clear.

Beneath the translucent layer is a layer of cells having many granules within them, the granular layer.

The innermost or fourth layer is called the germinal layer. This is made up of several tiers of columnar or cylindrical cells. The cells at the bottom of this layer divide repeatedly to produce new daughter cells. These push the older cells towards the skin surface.

As cells approach the surface, they are transformed successively into granular cells, with many granules, then clear cells with loss of granules, and finally into degenerated cells or scales, the horny cells.

The horny or outer layer is being constantly rubbed off or otherwise lost, and these scales are replaced by further degenerating clear cells. The horny layer is thin on most parts of the body, but is thicker on the palms of the hands and soles of the feet, more so in the callouses.

The pigment of the skin is contained in and around the cells of the germinal layer; this pigment determines the darkness of the skin.

F. 13 DIAGRAM OF SKIN - at right angles to surface

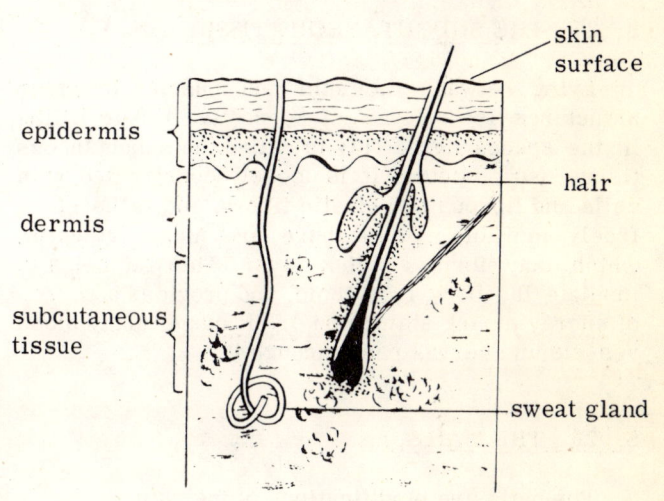

F. 14 DIAGRAM OF SKIN - greatly magnified -

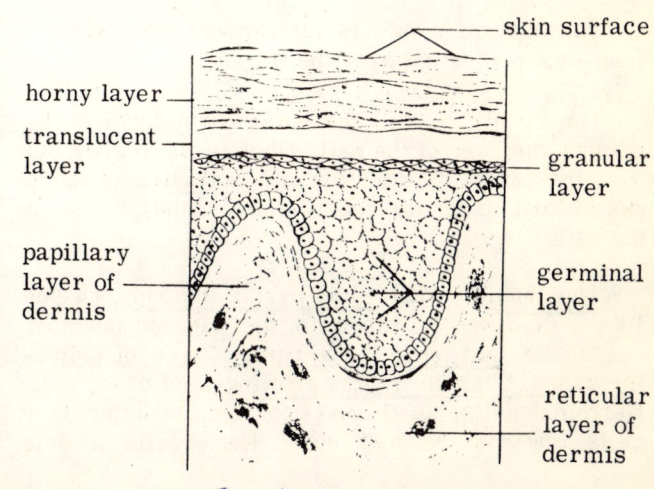

The Dermis, corium or true skin, lies under the epidermis. It is composed of widely separated cells with fibrous tissue bands and elastic fibers interlacing each other between the cell bodies. The dermis is derived from the mesoderm, or middle layer of the embryo. See section 16. Considerable fat may be deposited in the cells. Blood capillaries and nerves pass freely through the dermis to supply the epidermis.

The dermis is composed of two layers, the papillary layer, and the reticular layer.

The papillary layer lies next to the epidermis. It is elevated into tiny projections with hollows between them; hence the name papillary (papillae). The innermost layer of germinal cells of the epidermis fits into these papillae and hollows.

The reticular layer lies beneath the papillary layer. Its cells and fibers form an interlacing network which is therefore called reticular.

S. 27 THE SUBCUTANEOUS TISSUE.

Lying between the skin and muscles or other structures is a layer of connective tissue filling in the spaces here. This is called the subcutaneous tissue (sub, under). It is loosely constructed with cells and fibrous and elastic fibers, and is therefore freely movable. Often there are many fat cells, which may form a thick layer. This fat helps to insulate the body from cold, and provides a source of energy during starvation or sickness. Many blood vessels and nerves pass through it.

S. 28 THE NAILS.

The nails are modifications of the skin.

The root of a nail is the inner part, covered by a fold of skin.

The body of a nail is the exposed part, with its free edge projecting over the finger tip.

The eponychium is the outer horny layer of the skin at the base of the nail, which tends to grow out over the nail body. Infection of a hangnail may cause pus to form under the eponychium around the base of the nail.

The lunula is the white part of the body, shaped like a half moon, close to the base of the nail.

At the nail root the germinal layer of skin is thickened. This forms the growing point of the nail. Germinal cells, as they are formed, push the older cells towards the nail body. These cells become converted into the hardened or cornified flat nail. If a nail is torn off or otherwise destroyed, it will re-form as long as the germinal layer at the root is not also destroyed. The nails afford some protection to the tips of the fingers and toes.

F. 15 FINGER NAIL
- dorsal view -   - lateral view -

free edge
body
lunula
nail root
eponychium
nail root
growing point

S. 29 THE HAIR.

Hairs are, like the nails, modifications of epidermis. They are also derived from the germinal layer of skin.

The root of a hair is that part below the skin surface.

The shaft of a hair is the part that extends out beyond the skin surface.

A hair follicle, hair canal, is a small canal opening on the skin surface and extending down into the dermis or subcutaneous tissue. Each follicle is lined by epithelium, continuous with the epithelium of the skin. This epithelium forms the sheath of a hair. It is through this canal that the hair reaches the surface.

The bulb is an enlargement of the epithelium at the bottom of a follicle, and projects into the canal at its inner end. It is by division of germinal cells in the bulb that growth of a hair takes place. New cells are formed and push the older cells towards the skin surface. These older cells become elongated and hardened to form the rodlike hair. Epithelium in the bulb is like the germinal layer of the skin and nails.

Each hair has three layers of cells.

(a) The cuticle or outer layer is composed of several tiers of degenerated cells surrounding the hair. These cells overlap like the scales of a fish. This layer extends along the length of a hair.

(b) The cortex consists of several layers inside of the cuticle. These cells are soft at the bulb but become elongated and hardened towards the shaft.

(c) The medulla consists of cells in the center of a hair. In the shaft these degenerate, and the hair is hollow. The papilla of a hair is a projection of dermis into the bulb through its inner end. Each hair emerges through the skin at an angle. A small muscle, the arrector muscle, extends from the dermis down to the hair root. When this contracts, the hair is straightened.

The entire surface of the body, except the palms of the hands and soles of the feet, is covered by hair.

S. 30 SEBACEOUS GLANDS.

These are little glands which open into a hair follicle. They secrete an oily substance which lubricates the hair and passes out through the hair follicle to moisten the skin. They lie beside a hair follicle. The duct of each is formed by a single layer of cells continuous with the epithelium of the follicle. The secreting end may be single or branched and consist of two or three layers of epithelium. These cells become filled with fat globules, become distended, and degenerate to form the oily secretion. They are modified epithelial cells. New cells continue to form to replace those degenerated.

S. 31 SWEAT OR SUDORIFEROUS GLANDS.

Sweat glands are simple tubelike glands consisting of a single duct or canal opening upon the skin surface. The tube extends down in a spiral manner to end in the dermis or subcutaneous tissue. The duct or canal is formed by a single layer of cells continuous with the epithelium of the skin on the surface. The inner end is coiled upon itself. This secretory part consists of two or three layers of cells.

Sweat glands secret some oil but can also secrete a watery solution containing salt and water, and other waste products of the body in solution. During exertion, or illness accompanied by fever, there is an increased production of heat in the body. These glands then increase their secretion, and drops of sweat appear on the skin. Heat from the body is used to evaporate them. The body temperature is reduced. Treatment aimed at causing a patient to sweat accomplishes the same result in a fevered patient. Sweat glands have nerves supplying them, and the amount of secretion is regulated by nerve control. Sweat glands are most numerous on the palms and soles, but are present throughout the skin.

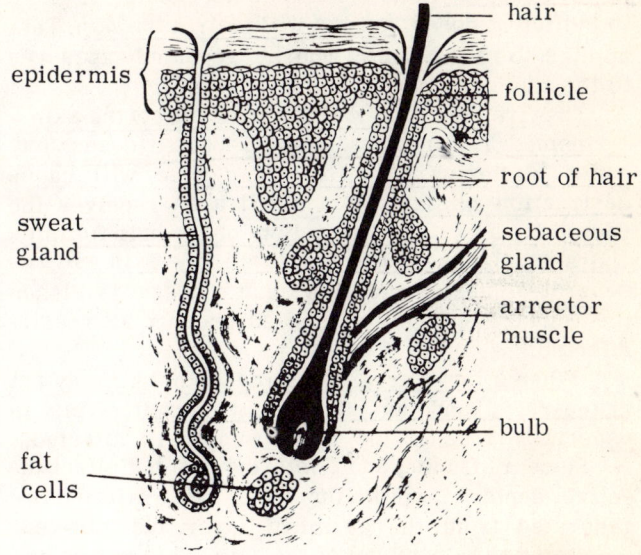

F. 16 DIAGRAM - HAIR, SEBACEOUS, SWEAT GLANDS

S. 32 FUNCTIONS OF THE SKIN.

1. Protection. The skin forms a protective covering for the body. As long as the skin remains unbroken, bacteria are prevented from reaching the body tissues by this route.

2. Insulation. Skin provides insulation from cold.

3. Temperature regulation. As stated in Section 31, secretion of sweat and its evaporation from the body provides a means of reducing body heat.

4. Excretory function. The sweat glands also excrete waste products from the body.

5. Protection from sun. The pigment in the skin helps protect underlying tissues from sunlight.

6. Sensory end-organs. Sensations of touch, pain, heat and cold are received by nerve endings in the skin and conveyed to the brain.

S. 33 RADIOLOGICAL APPLICATIONS.

Radiography does not help in the diagnosis of diseases of the skin. The radiographic technician must make certain that the skin does not receive a large dose of radiation when filming deeper structures.

The therapy technician must give treatments for some skin conditions. In addition, therapy to deeper structures must be applied through the skin.

It is important that the skin does not receive an overdose of radiation when treatments are given.

X-ray radiation has a destructive action on body tissue generally, and the skin is not exempt. If given in sufficient doses, x-rays will destroy the skin. This applies to radiography, wherein repeated exposures to the same skin area may destroy skin.

The first reaction will be a reddening of the skin - erythema. A larger dose or repeated doses may cause blistering. A still larger dose will cause destruction of skin. If a small area receives the radiation, and if the epithelium of the hair follicles and skin glands is not destroyed, the skin will regenerate. These structures lie at a deeper level than the surface epithelium and so are not as readily affected.

When a large area is destroyed, the skin may not regenerate, and an ulcer may result. This is especially true if the blood supply is affected.

Since reddening and blistering will not affect the entire depth of epithelium, the skin will be regenerated from the germinal layer and follicles.

Epilation is removal of the hair. This may be accomplished by using x-rays. Ringworm of the scalp may be treated in this way. Here again the hair will grow in provided the dose given did not destroy the epithelium.

Sometimes x-rays are used to remove superflous hair. This is dangerous as a sufficiently large dose must be given to destroy the hair roots. Cancer has been known to develop following too enthusiastic treatment.

When cancer is being treated, it may be necessary to sacrifice the skin in order to administer a dose large enough to destroy the cancer.

S. 34   TERMS USED IN CHAPTER IV.

THE SKIN.

1. Epidermis:

    (a) horny layer
    (b) translucent, clear layer
    (c) granular layer
    (d) germinal layer

2. Dermis, corium:

    (a) papillary layer
    (b) reticular layer

3. Nails:

    (a) nail root
    (b) nail body
    (c) lunula
    (d) eponychium (hangnail)

4. Hair:

    (a) root
    (b) shaft
    (c) hair follicle
    (d) bulb
    (e) cell layers:
        cuticle
        cortex
        medulla

5. Sweat glands:

    (a) duct
    (b) secretory part

6. Sebaceous glands:

    (a) duct
    (b) secretory part

7. Functions of skin:

    (a) protection from disease
    (b) insulation
    (c) temperature regulation
    (d) excretory function
    (e) protection from sun
    (f) sensory end organs

CHAPTER V. BONES: CLASSIFICATION: STRUCTURE: DEVELOPMENT.

Section 35 - 41 deal with:

1. bony prominences and depressions,
2. functions of bones,
3. classification of bones,
4. structure of bones,
5. development of bones,
6. congenital anomalies,
7. radiographic appearance of growing bone.

The skeletal or osseous system includes all the bones of the body which together make up the human skeleton. Joints or articulations are included with the skeletal system. A study of the various joints may be made most satisfactorily if they are related to the bones of the same part.

S. 35 TERMS - BONY PROMINENCES and DEPRESSIONS.

Many of the terms listed below are also used with reference to other parts of the body as well as to bones.

Os (pl. ossa; adj. osseous): the Latin word for bone. To ossify means to form bone; ossification is used in the same sense. These terms refer to the formation of bone cells, and the deposition of calcium phosphate about these cells and their processes.

Ossicle: a little bone; auditory ossicles of ear.

Calcification: refers to the deposition of calcium in any structure, with no bone cell formation.

Articulation (adj. articular): a joint.

Ala (pl. alae): a wing, e.g., ala of sacrum or ilium.

Body (L. corpus): the principal part of a structure, and the shaft of a long bone.

Cornu (pl. cornua): a horn; cornu of the hyoid bone.

Crest (L. crista): a narrow ridge of bone, e.g., the crest of the ilium.

Condyle (pl. condyles): a rounded knoblike projection; medial and lateral condyles of the femora.

Epicondyle (epi, upon): a bony projection on or above the condyle; epicondyles of the femur.

Fissure: a narrow slit; fissure fracture of skull.

Foramen (pl. foramina): a hole or orifice in a bone, e.g., foramen magnum of the occipital bone; vertebral and intervertebral foramina.

Fossa (pl. fossae): a depression or ditch, e.g., coronoid and olecranon fossae of the humerus.

Sulcus (pl. sulci): a groove or depression or furrow on a bone to accommodate a tendon, etc.

Head (L. caput): the expanded part of a structure, or the expanded end of a bone; heads of: radius, humerus, ulna, femur, tibia, fibula, metacarpal.

Capitulum or capitellum (L. caput, head; ulum, little): a little head; the capitulum of the humerus.

Lumen: a window or opening; the cavity in a hollow organ; lumen of the small intestines.

Meatus: a canal, a long tubelike passage or canal, e.g., external and internal auditory meatuses.

Neck (L. collum): The constricted part of an organ, the narrow part adjacent to the head, e.g., necks of humerus, radius, femur, tibia, scapula, etc.

Process: any definite or marked bony prominence, e.g., mastoid process of temporal bone; styloid processes of the radius, ulna and temporal bones.

Ramus (pl. rami): a branch; ramus of the mandible.

Shaft (Anglo-Saxon scaeft): the principal part of, or the body of, a bone, e.g., shafts of humerus, radius, ulna, femur, tibia, fibula, metacarpal.

Sinus (three different meanings)
  (a) a cavity within a bone: the paranasal or the accessory nasal sinuses; the frontal, ethmoidal, maxillary, and sphenoidal sinuses of the skull;
  (b) a passage from one body cavity to another, or to the outside: a sinus tract from an infected bone to the surface of the body;
  (c) a large lake-like cavity containing blood, e.g., the venous sinuses of the skull.

Spine or spinous process: a sharp, slender process or sharp process, e.g., spines of ischium, scapula, spinous process of a vertebra, etc.

Symphysis: a joining together, a joint with very little movement; the symphysis pubis between the pubic bones.

Trochanter: a very large rounded process; the greater and lesser trochanters of the femur.

Tubercle: a smaller rounded bony process; the greater and lesser tubercles of the humerus.

Tuberosity: a large rounded process.

S. 36   THE FUNCTIONS OF BONES.

1. Protection. Bones protect many important organs and other structures from injury. The skull protects the brain, eye and ear. The thorax encloses the heart and lungs. The pelvis affords some protection to the pelvic organs.

2. Support and framework. Like the steel or wooden framework of a building bones give support and shape to the body; they afford attachment to muscles and ligaments.

3. Levers. Bones, together with adjacent joints form levers of various kinds, and permit movement in restricted and definite directions.

S. 37   CLASSIFICATION OF BONES.

1. Long bones: humerus, radius, femur, tibia, etc.

2. Short bones: metacarpals.

3. Flat bones: scapula, and some of the bones of the skull.

4. Irregular bones: the vertebrae.

F. 17   PARTS OF A LONG BONE

example - femur -

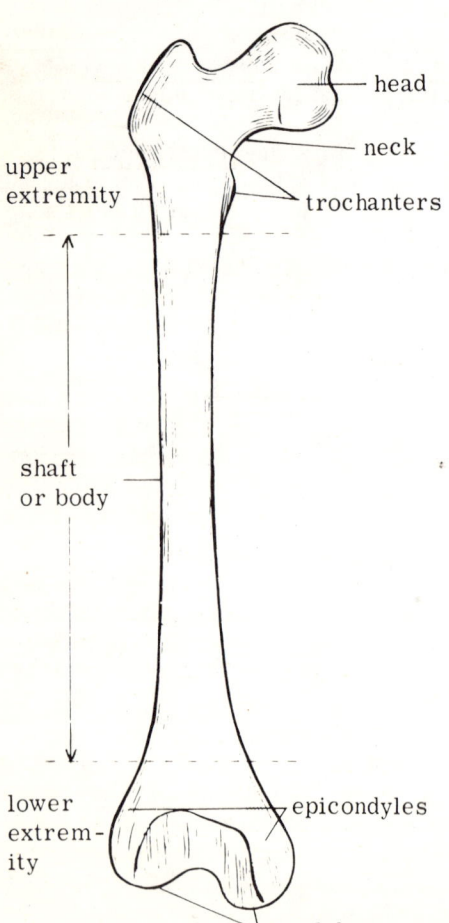

F. 18   STRUCTURE OF A LONG BONE

longitudinal section of femur -

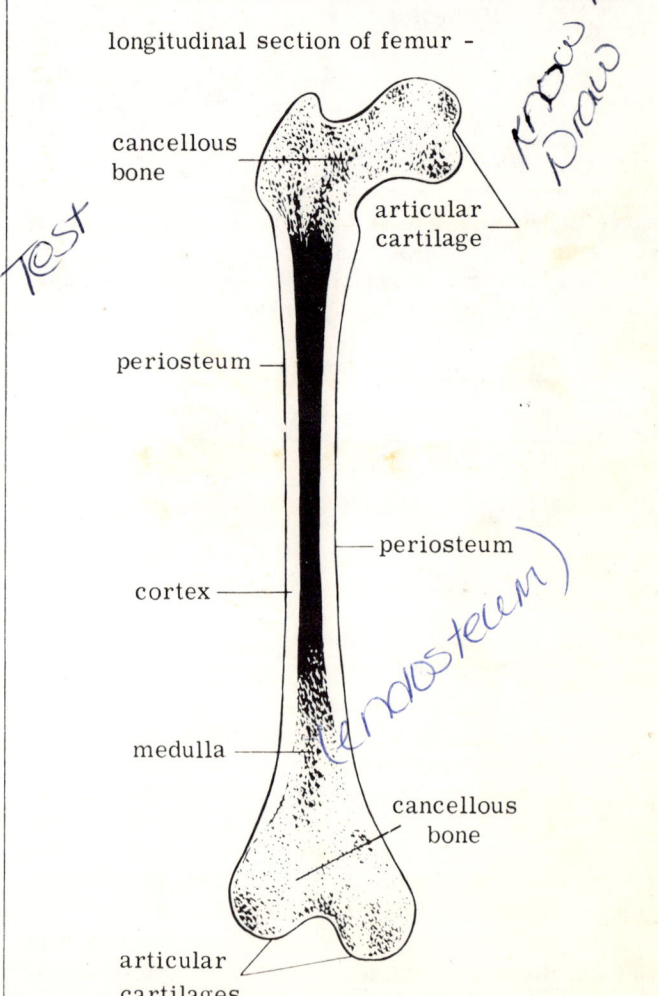

METHODS OF DESCRIBING BONES.

1. A long bone:
   (a) an upper, superior or proximal extremity or end,
   (b) a body or shaft,
   (c) a lower, inferior or distal extremity or end.

2. A short bone:
   (a) a base or proximal end,
   (b) a body or shaft,
   (c) a head or distal end.

3. Some other bones:
   (a) a body,
   (b) processes, e.g., vertebrae.

S. 38 STRUCTURE OF BONES.

1. The Periosteum is an outer layer of thin bone covering the entire bone, except the ends which help to form a joint. These ends are covered by articular cartilages. The periosteum may be stripped off. This often occurs when a bone is fractured. The periosteum assists in the healing of bones following fracture or infection. (adj. periosteal)

2. The Cortex is a layer of dense, compact bone under the periosteum. In the shafts of long bones a fairly thick layer of compact bone is present. At the extremities, under the articular (joint) cartilages, it is thin. In short, flat, and irregular bones, it forms a thin layer. (adj. cortical)

3. Cancellous bone is porous, loosely constructed bone like a sponge, with many spaces. It forms a layer under the cortex. In the extremities or ends of long bones, and in the bodies of many other bones, it forms all but the thin cortex and periosteum.

4. The Medulla is a central cavity in the shafts of long bones. This cavity is lined by the endosteum.

5. The Bone Marrow is the tissue occupying the medulla of the long bones, and the spaces in the loosely knit cancellous bone. Two types are present.
   (a) Red bone marrow is found in the bones of infants and children, and in adults in cancellous bone at the ends of long bones, as well as in the bodies of the sternum, vertebrae, ribs, etc. It forms new red blood cells which are discharged into the blood vessels of bones to enter the blood stream.
   (b) Yellow Bone Marrow replaces the red bone marrow in the long bones of adults, and contains much fat.

F. 19 RADIOGRAPHIC APPEARANCE OF GROWING BONE.

In a newborn infant — In a child of 13 years

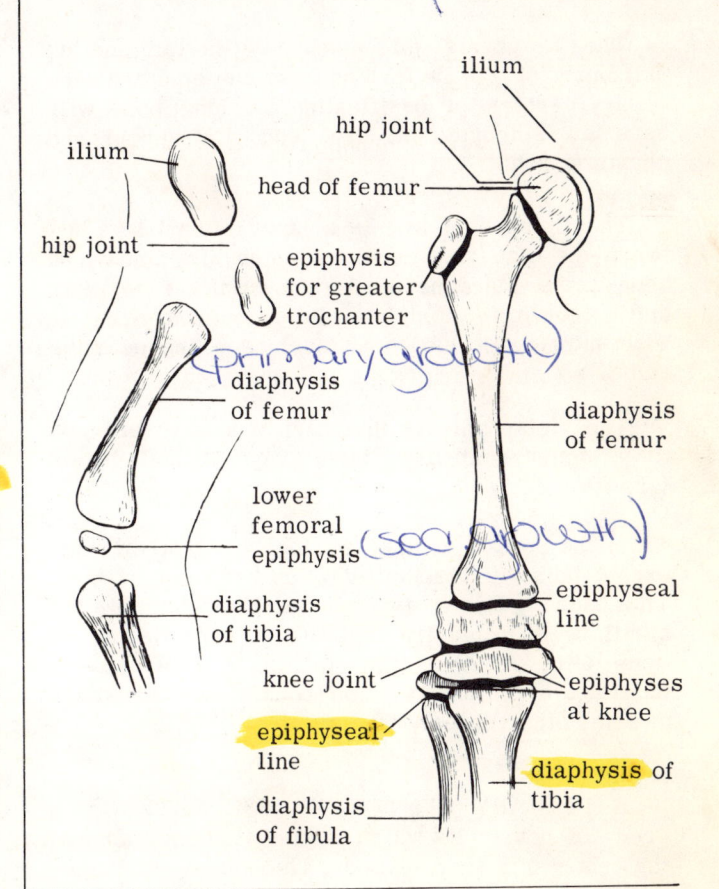

[Diagram labels: ilium, hip joint, head of femur, epiphysis for greater trochanter, diaphysis of femur (primary growth), lower femoral epiphysis (sec growth), diaphysis of tibia, knee joint, epiphyseal line, epiphyses at knee, diaphysis of tibia, diaphysis of fibula]

6. The Nutrient Foramen is a small canal passing through the periosteum and other layers of bone to reach the medulla. It contains blood vessels. In long bones it lies near the center of the shaft. In the radiographs it may be mistaken for a fracture.

7. Blood Supply. Bones receive their blood supply by means of the nutrient artery, which enters the bone through a nutrient foramen. Small arteries also penetrate the periosteum.

Test

8. The Bones of The Skull have a construction that is peculiar to them. The outer table is a layer of compact bone under the periosteum. The inner table is a similar layer of compact bone. The diploe is a layer of cancellous bone between the outer and inner tables.

it has no medulla — important

S. 39 DEVELOPMENT OF BONES.

The Diaphysis (pl. diaphyses) is that part of a bone formed from a primary center of ossification, and includes the shaft or body. Dia (through) and physis (growth).

The Epiphysis (pl. epiphyses) is the end or extremity of a bone formed from one or more secondary centers of ossification. A long bone will have an epiphysis at each end. Epi (upon) and physis (growth).

The Epiphyseal line is a layer of cartilage between the diaphysis and each epiphysis. Growth of bone takes place here, and the cartilage persists until growth is complete. In processed films it will show as a dark or translucent line near the ends.

The Metaphysis is that part of a diaphysis next to an epiphyseal line. Meta (beyond) and physis (growth).

In the human embryo all the bones of the body except those of the skull develop first as cartilage. This is complete in two months. Following this the cartilage is gradually replaced by bone tissue. At term (nine months) bone will have replaced the cartilage in the shafts of long bones and in the bodies of some other bones.

A PRIMARY CENTER OF OSSIFICATION is a group of bone cells which make their appearance at the center of a shaft or body. These bone cells multiply and replace the cartilage of the shaft or body. Calsium phosphate is deposited between the bone cells cementing them together. This is the diaphysis.

SECONDARY CENTERS OF OSSIFICATION are other groups of bone cells which make their appearance in each end of a bone, or bony process. In long bones, except those about the knees, these centers appear after birth. Any one center appears at a definite age in months or years. In girls the age of appearance is slightly younger than in boys. The replacement by bone tissue takes place gradually over a period of months or years. It is complete at a definite age for each bone. In some bones two or more secondary centers are present in the same end. Some bony prominences also have separate centers. Each of these forms bone, and they eventually fuse into a single solid bone mass, the epiphysis.

The epiphyseal line is a layer of cartilage that persists between a diaphysis and each epiphysis. It is here that longitundial growth of bone occurs, and the cartilage persists until growth is completed. Then this cartilage is replaced by bone. This also occurs at a definite age for each bone.

The short bones have a primary and only one other or secondary center, with one epiphysis. The first metacarpal, first metatarsal, and all phalanges have epiphyses at the bases or proximal ends only. The second, third, fourth and fifth metacarpals and metatarsals have a single epiphysis at the distal ends, with the epiphyseal lines adjacent to the epiphyses.

The bone age, and the approximate age of a child or young adult may be determined from radiographs of the joints. This is possible because the age of the appearance of any one epiphysis, the age at which it completely replaces cartilage, and the age when it becomes fused with the shaft, is fairly constant. Tables have been compiled from many normal cases giving this date, e.g., the head of the femur begins to ossify at the end of the first year, and unites with the shaft at eighteen years of age.

Radiographs are of some help in the diagnosis of diseases which affect growth of bones.
In cretinism (lack of thyroid) the epiphyses appear late.
In some types of dwarfism they appear prematurely, and fuse at an early age, stopping growth.

S. 40 CONGENITALS ANOMALIES.

1. The centers of ossification of a bone may not unite to form a single bone, but may remain as separate entities throughout life.
2. A bone may have more centers than usual, and these may not unite. The extra center will appear as a separate bone and may be mistaken for a fracture.
3. One center may not unite with the other centers of that bone but with an adjacent bone, e.g., vertebrae.

S. 41 RADIOGRAPHIC APPEARANCE OF GROWING BONES.

A pregnancy in a doubtful case may be diagnosed by a radiograph of the abdomen after about the twelfth week, when the fetal bones should have sufficient calcium to outline them.

In radiographs including the joints of young children the shafts of bones will be outlined, as they will be ossified.

The secondary centers will show as small bone islands close to, and in line with, the shafts, surrounded by a clear zone. This clear zone is occupied by cartilage and is not a gap. The entire bone is present and has the shape of the adult bone. Those parts that are still cartilage are not outlined. Cartilage is translucent (lucent).

The translucent lines close to the ends of long bones in older children are due to the translucent cartilage at the epiphyseal lines, not bone gaps.

Likewise the spaces between bones at joints in adults are not gaps but are due to the cartilage layers which cover the ends of bones at joints.

S. 42. TERMS DESCRIBED IN CHAPTER V.

os
ossify
ossification
calcification

Bony parts and prominences:

ala
alae
body
corpus
corpora
cornu
cornua
crest
crista
condyle
epicondyle
fissure
foramen
foramina
fossa

fossae
grove
sulcus
sulci
head
caput
capitulum
capitellum
lumen
meatus
neck
collum
process
shaft
paranasal sinus
venous sinus
ramus
rami
spine
spinous process
symphysis
trochanter
tubercle

Classification of bones:

long bones
short bones
irregular bones
flat bones

proximal end or extremity
distal end or extremity
head
body - shaft
base

Structure of bones:

periosteum
cortex
cancellous bone
endosteum
medulla
bone marrow
red bone marrow

yellow bone marrow
nutrient foramen
outer table
inner table
diploe

Development of bones:

diaphysis
diaphyses
epiphysis
epiphyses
metaphysis
metaphyses
epiphyseal line
primary center of ossification
secondary center of ossification
bone age
premature ossification
delayed ossification

F. 20 EPIPHYSES OF HUMERUS, RADIUS, ULNA

2 years   10 years   2 years   10 years

F. 21 EPIPHYSES OF TIBIA & FIBULA

2 years   14 years

F. 22 EPIPHYSES OF HAND

3 years

F. 23 EPIPHYSES OF PELVIC BONES

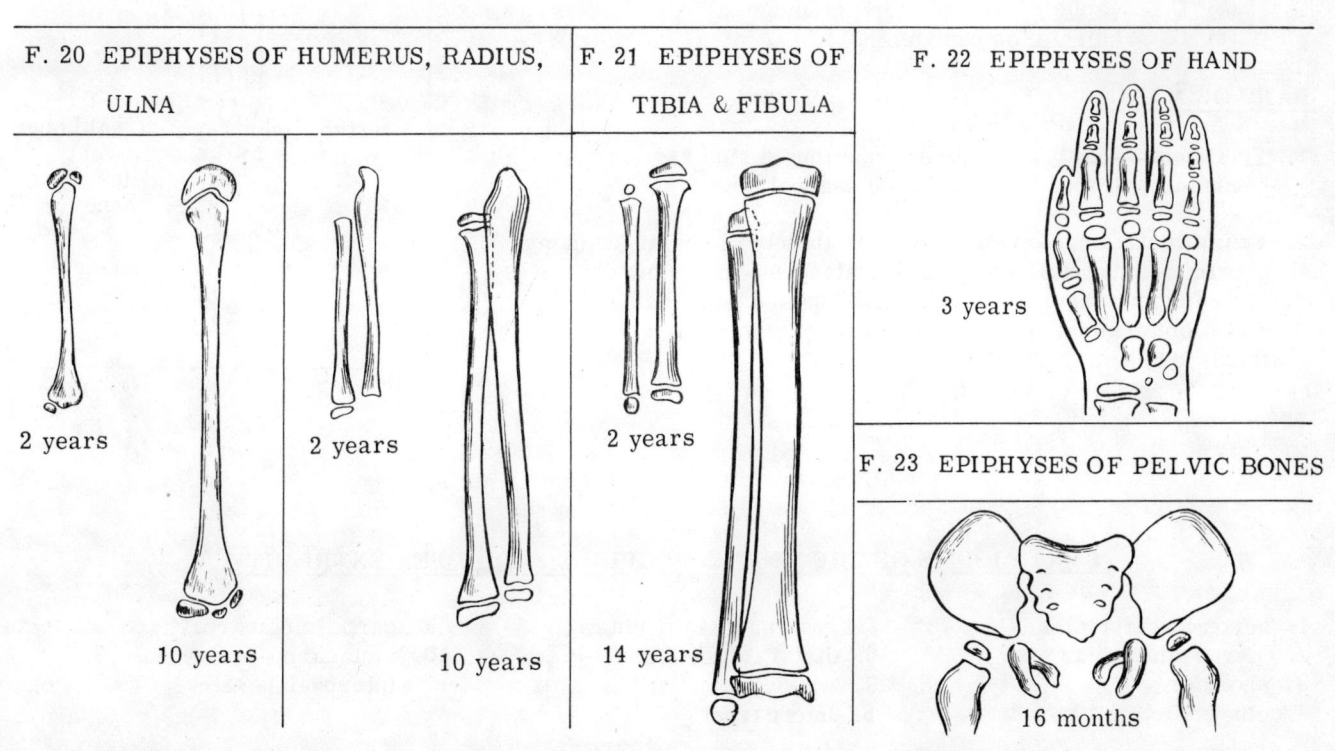

16 months

CHAPTER VI. THE SHOULDER GIRDLE AND UPPER EXTREMITY.

S. 43 BONES OF THE SHOULDER GIRDLE AND UPPER EXTREMITY.

SHOULDER GIRDLE:
1. Scapula (pl. scapulae), the shoulder blade.
2. Clavicle (pl. clavicles), the collar bone.

ARM OR BRACHIUM: "66" "99"
1. Humerus (pl. humeri), the arm bone.

FOREARM OR ANTIBRACHIUM (ANTEBRACHIUM): "66" "99"
1. Radius (pl. radii; adj. radial),
2. Ulna (pl. ulnae; adj. ulnar). (inside of arm)

WRIST OR CARPUS:
Eight carpal bones in two rows and called proximal row and distal row, named from thumb side as:

1. Proximal row: (thumb side of hand in PA projection)
    (1) N. navicular or scaphoid, os noviculare,
    (2) L. lunate or semilunar, os lunatum,
    (3) T. triangular or triquetral os triquetrum.
    (4) P. pisiform, os pisiforme.

2. Distal row:
    (5) M. greater multangular, trapezium, os multangulum majus,
    (6) M. lesser multangular, trapezoid, os multangulum minus,
    (7) C. capitate, os capitatum, os magnum,
    (8) H. hamate, os hamatum.

(use "saying")

HAND OR MANUS:

1. Five metacarpal bones, named from thumb side as: first, second, third, fourth, and fifth metacarpal bones,

2. Fourteen phalanges (sing, phalanx): thumb: 2 phalanges named proximal and distal or terminal phalanges, index, middle, ring, little fingers: each has 3 phalanges, named proximal, middle, distal or terminal phalanges. Alternate names: first, second, third, fourth, fifth digits.

F. 24 THE SHOULDER GIRDLE AND UPPER EXTREMITY.

- sterno-clavicular
- clavicle
- acromio-clavicular
- shoulder joint
- scapula
- humerus
- elbow joint
- radius
- ulna
- wrist joint
- carpal bones
- metacarpal bones
- phalanges

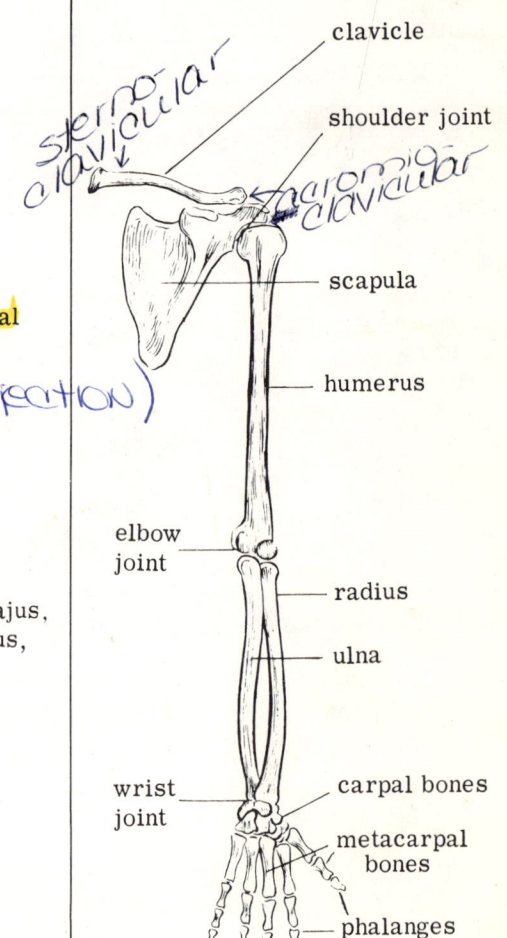

S. 44 JOINTS OF THE SHOULDER GIRDLE AND UPPER EXTREMITY:

1. acromio-clavicular
2. sterno-clavicular
3. shoulder
4. elbow
5. proximal radio-ulnar
6. distal radio-ulnar
7. wrist
8. intercarpal
9. carpo-metacarpal
10. metacarpo-phalangeal
11. interphalangeal

S. 45 IMPORTANT PARTS AND PROMINENCES OF THE BONES OF THE UPPER EXTREMITY.

SCAPULA:
1. head
2. neck
3. body
4. glenoid cavity
5. spine
6. acromion
7. coracoid process
8. angles:
    medial
    lateral
    inferior
9. borders:
    superior
    axillary
    vertebral

CLAVICLE:
1. body
2. sternal end, extremity
3. acromial end or extremity

HUMERUS:
1. upper end, or extremity
    head
    anatomical neck
    surgical neck
    greater tubercle
    lesser tubercle

2. shaft or body:
    deltoid tubercle
3. lower end, extremity:
    capitulum, capitellum
    trochlea
    medial epicondyle
    lateral epicondyle
    olecranon fossa
    coronoid fossa

RADIUS:
1. upper end (extremity)
    head
    neck
    radial tuberosity
2. shaft or body
3. lower end, or extremity
    styloid process
    ulnar notch
    articular surface

ULNA:
1. upper end (extremity)
    olecranon
    coronoid process
    semilunar notch
    radial notch

2. shaft or body.
3. lower end (extremity)
    head
    styloid process

CARPAL BONES: (eight)

navicular:
    navicular tubercle

greater multangular:
    a tubercle

hamate:
    hamulus

METACARPAL BONES: (five)
1. base or proximal end
2. body
3. head or distal end

PHALANGES: (fourteen)
1. base or proximal end
2. body
3. head or distal end

S. 46 DETAILED STUDY OF THE BONES OF THE SHOULDER GIRDLE AND UPPER EXTREMITY.

The upper extremity is called the upper limb or the arm by the laity. Medically it is termed the upper, superior or proximal extremity. It is superior to or above the lower limb, and lies closer to the head end of the body; hence proximal. Do not confuse this term with the upper, superior or proximal end of a long bone.

The upper extremity includes the shoulder, arm or brachium, forearm or antibrachium, and the hand or manus.
The hand includes the wrist.

THE BONES OF THE SHOULDER GIRDLE.

The shoulder has two bones: the scapula, and the clavicle. These bones form the shoulder girdle.

1. THE SCAPULA.

Scapula, shoulder blade (pl. scapulae; adj. scapular).

The scapula or shoulder blade is a flat triangular bone lying against the upper, lateral, posterior chest wall. It is separated from the chest wall by muscles. The sole connection with the bones of the trunk is at the acromio-clavicular joint. The clavicle, by its articulations with the sternum and acromion acts as a brace or prop for the scapula.

The scapula has a body, neck, head and two processes. These are the coracoid process and the spine of the scapula, which is continued out over the shoulder as the acromion.

Process = "sticks out"

The body of the scapula is flat and triangular and has three borders. Its inner border lies close to the vertebral column and is called the vertebral or medial border. The outer border lies behind and close to the armpit or axilla, and is called the axillary or lateral border. The upper or superior border is short, and at its lateral or outer end is a depression, the scapular notch. The inner end of this border, at its junction with the vertebral border, forms the medial angle. The lower end of the body is rounded and forms the inferior angle.

The spine of the scapula is a narrow ridge or crest of bone that projects back (posteriorly) from the posterior surface of the body above its middle. It passes transversely (crosswise) from the medial to the lateral border. It divides the posterior surface of the body into the supraspinatus fossa above, and infraspinatus fossa below. The supraspinatus and infraspinatus muscles are attached to the corresponding fossae. The spine can often be felt through the skin.

The acromion is a flat rounded bony prominence continuous with the lateral end of the spine of the scapula. It extends out over the shoulder joint. This process can often be felt through the skin at the shoulder tip.

The neck of the scapula is the thickened, slightly constricted part continuous with the upper, outer part of the body.

The head of the scapula is a poorly defined, slightly expanded part lateral to the neck. It does not present the usual enlargement found in the heads of most other bones.

The glenoid cavity or fossa is an oval depression on the outer surface of the head, somewhat cup-shaped, with slightly raised borders. It articulates with the head of the humerus to form the shoulder joint.

The coracoid process is a beaklike projection of bone continuous with, and projecting forward from, the neck of the scapula. It lies below the outer part of the clavicle. It can sometimes be felt in the infraclavicular fossa near its outer end.

2. THE CLAVICLE.

Clavicle, collar bone (pl. clavicles; adj. clavicular).

The clavicle is a long slender bone resembling somewhat an old-fashioned key, hence the Latin name clavicula, a key. It has a double curve, and lies almost horizontally in front of the upper thorax. Its inner or sternal end articulates with the sternum. Its outer or acromial end articulated with the acromion of the scapula. Depressions above and below the clavicle, visible in thin subjects, are called the supra and infraclavicular fossae. As groups of lymph glands (nodes) lie in these fossae, they are important to the technician doing therapy. The clavicle is visible through the skin in thin subjects and may be felt in the fat.

F. 25 THE SCAPULA AND CLAVICLE

1. Scapula - dorsal view -
2. Scapula - frontal view -
3. Scapula - lateral view -
4. Clavicle (collar bone)

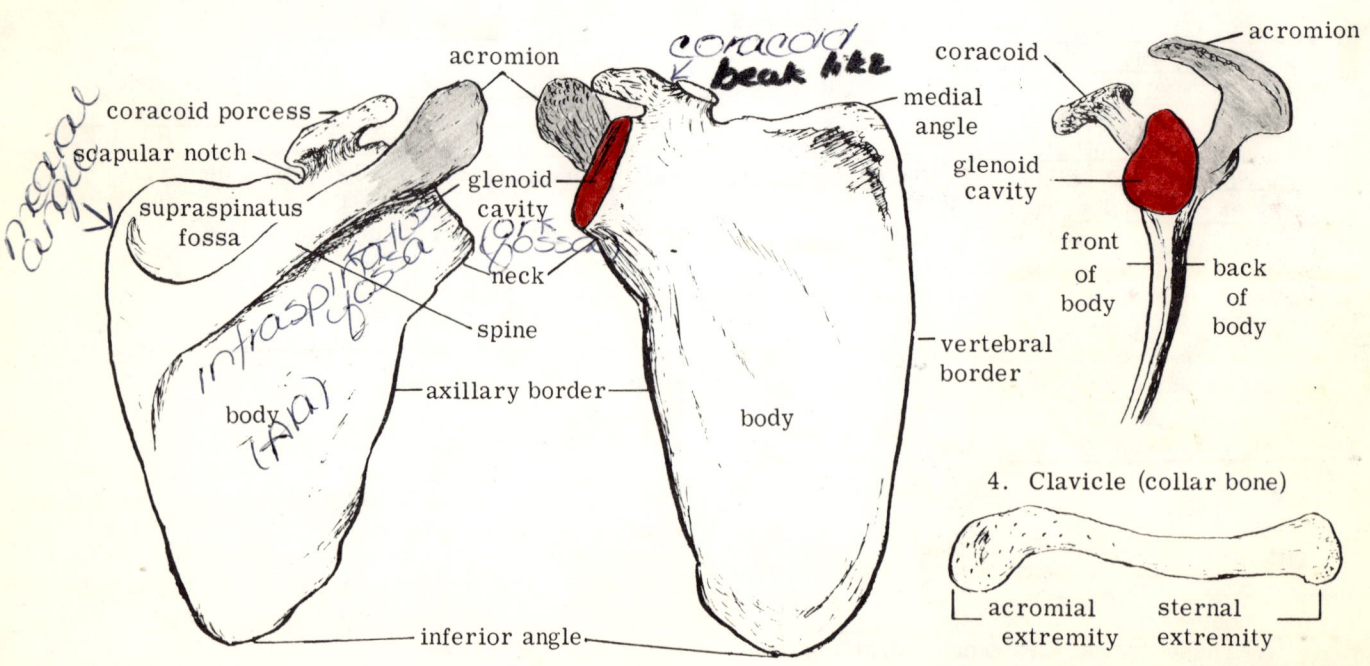

BONES OF THE UPPER EXTREMITY.

1. THE HUMERUS.

Humerus, arm bone (pl. humeri; adj. humeral).

The humerus or arm bone is a long cylindrical bone extending from the shoulder joint to the elbow. It is described as having: superior and proximal end or extremity (including a head, neck, greater and lesser tubercles); a shaft or body; and a lower, inferior or distal end or extremity (including a trochlea, capitulum, medial and lateral epicondyles, a coronoid fossa, and olecranon fossa).

The head of the humerus (L. caput humeri) is the smooth, expanded, rounded upper end that articulates with the glenoid cavity of the scapula to form the shoulder joint.

The anatomical neck is the slightly constricted obliquely directed part adjacent to the head.

The greater tubercle (L. tuberculum majus) is the large rounded bony prominence on the upper, lateral border just below the anatomical neck. It has small depressions for the insertions of the spinatus muscles.

The lesser tubercle (L. tuberculum minor) is a smaller bony prominence on the front of the upper humerus just below the anatomical neck.

The surgical neck is that constricted part of the upper humerus below the tubercles. It is called the surgical neck, as fractures may occur here.

The shaft or body is a long rounded part that becomes flattened from front to back as it nears the elbow.

The deltoid tubercle is a rough prominence on the front or anterior surface just above the midpoint of the humerus into which the deltoid muscle inserts.

The trochlea (pulley) is that part of the distal end of the humerus that articulates with the semilunar notch of the ulna. It occupies more than the medial half of the lower articular surface of the humerus. It is rounded from front to back with a depression like a pulley between its two halves.

The capitulum or capitellum (little head) is a small rounded prominence also on the lower end of the humerus. It lies on the outer or lateral side of the trochlea. The trochlea and capitulum are actually condyles.

The coronoid fossa is a depression on the front of the humerus immediately above the trochlea. The coronoid process of the ulna fits into this when the forearm is flexed (bent).

The olecranon fossa is a depression on the back or posterior surface of the humerus above the trochlea into which the olecranon fits when the forearm is extended (straightened).

The medial epicondyle (epi, upon, and condyle) is a knucklelike rounded bone prominence on the medial border of the lower humerus above the trochlea.

The lateral epicondyle is a similar smaller bony prominence on the outer border of the lower humerus above the capitulum.

The distal articular surface of the humerus which is made up of the trochlea and capitulum does not lie at right angles to the long axis of the shaft. It is directed obliquely laterally, giving the carrying angle.

THE FOREARM - ANTIBRACHIUM.

The forearm has two long bones, the radius and ulna, which extend from the elbow to the wrist. When the upper limb is in the anatomical position, with the palm of the hand to the front, these bones lie parallel to each other. The radius is on the outer (lateral) side, the ulna on the inner (medial) side.

2. THE RADIUS.

Radius (pl. radaii; adj, radial).

The radius has an upper, superior or proximal end or extremity (including a head, neck and a radial tuberosity); a body or shaft; and a lower inferior or distal end or extremity (including the distal articular surface, the styloid process, and ulnar notch).

The head of the radius is the upper expanded disclike end that articulates with the capitulum of the humerus.

The neck is the constricted part immediately below the head.

The radial tuberosity is a prominence below the neck on the antero-medial border. The biceps tendon is attached to it.

The shaft or body become gradually larger as it approaches the wrist joint and its articular surface.

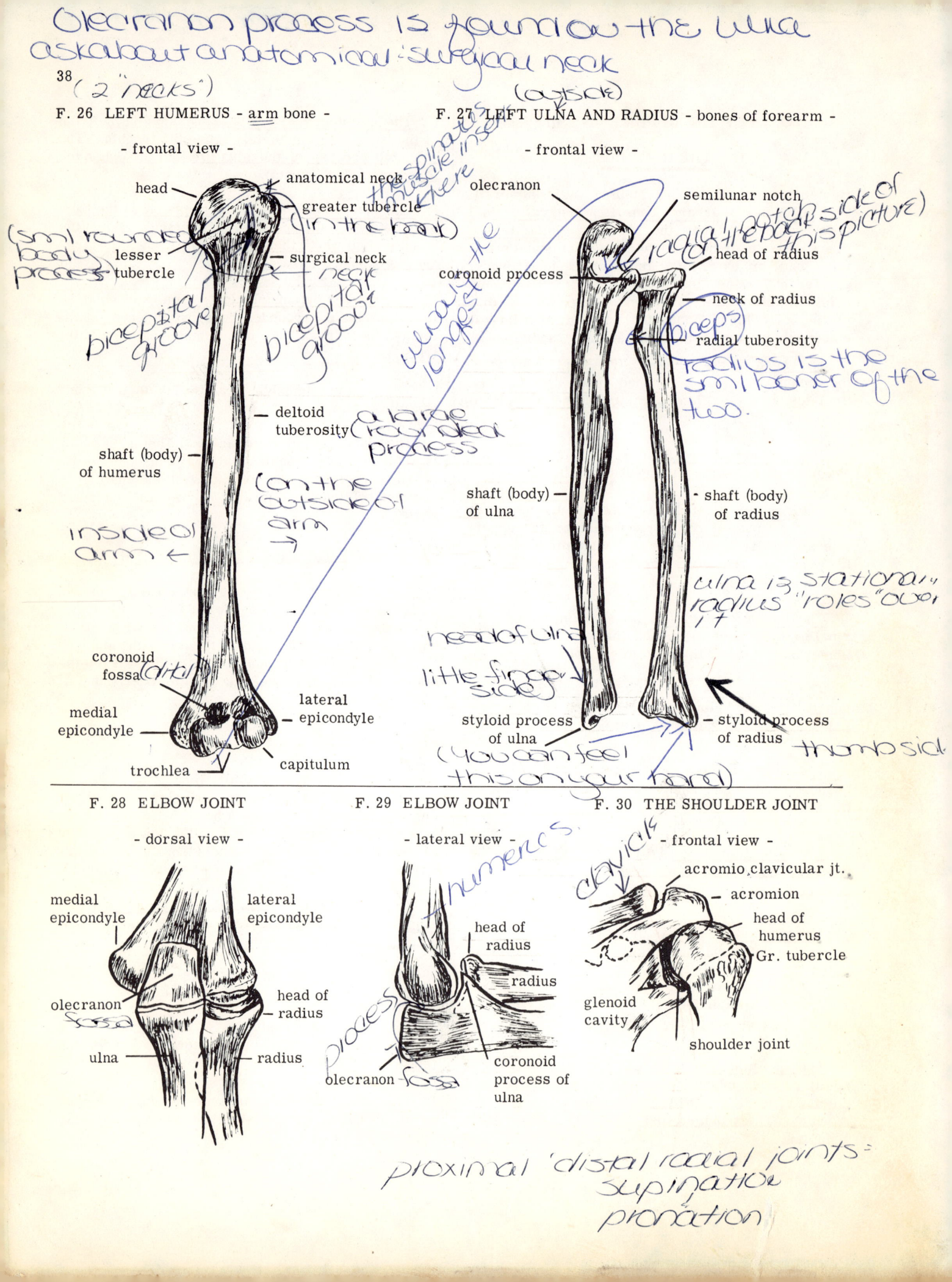

Olecranon process is found on the ulna
ask about anatomical : surgical neck
(2 "necks") (outside)

F. 26 LEFT HUMERUS - arm bone -
- frontal view -

F. 27 LEFT ULNA AND RADIUS - bones of forearm -
- frontal view -

this is where the muscle inserts there

Labels on F.26: head, anatomical neck, greater tubercle (in the head), lesser tubercle, surgical neck, bicipital groove, deltoid tuberosity (a large rounded process — on the outside of arm →), shaft (body) of humerus, coronoid fossa (orbit), medial epicondyle, lateral epicondyle, trochlea, capitulum

(sml rounded body process)
bicipital groove
inside of arm ←
ulna is the longest

Labels on F.27: olecranon, semilunar notch, radial notch (on the back side of this picture), coronoid process, head of radius, neck of radius, radial tuberosity (biceps), shaft (body) of ulna, shaft (body) of radius, styloid process of ulna, styloid process of radius

radius is the sml bone of the two.
ulna is stationary, radius "roles" over it
head of ulna — little finger side
(you can feel this on your hand)
thumb side

F. 28 ELBOW JOINT
- dorsal view -

Labels: medial epicondyle, lateral epicondyle, olecranon fossa, head of radius, ulna, radius

F. 29 ELBOW JOINT
- lateral view -

humerus
process

Labels: head of radius, radius, olecranon fossa, coronoid process of ulna

F. 30 THE SHOULDER JOINT
- frontal view -

clavicle

Labels: acromio clavicular jt., acromion, head of humerus, Gr. tubercle, glenoid cavity, shoulder joint

proximal / distal radial joints = supination / pronation

handwritten at top: never lower Tillies pants mommy might come home (wrist)
navicular (lesser) triangular pisiform (etc)
lunate bone   bone

39

F. 31 THE LEFT HAND - viewed from the back - postero-anterior -

- middle finger 3rd digit
- index finger 2nd digit
- distal phalanx
- distal interphalangeal joint
- ring finger 4th digit
- middle phalanx
- proximal interphalangeal joint
- proximal phalanx
- little finger 5th digit
- thumb, 1st digit
- distal phalanx, thumb
- interphalangeal joint, thumb
- head of proximal phalanx
- body of proximal phalanx
- base of proximal phalanx
- proximal phalanx, thumb
- fifth metacarpo-phalangeal joint
- first metacarpo-phalangeal joint
- head, 5th metacarpal bone
- sesamoid bone
- body, 5th metacarpal bone
- capitate bone
- base, 5th metacarpal bone
- first metacarpal bone
- carpo-metacarpal joint
- carpo-metacarpal joint
- hamate bone
- greater multangular bone
- pisiform bone
- lesser multangular bone
- triangular bone
- navicular (scaphoid) bone
- lunate (semilunar) bone
- radial styloid process
- ulnar styloid process
- radius
- head of ulna

handwritten annotations:
- 2 interphalangeal joint
- wrist it = radius a navicular lunate Triangular not Pisi.
- there is no mp in thumb
- looklike (can be felt) (triquetal?)
- (can be felt) (triquetal)
- ulna / radius
- shortest (1st bone of the)
- (everything # from thumb side)
- 8, 4, 3, 2 (circled beside hamate, pisiform, triangular, lunate)
- 5, 6, 7 (circled beside greater multangular, lesser multangular, navicular)

Carpal Bones, proximal row,

N. navicular (scaphoid)
L. lunate (semilunar)
T. triangular (triquetral)
P. pisiform

Carpal Bones, distal row.

G M. Greater multangular (trapezium
L M. lesser multangular (trapezoid)
C. capitate (os magnum)
H. hamate

Metacarpal bones.

first, second, third, fourth, fifth.

Phalanges

Thumb.
1. proximal
2. distal

Fingers,
1. proximal
2. middle
3. distal (terminal)

handwritten: Pisiform can be felt through skin

F. 32 WRIST - lateral view -

- metacarpal
- capitate bone
- lunate bone
- radius

The styloid process is a large bony prominence on the outer (lateral) border and distal end of the radius. This can be felt through the skin.

The ulnar notch is a depression on the inner border of the lower radius, just above its lower end. The outer border of the head of the ulna fits into this notch.

The lower articular surface is large and forms the wrist joint along with the proximal carpal bones.

3. THE ULNA.

Ulna (pl. ulnae; adj. ulnar).

The ulna lies on the inner (medial) side of the radius. It has: an upper end or extremity (including the olecranon, coronoid process, and semilunar notch); a shaft or body; and a lower end or extremity (including a head and styloid process).

The olecranon is the blunt rounded upper end of the ulna that lies behind the elbow joint. It forms the tip of the elbow, and is palpable through the skin. The tip of the olecranon fits into the olecranon fossa of the humerus when the forearm is extended (straightened).

The coronoid process forms a beaklike projection from the anterior surface of the ulna below and in front of the olecranon. It fits into the coronoid fossa of the humerus when the forearm is flexed.

F. 33 UPPER END OF ULNA
- lateral view -
- olecranon
- semilunar notch
- coronoid process
- radial notch
- shaft

F. 34 LOWER END OF ULNA
- lateral view -
- head of ulna
- shaft
- styloid process

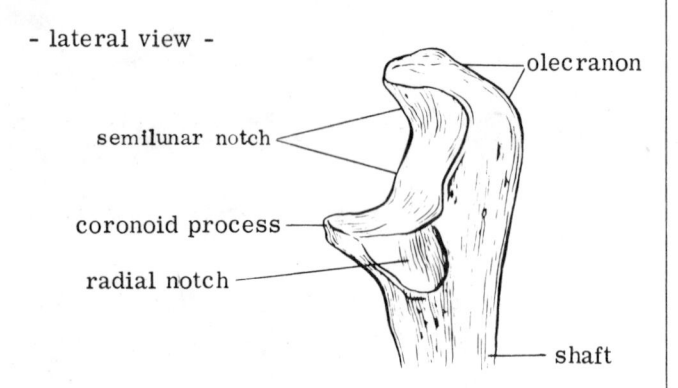

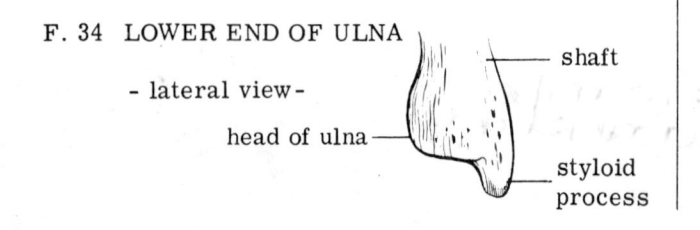

The semilunar notch or trochlear notch is a small, half-moon shaped, concave hollow on the front of the upper ulna. It is formed by the anterior surface of the olecranon and the upper border of the coronoid process. It accommodates the trochlea of the humerus.

The radial notch is a small hollow or concavity on the outer or lateral border of the semilunar notch of the ulna. The inner border of the head of the radius fits into this notch.

The shaft of the ulna is somewhat rounded and becomes smaller as it approaches the wrist.

The head of the ulna is its lower, expanded end, and can be felt through the skin.

The styloid process of the ulna is a very small bony prominence extending down from the posteromedial border of the head. It can be felt through the skin. The student should note that the radial styloid process is much larger than the ulnar and extends down beyond the wrist joint.

THE HAND.

The hand includes the bones of the wrist or carpus, the bones of the palm or metacarpals, and the bones of the digits, the phalanges.

4. THE WRIST OR CARPUS.

There are eight carpal bones. Four of them form a proximal row adjacent to the lower end of the radius. The other four form a distal row adjacent to the metacarpal bones. It is customary to name the proximal row first, beginning at the thumb or radial side, and to follow with the distal row in the same order. Some of these bones have two names in common use, either one of which may appear on a requisition to the x-ray department. The student must know both names.

Proximal row. From the thumb side these bones are named:
- navicular or scaphoid bone
- lunate or semilunar bone
- triangular or triquetral bone
- pisiform bone.

Distal row. From the thumb these bones are named:
- greater multangular or trapezium
- lesser multangular or trapezoid
- capitate or os magnum
- hamate bone.

"navicular view)

The navicular or scaphoid bone is frequently fractured in injuries to the wrist. Its blood supply is poor, and healing takes place slowly, or not at all. Occasionally one fragment becomes dense and appears while on radiographs; it has died. This bone has a tubercle or bony projection in front.

The pisifrom bone lies in front of the triangular bone. Films of the wrist in the postero-anterior projection will show its image superimposed upon that of the triangular bone.

The greater multangular bone has a small tubercle projecting forward from its anterior surface.

The hamate bone has a hook-like process arising from its front or anterior surface, the hamulus.

5. THE METACARPAL BONES.

The five metacarpal bones form the bony framework of the palm and support it. They are also named from the thumb side of the hand as: the first, second, third, fourth, and fifth metacarpal bones.

6. THE PHALANGES.

Phalanx (pl. phalanges; adj. phalangeal). (14 phalanges).
The thumb has two phalanges: proximal, and distal or terminal.
Each of the other digits or fingers has three phalanges: a proximal, middle, and distal or terminal. Some anatomists use the term digit. By some, each digit is termed a finger: hence the thumb would be the first finger. This leads to considerable confusion as other doctors call the index the first finger. It seems more logical to name them as: the thumb, index, middle, ring, and little fingers.

Each metacarpal bone and each phalanx has a base or proximal end, a body, and a head or distal end.

S. 47 JOINTS OF THE UPPER EXTREMITY.

Sterno-clavicular joints:
  (a) clavicular notch of sternum
  (b) inner end of clavicle

Acromio-clavicular joint:
  (a) acromion of scapula
  (b) outer end of clavicle

Shoulder joint:
  (a) glenoid cavity of scapula
  (b) head of humerus

F. 35 SHOULDER AND ACROMIO-CLAVICULAR JOINTS

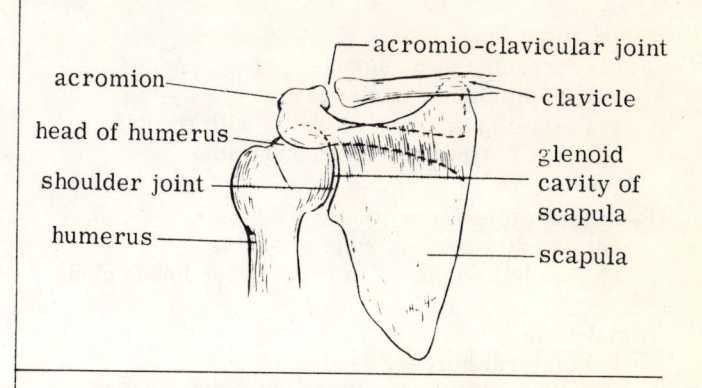

- acromio-clavicular joint
- acromion
- clavicle
- head of humerus
- shoulder joint
- glenoid cavity of scapula
- humerus
- scapula

F. 36 ELBOW JOINT - frontal view -

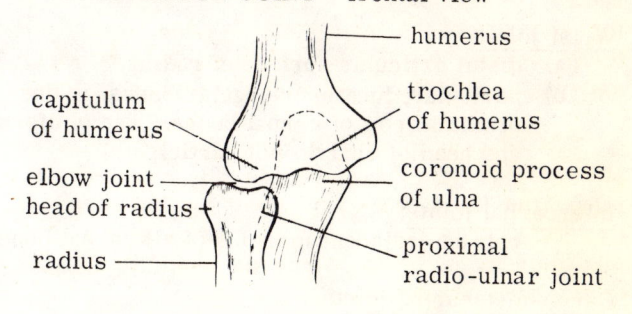

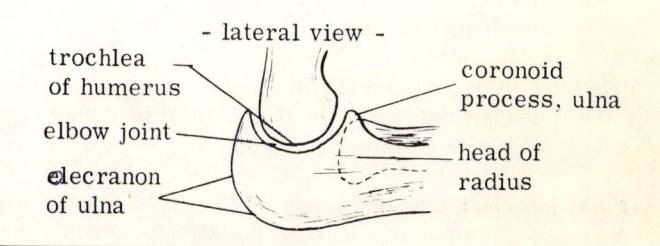

- humerus
- capitulum of humerus
- trochlea of humerus
- elbow joint
- head of radius
- coronoid process of ulna
- radius
- proximal radio-ulnar joint

- lateral view -

- trochlea of humerus
- coronoid process, ulna
- elbow joint
- olecranon of ulna
- head of radius

F. 37 WRIST JOINT and FINGER JOINTS

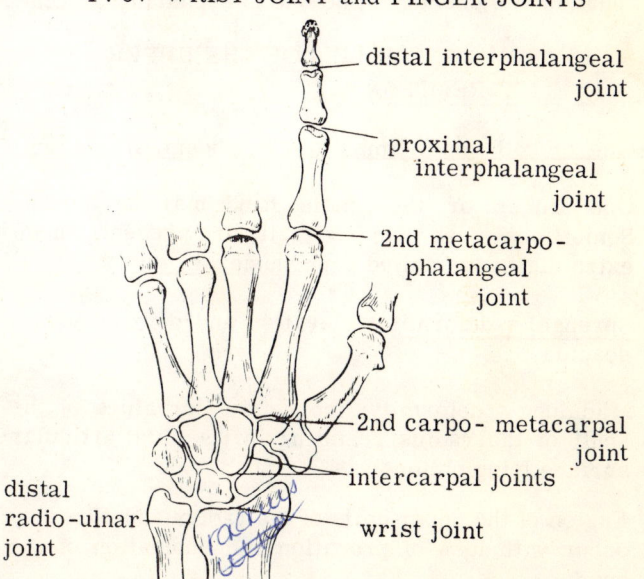

- distal interphalangeal joint
- proximal interphalangeal joint
- 2nd metacarpo-phalangeal joint
- 2nd carpo-metacarpal joint
- intercarpal joints
- distal radio-ulnar joint
- wrist joint

(not palpable because of thick deltoid muscle).

Elbow joint:
(a) trochlea of humerus
(b) capitulum of humerus
(c) semilunar notch of ulna - with trochlea
(d) head of radius - with capitulum

Proximal radio-ulnar joint:
(a) medial border, head of radius
(b) radial notch, on lateral border upper ulna

Distal radio-ulnar joint:
(a) lateral border, head of ulna
(b) ulnar notch of radius, on medial border

Wrist joint:
(a) distal articular surface of radius
(b) navicular, lunate, triangular bones, in the proximal row of carpal bones. The pisiform and head of ulna do not participate.

Intercarpal joints:
between adjacent margins of all carpal bones

Carpo-metacarpal joints:
(a) distal row of carpal bones
(b) bases of five metacarpal bones

Proximal interphalangeal joints:
(a) heads or distal ends of proximal phalanges
(b) bases of middle phalanges

Distal interphalangeal joints:
(a) heads or distal ends of middle phalanges
(b) bases of distal or terminal phalanges.
(Thumb: two phalanges; so one interphalangeal joint).

S. 48 SOME ANOMALIES OF THE UPPER EXTREMITY.

One or both upper limbs may be absent: abrachium.

One finger or the whole hand may be absent. Sometimes more than five digits are present. These extra digits are called supernumerary digits.

Sprengel's deformity: elevation and deformity of a scapula.

Madelung's deformity: there is a curvature of the shaft of the radius resulting in its distal articular surface lying obliquely.

Fusion of the upper cells of the radius and ulna may occur with loss of pronation and supination of the hand.

S. 49 BONY PROMINENCES - UPPER EXTREMITY.

Shoulder: the spine and inferior angle of the scapula can be felt through the skin.
The tip of the acromion overhangs the shoulder joint and can be palpated here.
The coracoid process of the scapula can sometimes be felt below the clavicle near its outer end.
The clavicle can be felt throughout its entire length and in thin subjects is also visible.
The deltoid tubercle cannot be felt but may be located by the depression at the lower end of the deltoid muscle.

Elbow: The medial epicondyle of the humerus may be seen and felt at the inner margin of the elbow, as it forms a prominent projection here.
The lateral epicondyle is smaller, but can also be seen and felt at the lateral (outer) border of the elbow with the forearm flexed (bent).
The olecranon forms the tip of the elbow-joint and can be seen and felt with the elbow flexed.
The head of the radius can be felt as a bony ridge passing transversely across the back of the elbow at the outer border of the joint. Rotating the wrist will help as it may be felt in motion.

Wrist: The styloid process of the radius is large and can be palpated at the outer border of the wrist. The head of the ulna forms a rounded prominence on the medial or ulnar border of the wrist particularly behind, and can be palpated readily. The ulnar styloid process can be felt at the lower end of the head of the ulna posteriorly.
The pisiform is the only carpal bone that is palpable as a separate structure. It lies in front of the triangular bone and can be felt on the ulnar border of the wrist anteriorly.

Metacarpals and digits: The metacarpo-phalangeal joints are prominent on the dorsum of the hand when the fist is closed, and are readily visualized. They are frequently called the knuckles.
The digits and their joints present no difficulty.

S. 50 APPLICATION TO RADIOGRAPHY.

The student should again read section 24, and note the general remarks on this topic. It must be emphasized that in any description of the upper extremity it is always assumed that the subject is in the anatomical position. When the subject is upright, the palms of the hands must be to the front; when the subject is lying down, the palms must be up - in supination, e.g., the radius lies lateral to the ulna only if the anatomical position is maintained.

Find out surgical anatomical

The student should obtain a mounted skeleton and illustrative films to verify the following points.

Scapula and shoulder joints: The scapula lies obliquely against the upper posterior chest. When viewed from the front it is seen, not face on but obliquely. The glenoid cavity also lies obliquely. When viewed from the front, the head of the humerus and glenoid overlap at the shoulder joint.

To obtain true antero-posterior views of the scapula or shoulder joint, the student should rotate the patient slightly. If the subject is lying down, the opposite shoulder must be elevated from the table top. If the patient is upright, the opposite shoulder must be forward. A true lateral cannot be obtained by having the patient in the lateral position. The subject must be turned so that the opposite shoulder is not superimposed.

Calcifications about the shoulder. These usually lie above or behind the greater tubercle of the humerus, in or about the tendons here. They may be demonstrated by turning the arm in or out, i.e., by internal or external rotation.

Humerus: An antero-posterior view is obtained by having the arm in the anatomical position. A lateral view taken at right angles to this may be taken by rotating the arm across the chest or with the hand on the hip. Following injury, the arm is often in a sling. No attempt must be made to move the arm, but the whole body may be rotated to get a lateral view.

Elbow and forearm: In the anatomical position the radius and ulna are parallel. With the palm down the radius crosses the ulna. An antero-posterior view is obtained with the forearm extended, the back of the arm and forearm resting on the film holder, and the shoulder AT THE SAME LEVEL. This is accomplished with the patient supine on a table, or with the patient sitting on a low stool beside the table so that the shoulder is on a level with the rest of the limb. If the patient leans over to the same side as the affected limb, overlapping of the radius and ulna may be avoided. To get a true lateral view of the elbow and forearm, the shoulder must be at the same level as the elbow. This may be done by building up the table top or by having the patient sit on a low stool beside the table. The ulnar side of the forearm must rest upon the film, with the wrist in the lateral position. Following injury, the patient usually holds the forearm in partial flexion as this seems more comfortable. No attempt should be made to straighten the elbow. A film taken with the tip of the elbow only touching the film holder is not sufficient for the A P view. Two A P views should be taken: one with the back of the forearm resting on the film holder, the other with the humerus on the holder and the forearm supported in its flexed position.

Wrist: There is considerable overlapping of the bones at the wrist, regardless of what position is assumed. Therefore, antero-posterior, postero-anterior and oblique views are taken. In addition, adducting the hand will open up the outer part of the wrist, while abduction will open up the inner part.

Metacarpal bones: Because these bones lie so close together and have such limited movement, true lateral views will show overlapping of bones. For this reason oblique views are also routine.

Digits: When only one finger is injured, it is a simple matter to get a lateral view by having the patient hold the other fingers out of the way. This is a "must" in baseball injuries. When several fingers are injured, lateral views may be obtained by flexing each finger to a different degree, so that the images are not superimposed.

S. 51 TERMS USED IN CHAPTER VI.

acromion
acromial (adj.)
acromial extremity, end of clavicle
acromio-clavicular joint
anatomical neck of humerus
angles of scapula *(inferior, medial, axillary)*
antibrachium - forearm
arm bone
axilla *(arm pit)*
axillae (pl.)
axillary (adj.)
axillary border of scapula

bones of upper, superior or proximal extremity
borders of scapula *axillary vertebral*
brachium - arm
brachial (adj.)
capitate bone
capitellum or capitulum of humerus
carpus - wrist
carpal (adj.)
carpal bones
carpo-metacarpal joints
clavicle

clavicles (pl.)
clavicular (adj.)
collar bone
coracoid process of scapula
coronoid fossa of humerus
coronoid process of ulna
deltoid tubercle or tuberosity
distal end or extremity of:
 humerus
 radius
 ulna
distal interphalangeal joints

distal radio-ulnar joints
elbow
forearm - antibrachium
glenoid cavity
greater multangular bone
hamate bone
greater tubercle of humerus
heads of:
    scapula
    humerus
    radius
    metacarpal bones
    phalanges
hamulus of hamate bone
humerus
humeri (pl.)
humeral (adj.)
inferior angle of scapula
infraspinatus
intercarpal joints
interphalangeal joints
lateral angle of scapula
lateral epicondyle of humerus
lesser multangular bone
lunate bone
medial angle of scapula
metacarpal bones
metacarpo-phalangeal joints
middle phalanx
multangular bones
navicular bone

necks of:
    scapula
    humerus
    radius
olecranon
olecranon fossa of humerus
phalanx
phalanges (pl.)
phalangeal (adj.)
pisiform bone
proximal phalanx
proximal interphalangeal joints
proximal radio-ulnar joints
radius
radii (pl.)
radial (adj.)
radial tuberosity
radio-ulnar joints
radial notch of ulna
scaphoid bone
scapula
scapulae (pl.)
scapular (adj.)
semilunar bone
semilunar notch of ulna
sesamoid bone
shafts of:
    humerus
    radius
    ulna
    metacarpal bones
    phalanges

shoulder blade
shoulder girdle
shoulder joint
spine of scapula
sterno-clavicular joint
sternal extremity of clavicle
styloid process of:
    radius
    ulna
superior border of scapula
supracondylar notch
supraspinatus fossa
surgical neck of humerus
terminal phalanx
triangular bone
triquetral bone
trochlea of humerus
trochlear (adj.)
tubercles of:
    humerus
    navicular bone
    greater multangular bone
tuberosity of radius
upper extremity
ulna
ulnae (pl.)
ulnar (adj.)
ulnar notch of radius
vertebral border of scapula
wrist
wrist joint

F. 38 MIDDLE FINGER and THUMB - anatomical names -

1. Middle finger

- distal phalanx
- distal inter-phalangeal joint
- middle phalanx
- proximal inter-phalangeal joint
- proximal phalanx
- 3rd metacarpo-phalangeal joint
- 3rd metacarpal

- head (distal end)
- body
- base of distal phalanx
- head of middle phalanx
- body of middle phalanx
- base of middle phalanx
- head of proximal phalanx
- body of proximal phalanx
- base of proximal phalanx
- head 3rd metacarpal

2. Thumb

(two phalanges only)

- distal or terminal phalanx
- interphalangeal joint (one)
- proximal phalanx
- 1st metacarpo-phalangeal joint
- 1st metacarpal bone

CHAPTER VII. THE PELVIS AND LOWER EXTREMITY.

S. 52 BONES OF THE PELVIS AND LOWER EXTREMITY.

PELVIS:
1. innominate bone (hip bone or os coxae or os innominatum)
   - (a) ilium or flank bone (pl. ilia; adj. iliac)
   - (b) ischium (pl. ischia; adj. ischial)
   - (c) pubis, pubic bone (pl. pubes; adj. pubic)
2. sacrum and coccyx

THIGH:
1. femur, thigh bone (pl. femora or femurs; adj. femoral)
2. patella or knee cap (pl. patellae; adj. patellar)

LEG:
1. tibia or shin bone (pl. tibiae; adj. tibial)
2. fibula or calf bone (pl. fibulae; adj. fibular)

FOOT:
1. Bones of ankle, tarsal bones (tarsus):
   1. talus or astragalus
   2. calcaneus (os calcis or heel bone, pl. calcanei or ossa calci; adj. calcaneal)
   3. navicular or tarsal scaphold, os naviculare.
   4. first cuneiform, medial cuneiform (cuneiform, wedge-shaped)
   5. second cuneiform, or intermediate cuneiform bone.
   6. third cuneiform or lateral cuneiform bone
   7. cuboid bone or os cuboideum.
2. Metatarsal bones, bones of instep:
   5 metatarsal bones, named from inner or medial side as: first, second, third, fourth and fifth metatarsal bones.

3. Toes or digits:
   great toe or hallux (two phalanges: proximal and distal). second, third, fourth, fifth toes (3 phalanges each: proximal, middle, distal or terminal phalanges).

F. 39 BONES OF PELVIS AND LOWER EXTREMITY

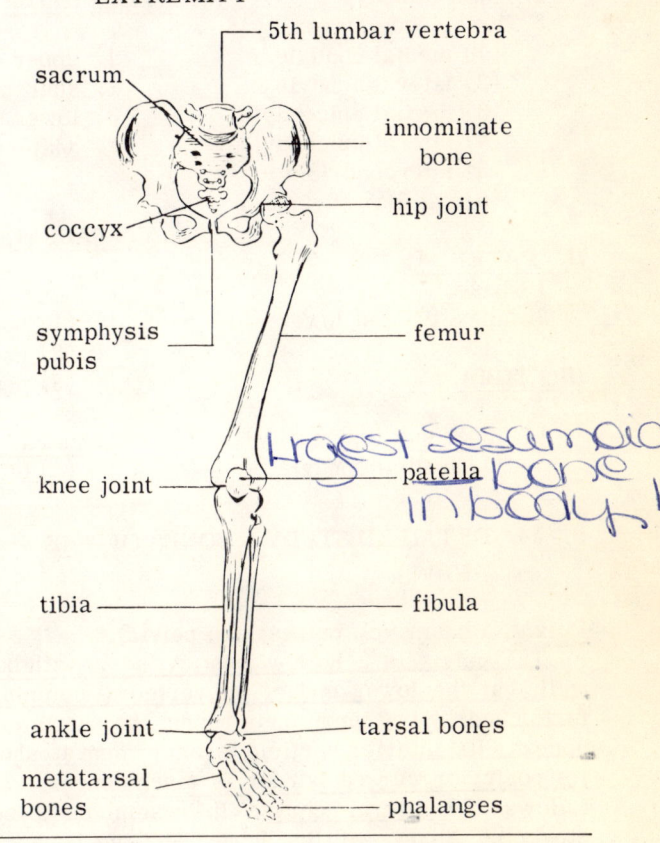

[Diagram labeled: 5th lumbar vertebra, sacrum, innominate bone, hip joint, coccyx, femur, symphysis pubis, knee joint, patella (largest sesamoid bone in body!), tibia, fibula, ankle joint, tarsal bones, metatarsal bones, phalanges]

S. 53 IMPORTANT PARTS AND PROMINENCES OF THE BONES OF THE PELVIS AND LOWER EXTREMITY.

PELVIS

I. **INNOMINATE BONE:**
1. acetabulum
2. obturator foramen
3. three fused bones (ilium, ischium, pubis)

   (1) Ilium:
   - (a) crest
   - (b) body
   - (c) four spines:
     - anterior-superior
     - anterior-inferior
     - posterior-superior
     - posterior-inferior

   (2) Ischium:
   - (a) body
   - (b) superior ramus
   - (c) inferior ramus
   - (d) spine of ischium
   - (e) tuberosity of ischium

   (3) Pubis:
   - (a) body
   - (b) superior ramus
   - (c) inferior ramus
   - (d) pubic tubercle

SUMMARY OF THE WHOLE PELVIS

1. pelvic brim or outlet
2. pelvic outlet
2. false pelvis
4. true pelvis

II. SACRUM and COCCYX:
   (P. 48)

THE LOWER EXTREMITY:

I. FEMUR:

1. upper end (extremity).
   (1) head
   (2) neck
   (3) greater trochanter
   (4) lesser trochanter
   (5) intertrochanteric
2. shaft of body
3. lower end (extremity):
   (1) medial condyle
   (2) lateral condyle
   (3) medial epicondyle
   (4) lateral epicondyle
   (5) intercondyloid fossa
   (6) patellar surface

II. PATELLA:
1. base
2. apex, pointed lower end

III. TIBIA:

1. upper end (extremity):
   (1) medial condyle
   (2) lateral condyle
   (3) intercondyloid eminence
   (4) tibial tuberosity
   (5) facet for head of fibula
2. shaft or body
3. lower end (extremity):
   (1) medial malleolus
   (2) fibular notch
   (3) articular notch

IV. FIBULA:

1. upper end (extremity)
2. shaft or body
3. lower end (extremity)
   (lateral malleolus)

V. TARSAL BONES - (seven)

1. talus or astragalus:
   (1) body
   (2) neck
   (3) head
   (4) trochlea
2. calcaneus or os calcis
   (1) tuberosity
   (2) body
   (3) sustentaculum tali

VI. METATARSAL BONES
    (five)

VII. PHALANGES (fourteen):

1. base or proximal end
2. body
3. head or distal end

JOINTS LOWER LIMB

1. sacroiliac joints
2. hip joints
3. symphysis pubis
4. knee joints
5. proximal tibio-fibular
6. distal tibio-fibular
7. ankle joints
8. intertarsal joints
9. intermetatarsal joints
10. tarso-metatarsal joints
11. metatarso-phalangeal joints
12. proximal interphalangeal
13. distal interphalangeal

S. 54   DETAILED STUDY - BONES OF THE PELVIS.

Pelvis, a basin, (pl. pelves; adj. pelvic).
   The pelvis is a hollow, bent cylinder, with bony walls, at the lower end of the vertebral column. It is formed by two innominate bones, the sacrum and coccyx. Its anterior verticle measurement is short. Its posterior curved border is much longer, as it follows the sacral curve. It resembles a bent stovepipe elbow. At the lower end the bony ring is incomplete. The gaps between the pubic arch, ischial tuberosities, and coccyx are completed by ligaments which stretch between these bony structures on each side. Muscles attached to these ligaments and bones form a hammock to complete the floor of the pelvis. There are openings for the anus, urethra and vagina. Seen from above, this hollow structure looks somewhat like a basin; hence the Latin name pelvis, a basin.

I. THE INNOMINATE BONE.

Innominate or hip bone (os coxae, or os innominatum).
   The innominate bone consists of three parts: the ilium, ischium and pubis. In early life these are three distinct, separate bones, which meet at the acetabulum. Here a Y-shaped cartilage separates them. By the eighteenth or twentieth year of life they will have united, and the cartilage will be replaced. There are two innominate bones: the left and right.

1. The acetabulum is a cup-shaped cavity or socket on the outer surface of the innominate bone at the junction of its three parts. It accommodates the head of the femur to form the hip joint. In normal subjects it lies obliquely, is deep and cannot be palpated.

2. The obturator foramen is a large opening in the lower part of the innominate bone. Its margins are formed by the rami of the ischium and pubis.

3. Three fused bones (ilium, ischium, pubis)

   (1) Ilium or flank bone: (pl. ilia; adj. iliac)
   The name of this bone must not be confused with that for a part of the small bowel, the ileum. note the "i" in the spelling for the bone. The ilium forms the upper two-fifths of the acetabulum, and all of the innominate bone above this

Ischium composed of:
Tuberosity
Spine
Rami & Body

socket. It has a body, ala or wing, fossa crest and four spines.

The body of the ilium is the thickened part close to, and above, the acetabulum.

The ala or wing (pl. alae) is the thin, upper, flat curved part above the body.

The iliac fossa is the curved depression formed by the inner surface of the wing.

The crest of ilium is the upper curved border of the ala or wing. It can be felt throughout its entire length through the lateral wall of the abdomen. It is an important landmark for the technician.

The anterior superior spine is the prominent anterior or front end of the iliac crest, and can be readily palpated through the skin.

The anterior inferior spine lies on the front or anterior border about one inch below the anterior superior spine. It cannot be palpated.

The posterior superior spine is a prominence at the posterior end of the crest. A dimple in the

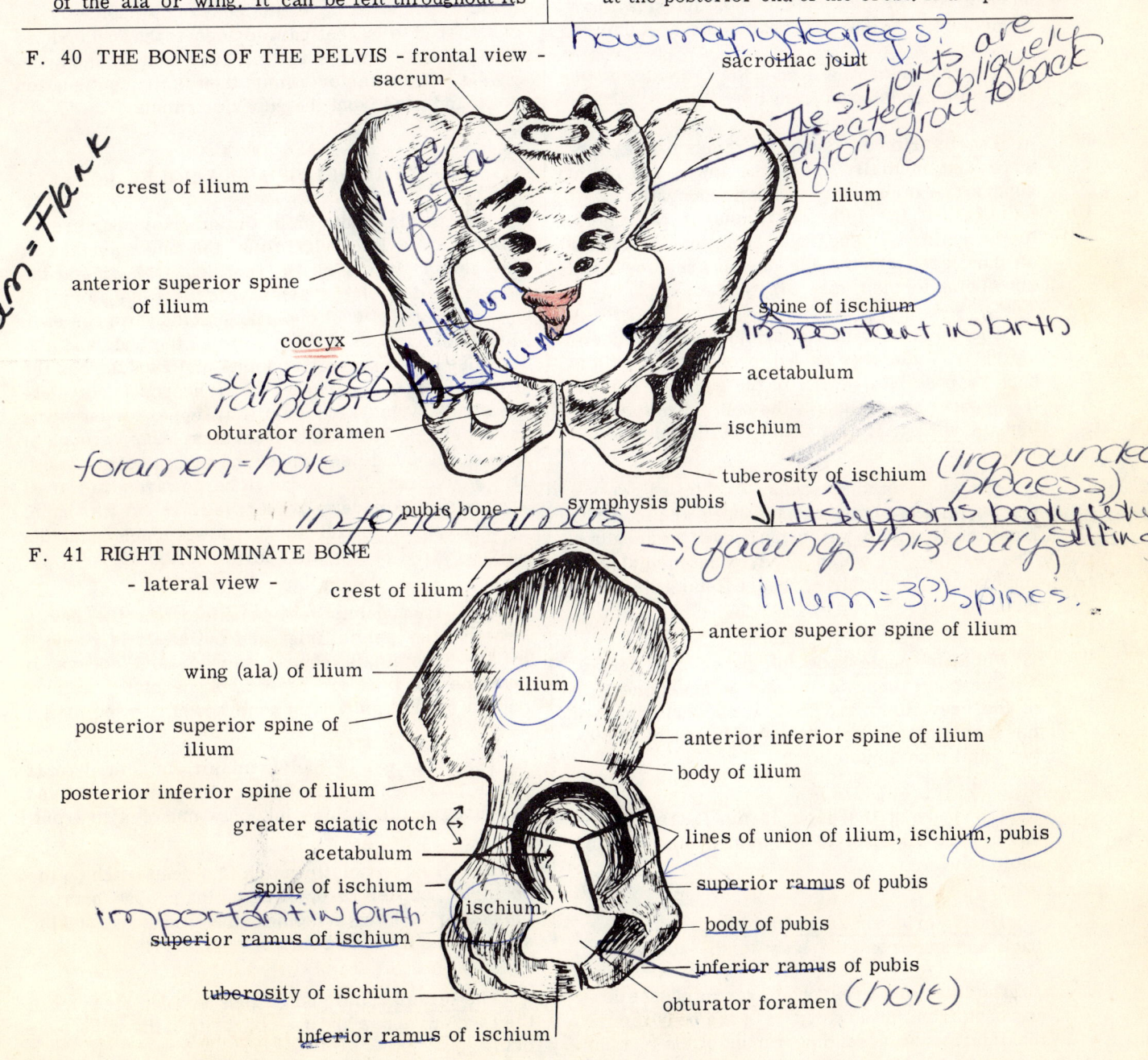

F. 40 THE BONES OF THE PELVIS - frontal view -

ilium = flank

Labels: sacrum, sacroiliac joint, crest of ilium, iliac fossa, ilium, anterior superior spine of ilium, spine of ischium, coccyx, acetabulum, ischium, obturator foramen, tuberosity of ischium, pubis bone, symphysis pubis

how many degrees?
The S.I. joints are directed obliquely from front to back
important in birth
foramen = hole
superior ramus pubis
inferior ramus
(lrg rounded process)
It supports body when sitting — facing this way
ilium = 3(?) spines

F. 41 RIGHT INNOMINATE BONE - lateral view -

Labels: crest of ilium, anterior superior spine of ilium, wing (ala) of ilium, ilium, posterior superior spine of ilium, anterior inferior spine of ilium, body of ilium, posterior inferior spine of ilium, greater sciatic notch, lines of union of ilium, ischium, pubis, acetabulum, spine of ischium, superior ramus of pubis, ischium, body of pubis, superior ramus of ischium, inferior ramus of pubis, tuberosity of ischium, obturator foramen (hole), inferior ramus of ischium

important in birth

skin marks its position as well as the midpoint of the sacroiliac joint.

The posterior inferior spine lies at a lower level.

(2) Ischium (pl. ischia; adj. ischial).
The ischium forms the lower posterior two-fifths of the acetabulum and that part of the innominate bone below and behind this cavity. The ischium has: a body, two rami, a spine, and a tuberosity.

The body of the ischium is the thickened part immediately below and behind the acetabulum.

The superior or descending ramus of the ischium extends down from the body.

The inferior or ascending ramus passes forward and medially from the lower end of the superior ramus, and is continuous with it. It unites with the inferior ramus of the pubis. In the child it is separated from this by a layer of cartilage, which later disappears, one solid bone being formed. (see films).

The tuberosity of the ischium (ischial tuberosity) is a large rounded prominence on the back or posterior border of the superior ramus. It supports the weight of the body when the subject is sitting. It is palpable to the side of the anus.

The spine of the ischium (ischial spine) is a pointed process that extends back and medially from the posterior part of the body of the ischium. The extent to which it extends medially is important in childbirth, as the fetal head must pass through.

(3) Pubis or pubic bone (pl. pubes; adj. pubic).
The pubic bone forms the anterior one-fifth of the acetabulum and the lower anterior part of the innominate bone. The pubic bone has a body, two rami, and a pubic arch.

The body of the pubis is the flat medial or inner part adjacent to the symphysis pubis or pubic joint.

The superior or ascending ramus extends up, back and out from the body to the acetabulum.

The inferior or descending ramus passes down and back from the lower part of the body to meet the inferior or ascending ramus of the ischium.

The pubic tubercle is a very small prominence on the upper surface of the pubic bone near its inner end.

The symphysis is the joint between the bodies of the two pubic bones.

The pubic arch is the curved arch formed by the lower curved borders of the two pubic bones and the lower border of the symphysis pubis. It is narrow in the male but forms a broad rounded curve in the female.

Note: in some textbooks the body of the pubic bone is considered to be that part adjacent to the acetabulum. The superior ramus is that part next to the symphysis. The inferior ramus then is the continuation down and back from the superior ramus.

THE PELVIS AS A WHOLE.

The pelvic inlet, brim or superior aperture, is marked by a line encircling the inner surface of the pelvis. It begins in front, on each side at the upper border of the symphysis. It runs along the upper margin of each pubic bone. It then crosses each ilium obliquely as a ridge between the body and ala. It crosses the sacroiliac joints and runs across the prominent anterior border of the sacrum to complete the circle. It marks the artificial upper border of the true pelvis. The fetal head must pass through it during childbirth; so its size and shape are important. By angulating the x-ray tube towards the feet, attempts are made to get a true image of its shape.
The pelvic outlet is the lower opening of the pelvic cavity. See pelvis above, section 54.

The true pelvis (pelvis minor) is the cavity between the pelvic inlet and outlet. It is bounded by the innominate bones, sacrum and coccyx. It contains the bladder, rectum, some of the reproductive organs, as well as some bowel. See section 15.

The false pelvis (pelvis major) is actually part of the abdomen. It lies above the pelvic inlet, and has bony walls behind but only muscles in front.

The greater sciatic notch is a deep notch on the posterior border of each innominate bone between the posterior inferior spine of the ilium above and the spine of the ischium below.

The lesser sciatic notch lies between the spine of the ischium above and the tuberosity of the same bone below.

You can feel the head of the tibia on the lat. side of the knee.

Fib on lat side of leg

FEMUR, TIBIA, FIBULA; KNEE AND ANKLE JOINTS.

Knee joint is located above the ridge formed by the tibial condyles.

F. 42 LEFT FEMUR OR THIGH BONE   F. 43 LEFT TIBIA AND FIBULA - LEG BONES

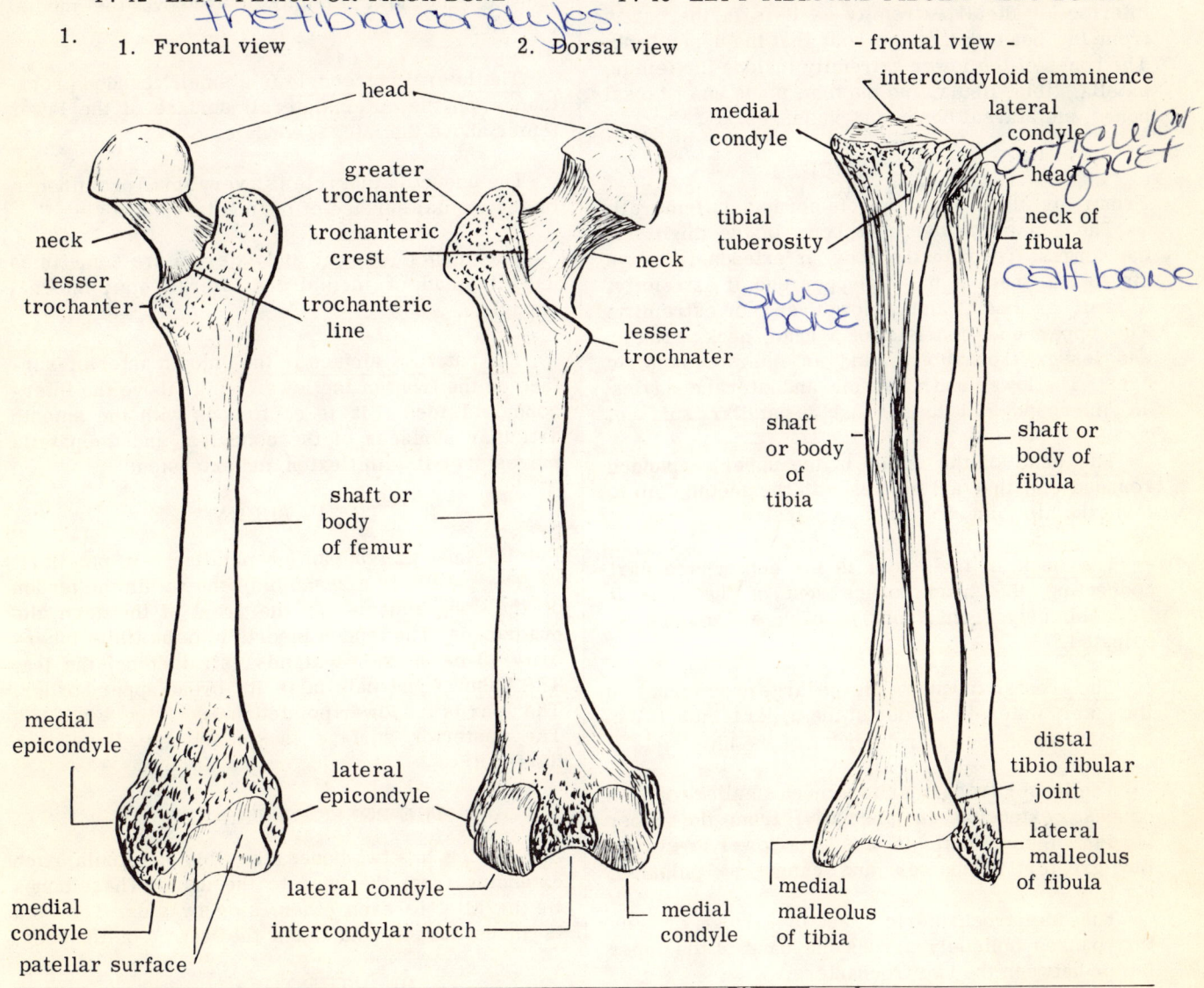

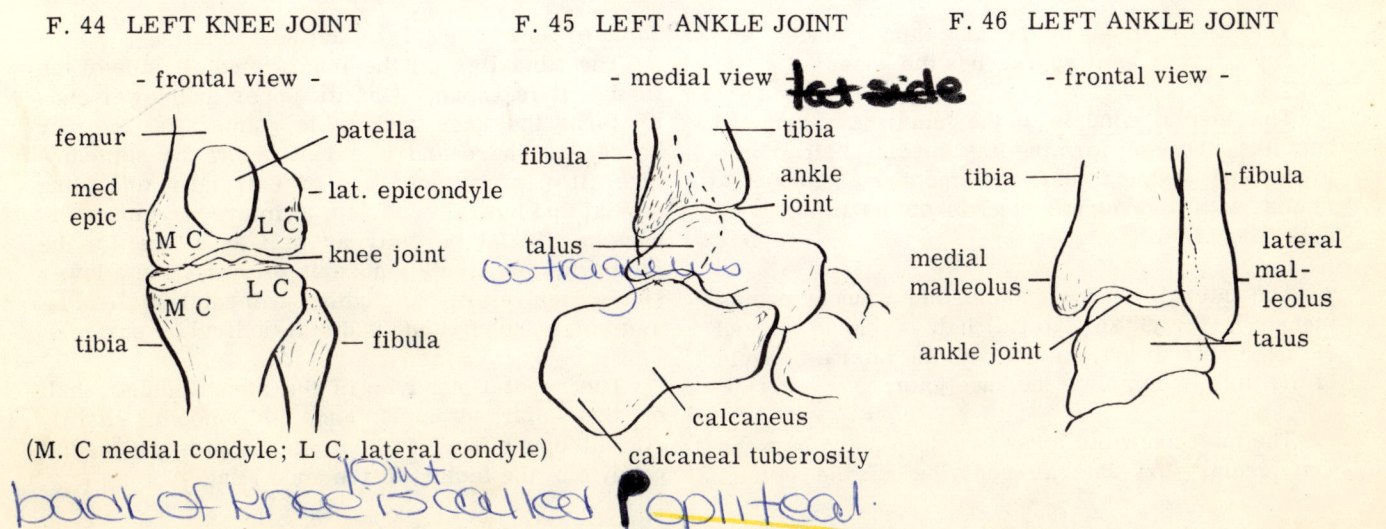

1. Frontal view   2. Dorsal view   - frontal view -

Labels on F.42: head, neck, greater trochanter, trochanteric crest, trochanteric line, lesser trochanter, shaft or body of femur, medial epicondyle, medial condyle, patellar surface, lateral epicondyle, lateral condyle, intercondylar notch, neck, lesser trochanter

Labels on F.43: intercondyloid emminence, medial condyle, lateral condyle, *articular facet*, head, tibial tuberosity, neck of fibula, *shin bone*, *calf bone*, shaft or body of tibia, shaft or body of fibula, distal tibio fibular joint, lateral malleolus of fibula, medial malleolus of tibia

F. 44 LEFT KNEE JOINT   F. 45 LEFT ANKLE JOINT   F. 46 LEFT ANKLE JOINT

- frontal view -   - medial view ~~lat side~~ -   - frontal view -

Labels F.44: femur, patella, med epic, lat. epicondyle, M C, L C, knee joint, M C, L C, tibia, fibula

Labels F.45: fibula, tibia, ankle joint, talus, *ostragalus*, calcaneus, calcaneal tuberosity

Labels F.46: tibia, fibula, medial malleolus, lateral malleolus, ankle joint, talus

(M. C medial condyle; L C. lateral condyle)

back of knee joint is called Popliteal.

When patella doesn't meet - but is in several parts. It is called Bipartite.

S. 55 THE BONES OF THE LOWER EXTREMITY.

The lower extremity or limb is also called the inferior or distal extremity as it is farther away from the head end of the body that the upper limb. The bones of the lower extremity include the femur, patella, tibia, fibula, and the foot, made up of tarsal bones, metatarsal bones and phalanges.

I. THE FEMUR.

Femur or thigh bone *(& patella)* (pl. femora; adj. femoral).

The femur is the only bone in the thigh, and the longest bone in the body. It extends from the hip to the knee. It has an upper end or extremity, a shaft or body, and a lower end or extremity. The upper end consists of a head, neck, greater and lesser trochanters, and an intertrochanteric crest. The lower end has medial and lateral condyles, an intercondyloid fossa, and a patellar surface.

The head of the femur is the upper, expanded rounded end that articulates with the acetabulum to form the hip joint. It cannot be palpated.

The neck of the femur is the constricted part connecting the head to the rest of the bone. It lies obliquely from front to back and cannot be palpated.

The greater trochanter is the large prominence on the outer (lateral) border of the upper femur. It can be palpated on the lateral border of the hip.

The lesser trochanter is a much smaller rounded process extending in (medially) from the upper border of the shaft. It lies at a lower level than the greater trochanter and cannot be palpated.

The intertrochanteric crest is a ridge of bone that passes obliquely across the back of the upper femur between the two trochanters.

The shaft or body is long and rounded and becomes larger as it approaches the knee.

The medial condyle of the femur is a rounded knoblike process forming the medial half of the lower end of the femur. Its smooth surface articulates with the medial condyle of the tibia. (condyle, knuckle)

The lateral condyle is a further rounded prominence on the outer (lateral) half of the lower end of the femur. It articulates with the lateral condyle of the tibia to complete the knee joint.

The intercondyloid fossa is a deep notch between the medial and lateral condyles of the femur.

The medial epicondyle (epi, upon) of the femur is a large prominence on the inner (medial) surface of the lower femur just above the medial condyle.

The lateral epicondyle is a small rounded prominence on the outer (lateral) surface of the lower femur above the lateral condyle.

The adductor tubercle is a very small prominence on the medial surface of the medial epicondyle.

The terms internal and external are sometimes used instead of medial and lateral, e.g., internal condyle.

The patellar surface is the smooth anterior surface on the front of the lower femur above the intercondyloid fossa. It is continuous with the smooth articular surfaces of the condyles, and the patella moves over it with flexion and extension.

II. THE PATELLA.

Patella, knee cap or pan (pl. patallae; adj. patellar).

The patella is a sesamoid bone within the tendon of the long muscle on the front of the thigh, the quadriceps. The tendon inserts into the tibial tuberosity. This muscle extends (straightens) the leg. The base of the patella is its broad upper border. The apex is its lower pointed end.
The posterior surface is smooth and glides over the femur.

THE BONES OF THE LEG.

The leg has two bones, the tibia and fibula, each extending from the knee to the ankle. These bones lie parallel to each other, side by side. The tibia is much larger and takes the weight of the body.

III. THE TIBIA.

Tibia or shin bone (pl. tibiae; adj. tibial).

The tibia lies on the inner (medial) side of the fibula. It is expanded at its upper and lower ends to form the knee and ankle joints. Its anterior border is sharp and lies just below the skin surface. It has an upper end or extremity (including medial and lateral condyles, an intercondyloid eminence, a tibial tuberosity as well as a facet for the joint with the fibula); a shaft or body; and a lower end or extremity (including a medial malleolus, a fibular notch and a distal articular surface).

The medial condyle is the medial (inner) half of the enlarged upper end. Its smooth, slightly cupped upper surface articulates with the medial condyle of the femur, at the knee joint.

The lateral condyle of the tibia is the outer half of its expanded upper end. Its smooth surface articulates with the lateral condyle of the femur to complete the knee joint.

The intercondyloid eminence is a small double pointed prominence on the upper articular surface of the tibia about its midpoint. It extends up into the intercondyloid fossa of the femur.

The tibial tuberosity is a rounded prominence on the anterior (front) surface of the upper tibia below the condyles. It can be felt through the skin. The quadriceps tendon inserts into it.

The articular facet is a smooth pit on the outer or lateral surface of the lateral condyle of the tibia. It accommodates the medial border of the head of the fibula, forming the proximal tibio-fibular joint.

The shaft or body is rounded in its mid portion, but is flattened and enlarged at its lower end.

The medial malleolus (little hammer) projects down from the medial border of the distal end of the tibia. It forms a large prominence on the medial or inner border of the ankle which is visible and can be palpated. It lies medial to the talus.

The distal articular surface of the tibia is a four sided (quadrilateral) smooth surface on the lower end of the tibia. It articulates with the trochlear surface of the talus.

The fibular notch is a small depression on the lateral border of the tibia just above the ankle joint. It articulates with the adjacent lower fibula and helps to form the distal tibio-fibular joint.

IV. THE FIBULA.

Fibula or calf bone: (pl. fibulae; adj. fibular).
The fibula is a long slender bone lying lateral to and parallel with the tibia. It does not reach the knee joint, and forms a small part of the ankle joint. It has a head, shaft or body, and a distal end or lateral malleolus.

The head is the upper expanded end and articulates with the articular facet of the tibia to form the proximal tibio-fibular joint. It can be seen and felt on the outer surface of the leg just below and behind the lateral condyle of the tibia.

The shaft or body is long and slender.

The lateral malleolus is the lower expanded end or extremity of the fibula. It extends down on the lateral border of the ankle lateral to the talus. It, along with the medial malleolus of the tibia, forms the ankle mortice. Its tip lies at a lower level than that of the medial malleolus. Its medial border above the ankle joint articulates with the fibular notch of the tibia to form the distal tibio-fibular joint.

THE BONES OF THE FOOT.

The bones of the foot include the seven tarsal bones, five metatarsal bones, and fourteen phalanges.

V. THE BONES OF THE ANKLE - TARSUS.

There are seven tarsal or ankle bones as compared to eight carpal or wrist bones. Named from back to front they are: the calcaneus or os calcis, talus or astragalus, navicular or tarsal scaphoid, three cuneiform, and a cuboid bone.

1. CALCANEUS - OS CALCIS.

Calcaneus or heel bone (os calcis; adj. calcaneal). The calcaneal bone forms the heel. It has a body, and an expanded posterior end or tuberosity, which can be felt as the heel. The sustentaculum tali is a small shelf of bone projecting in from the medial border of the body. It supports the talus above.

2. TALUS - ASTRAGALUS.

The talus, along with the lower ends of the tibia and fibula, forms the ankle joint. Unlike the wrist, it is the only tarsal bone helping to form this joint. It bears the body weight and has a body, neck and trochlea.

The body is the posterior part.
The neck is the somewhat constricted part in front of the body.
The head is the slightly expanded anterior end.
The trochlea is the upper smooth part that helps to form the ankle joint.
The talus articulates with the calcaneus below, the navicular in front, and tibia and fibula at the ankle joint.

3. THE NAVICULAR OR SCAPHOID BONE.

The navicular bone is boat-shaped; hence the name navicular. It lies between the talus behind, and the three cuneiform bones in front. The tuberosity is the prominent medial part that can be felt below and in front of the medial malleolus.

52

14 phalanges
5 metatarsals
7 carpal bones.

F. 47 BONES OF THE FOOT - viewed from above -

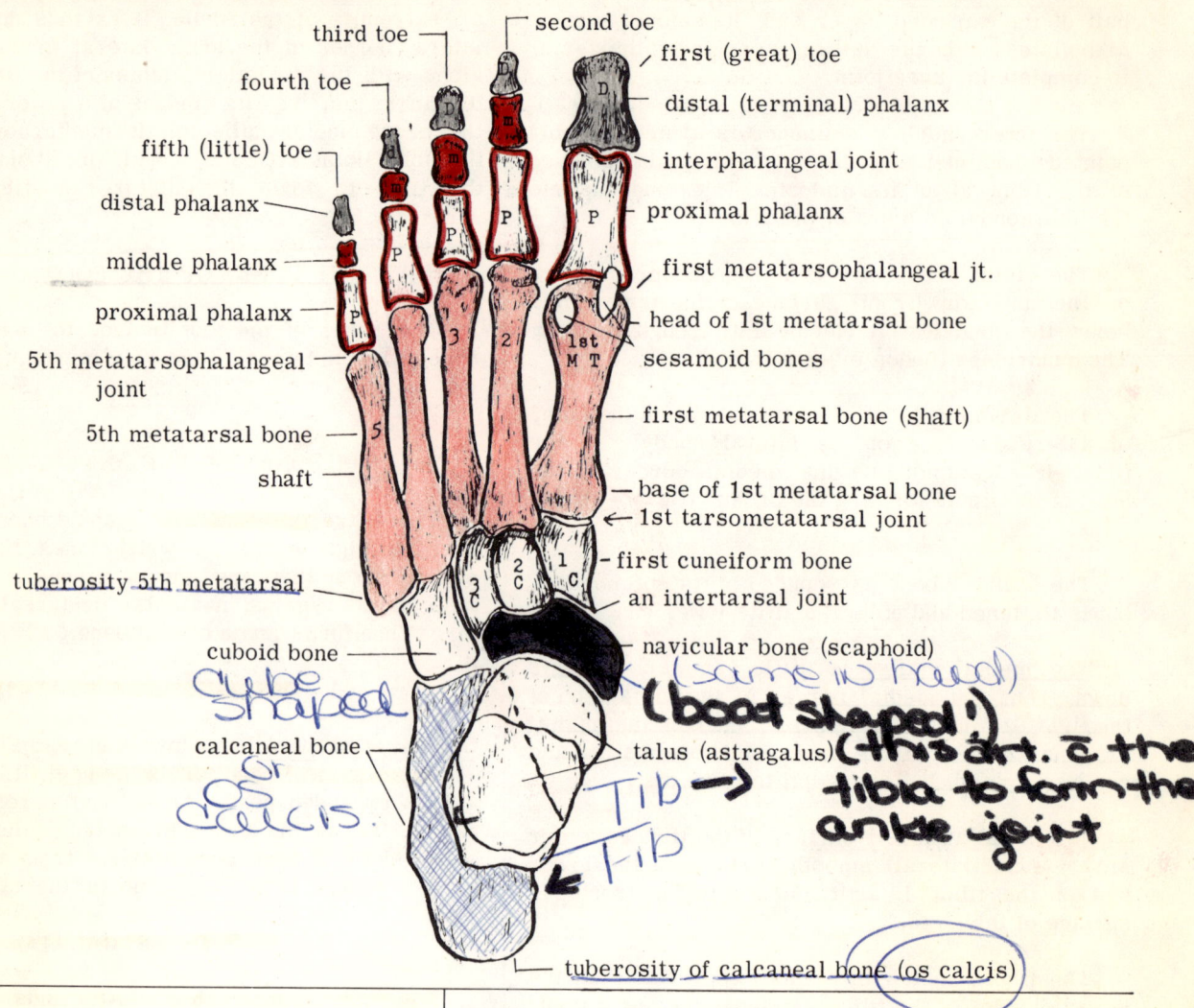

Labels (clockwise from top):
- third toe
- second toe
- fourth toe
- first (great) toe
- fifth (little) toe
- distal (terminal) phalanx
- distal phalanx
- interphalangeal joint
- middle phalanx
- proximal phalanx
- proximal phalanx
- first metatarsophalangeal jt.
- 5th metatarsophalangeal joint
- head of 1st metatarsal bone
- 5th metatarsal bone shaft
- sesamoid bones
- first metatarsal bone (shaft)
- base of 1st metatarsal bone
- 1st tarsometatarsal joint
- tuberosity 5th metatarsal
- first cuneiform bone
- an intertarsal joint
- cuboid bone
- navicular bone (scaphoid) *(same in hand)*
- calcaneal bone *or os calcis* — *cube shaped*
- talus (astragalus) *(boat shaped!)* *(this art. c̄ the tibia to form the ankle joint)*
- Tib → , ← Fib
- tuberosity of calcaneal bone (os calcis)

Seven Tarsal Bones.

calcaneus or os calcis.
talus or astragalus
navicular or tarsal scaphoid
cuboid
cuneiform, first, second, third.

Metatarsal bones.

first.
second
third
fourth
fifth

Phalanges (fourteen)

great toe, proximal, distal (terminal).
 other toe. proximal, middle, distal (terminal).

F. 48 LEFT FOOT - from lateral side -

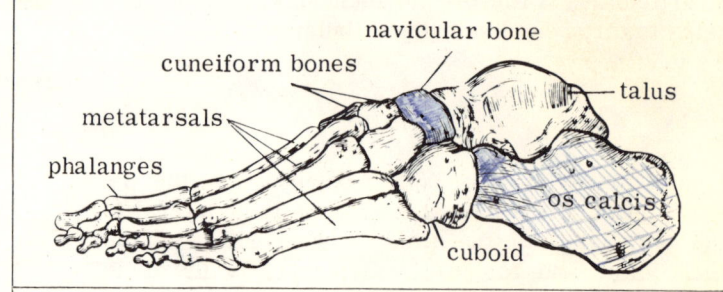

Labels: navicular bone, cuneiform bones, talus, metatarsals, phalanges, os calcis, cuboid

F. 49 RIGHT FOOT - from medial side -

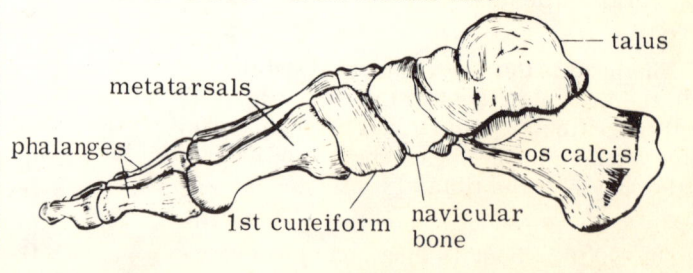

Labels: talus, metatarsals, phalanges, os calcis, 1st cuneiform, navicular bone

Sml △ accessory bone located behind the talus is called the; Os trigonum

53

4. THE CUNEIFORM BONES.

The three cuneiform (wedge-shaped) bones lie side by side in front of the navicular and behind the three medial metatarsal bones. They are named from the inner side of the foot as: the first or medial, second or intermediate, and third or lateral cuneiform.

5. THE CUBOID BONE. *lat.*

This cube-shaped bone lies on the outer border of the foot. The calcaneus is behind; the fourth and fifth metatarsal bones are in front.

VI. THE METATARSAL BONES.

The five metatarsal bones form the instep. They are named from the inner side of the foot as: first, second, third, fourth and fifth metatarsals.

VII. THE PHALANGES.

There are fourteen phalanges in the toes with the same arrangement as in the fingers. The great toe or hallux has two, and each of the other toes has three phalanges, a proximal, middle and distal phalanx.

Each metatarsal bone and phalanx has a base or proximal end, a body and a head or distal end.

F. 50 TIBIA AND FIBULA - distal

The ankle lies about 3/4" above the tips of the malleoli

- fibula
- distal tibio-fibular joint
- lateral malleolus
- talus or astragalus
- tibia
- medial malleolus
- ankle joint

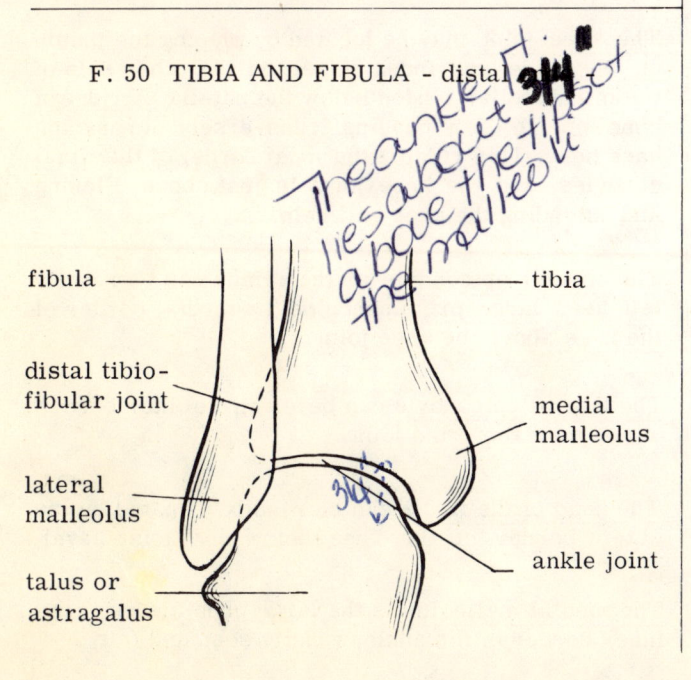

S. 56 JOINTS of the PELVIS and LOWER EXTREMITY.

Sacroiliac joints:
    (a) ala of sacrum
    (b) ala of ilium

Hip joints:
    (a) acetabulum of innominate bone
    (b) head of femur

Symphysis pubis:
    (a) body of pubic bone
    (b) body of other pubic bone

Knee joints:
    (a) medial and lateral condyles of femur
    (b) medial and lateral condyles of tibia
    (c) posterior surface of patella

Proximal tibio-fibular joints:
    (a) articular facet, lateral condyle of tibia
    (b) medial border of head of fibula

Distal tibio-fibular joints:
    (a) fibular notch on lateral border of tibia
    (b) lateral malleolus of fibula, medial border

Ankle joints:
    (a) distal articular surface of tibia
    (b) medial malleolus of tibia
    (c) lateral malleolus of fibula
    (d) trochlear surface of talus or astragalus

Intertarsal joints:
    between adjacent margins of all tarsal bones

Tarso-metatarsal joints:
    (a) distal ends of three cuneiform bones
    (b) distal end of cuboid bone
    (c) bases of metatarsal bones

Metatarso-phalangeal joints:
    (a) heads of metatarsal bones
    (b) bases or proximal ends of proximal phalanges

Proximal interphalangeal joints:
    (a) heads of proximal phalanges of the toes
    (b) bases of middle phalanges of the toes

Distal interphalangeal joints:
    (a) heads of middle phalanges of the toes
    (b) bases of distal phalanges of the toes

The arches of the feet:
The plantar surface or sole of the foot is curved in two directions. The longitudinal arch is seen when the foot is viewed from the inner side. The tuberosity of the os calcis and the heads of the metatarsal bones lie close to the skin surface and, in the upright position, rest upon the floor. The remaining tarsal bones and posterior parts of the metatarsals form a curve, with concavity down, and do not touch the floor. The transverse arch is a curve from the inner side of the plantar surface to the outer, at the instep. In flat feet these curves diappear, and the whole instep rests upon the floor.

S. 57 CONGENITAL ANOMALIES - PELVIS - LOWER LIMB.

Congenital dislocation of hip: the head of the femur lies outside of and above the acetabulum. This socket is either absent or shallow and lies almost vertically. One or both hips may be affected. It may be the first be noticed as a limp when the child begins to walk.

Absence of patella: this bone may fail to develop.

Bipartite patella: the patella may show as two or more bones. It has developed from two or more centers of ossification which have failed to fuse together.

Os trigonum: a small triangular bone behind the talus which has formed from a separate center, and has not united with the talus. It may be mistaken for a break.

Accessory navicular: the medial part of the navicular bone may form a separate center and fail to unite with the remainder of this bone.

Many other anomalies may occur.

S. 58 LANDMARKS: PROMINENCES: PELVIS: LOWER LIMB

Pelvis. The crest of the ilium can be felt as a curved ridge of bone on the lateral wall of the abdomen. It lies at the level of the naval usually, but is a much more reliable landmark, as the position of the naval varies.

The anterior superior spine of the ilium forms a very definite prominence at the anterior end of the iliac crest. It is readily felt and is a useful landmark.

The posterior superior spine of the ilium corresponds to a dimple of the skin on the medial border of the buttock behind.

The tuberosity of the ischium is a definite prominence lateral to the anus, and is palpable.

Only a small part of the sacroiliac joint can be felt through the skin in the region of the dimple marking the position of the posterior superior spine.

The symphysis pubis can be felt as a depression in the midline between the two pubic bones.

The pubic arch can be felt below the symphysis as a curved bony border.

The greater trochanter of the femur lies close to the skin surface and can be readily palpated as a large prominence on the lateral border of the hip.

The head of the femur lies deeply and cannot be felt. If a line be drawn from the anterior superior spine of the ilium to the upper border of the sumphysis and this line be bisected, the hip joint will lie at the point of bisection.

Knee. The patella can be seen and felt on the anterior surface of the knee above the joint.

The tibial tuberosity is palpable as a definite prominence on the front of the upper tibia. The infrapatellar ligament may be followed from the lower end of the patella to this tuberosity.

The knee joint may be located by placing the thumb on one side and index finger on the other side of the infrapatellar tendon below the patella. A ridge of bone may be felt passing transversely across the knee here. This ridge is the upper border of the tibial condyles, and the knee joint is just above. Flexing and extending the knee will help.

The medial epicondyle of the femur can be readily felt as a large prominence on the medial border of the knee above the knee joint.

The lateral epicondyle can be felt on the outer border of the knee above the joint.

The head of the fibula can be readily palpated on the outer border of the knee below the joint level.

The medial malleolus is the large prominence on the inner border of the ankle, readily seen and felt.

The lateral malleolus of the fibula is the prominence on the lateral (outer) border of the ankle. It is visible and palpable.

The ankle joint lies about three-quarters of an inch above the tips of the malleoli; so these tips must not be used in centering for the joint.

The calcaneal tuberosity forms the heel and is visible and palpable.

The tuberosity of the navicular bone can be felt on the inner border of the ankle, below and in front of the medial malleolus.

The tuberosity of the fifth metatarsal bone is a definite prominence on the outer border of the foot, well below and in front of the lateral malleolus. The metatarsal bones and phalanges can be readily located. The metatarso-phalangeal joints are not opposite the web between the toes but well behind them.

S. 59 APPLICATION TO RADIOGRAPHY - PELVIS AND LOWER EXTREMITY.

Using a mounted skeleton and illustrative films, the student should verify the following points.

The sacroiliac joints are directed obliquely from front to back so that their posterior borders lie closer to the median line than the anterior. To look through a sacroiliac joint on one side of the body the student must raise this side from the table top so that the pelvis lies obliquely. To view the other sacroiliac joint the student must elevate this side of the pelvis.

The best "face on" view of the innominate bone is obtained by raising the opposite hip so that the pelvis lies oblique to the table top. This is done by bending the knee and flexing the thigh.

The necks of the femora lie obliquely, and are directed out and back. The necks are therefore foreshortened when viewed with the toes turned out in their natural position. To offset this the inner borders of the great toes must be touching, or better still, the great toes should touch each other and the heels be separated.

In the lateral position, with the patient lying on the side, the femoral heads and necks are superimposed. If, instead, the subject lies supine, and the one thigh is flexed, the other femoral head and neck may be filmed by directing the beam laterally under the flexed thigh. Instead, when it is possible to rotate the thigh, a lateral view may be obtained by flexing the hip and knee and abducting and rotating the thigh laterally into the "frog" position. If there is a recent injury, this should not be attempted, but a lateral view must be obtained by flexing the oppo-

F. 51 SACROILIAC, HIP JOINTS, and SYMPHYSIS

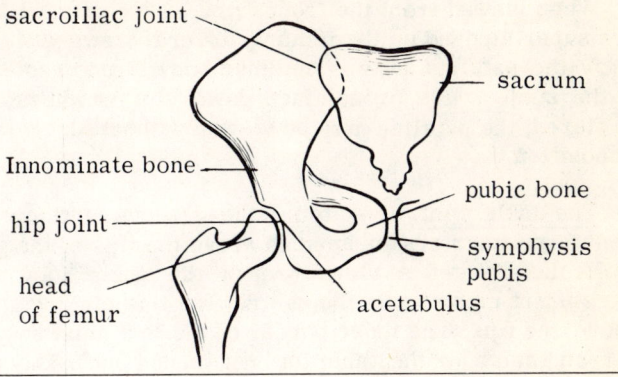

F. 52 THE KNEE JOINT

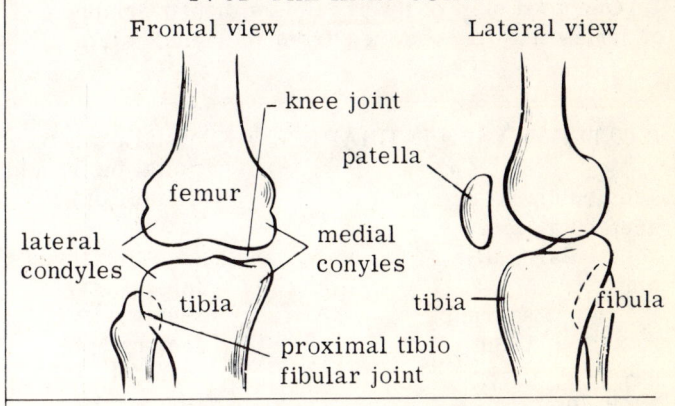

F. 53 THE ANKLE JOINT

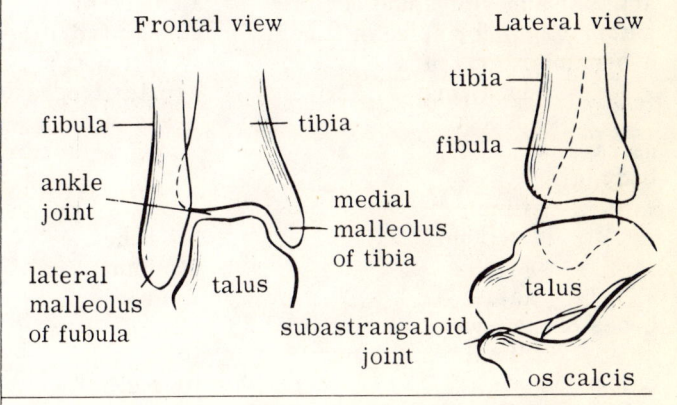

F. 54 JOINTS OF THE FOREFOOT - second toe -

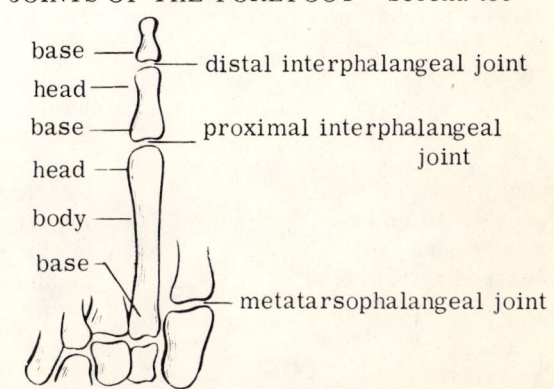

site thigh and directing the beam laterally as suggested above with the patient remaining supine.

When viewed from the front or back, the patellae are superimposed on the femora. Lateral views will show the patellae away from other bony structures. If the subject lies prone (face down) and the knees be flexed, the patellae may be viewed without superimposition.

The ankle joint, as stated in the previous section, lies three-quarters of an inch above the tips of the malleoli. To get a view through the ankle joint the student must direct the central ray this distance above the tips. The inner border of the foot must be perpendicular to the table top, not turned out in the natural position.

One good view of the os calcis without overlapping of bones may be obtained from the side, a lateral view. A further view may be obtained with the patient lying face down. The os calcis may then be viewed from the head end without superimposition.

The metatarsal bones overlap each other when seen from above. Part of this is due to the arching of the foot. If the outer border of the foot be elevated from the table top, with the medial border resting upon the table, there is much less overlapping of bones.

Because the toes are normally flexed, they must be straghtened out by pressing them against the table top. Oblique views are valuable because in the lateral view the toes overlap.

It requires ingenuity and some experience to deal with each case and region. The student should take the various bones, and using the eye as the focal spot, turn these bones into positions showing the least overlapping at joints, etc.

S.60 TERMS USED IN CHAPTER VII.

acetabulum
acetabula (pl.)
acetabular (adj.)
ala of:
    sacrum
    ilium
ankel
ankle joint
anterior superior spine of ilium
anterior inferior spine of ilium
ascending ramus of:
    ischium
    pubis
astragalus
body of:
    ilium
    ischium
    pubis
    talus
bones of the lower, inferior or
    distal extremity
calcaneus
calcaneal (adj.)
calcaneal tuberosity
calf bone
condyles of:
    femur
    tibia
coccyx
coccygeal (adj.)
crest of ilium
cuboid bone
descending ramus of:
    ischium
    pubis

distal phalanx
distal interphalangeal joint
distal tibio-fibular joint
fabella
facet for fibula
false pelvis
femur
femora (pl.)
femoral (adj.)
fibula
fibulae (pl.)
fibular (adj.)
fibular notch
greater trochanter of femur
heads of:
    femur   talus
    tibia   metatarsal bones
    fibula   phalanges
hip bone
hip joint
ilium
ilia (pl.)
iliac (adj.)
iliac crest
inferior, lower or distal extremity
inferior ramus of:
    ischium
    pubis
inferior aperture of pelvis
intermetatarsal joints
intercondyloid fossa of femur
interphalangeal joints
intertarsal joints
intertrochanteric crest of femur
ischium
ischia (pl.)
ischial (adj.)

ischial spine
ischial tuberosity
knee
knee joint
lateral condyles of:
    femur
    tibia
lateral epicondyle of femur
lateral malleolus of fibula
lower extremity
lesser trochanter of femur
lumbosacral joint
malleolus
malleoli (pl.)
medial condyles of:
    femur
    tibia
medial epicondyle of femur
medial malleolus of tibia
metatarsal bones
metatarso-phalangeal joints
middle phalanx
necks of;
    femur
    talus
navicular bone
obturator foramen
os calcis
patella
patallae (pl.)
patellar (adj.)
pelvis
pelves (pl.)
pelvic (adj.)
pelvic brim
pelvic inlet
pelvic outlet

pelvis major
pelvis minor
phalanx
phalanges (pl.)
phalangeal (adj.)
posterior inferior spine of ilium
posterior superior spine of ilium
promontory of sacrum
proximal tibio-fibular joint
proximal interphalangeal joints
pubis
pubes (pl.)
pubic (adj.)
pubic tubercle
ramus
rami (pl.)

ramus of:
    ischium
    pubis
sacrum
sacral (adj.)
sacrococcygeal joint
sacroiliac joint
scaphoid bones (tarsal)
shin bone
spine of ischium
superior ramus of:
    ischium
    pubis
sustentaculum tali
symphysis pubis
talus

tarsal bones
tarsus
tarso-metatarsal joints
thigh bone
tibia
tibiae (pl.)
tibial (adj.)
tibial tuberosity
tibio-fibular joints
trochanters of femur
trochlea of talus
tuberosity of:
    calcaneus
    ischium
    tibia
    fifth metatarsal bone

F. 55 VERTEBRAL COLUMN - lateral view demonstrating normal curves.

Seven cervical vertebrae (lordotic curve)

Disc between second and third dorsal is opposite suprasternal notch in front

Disc between fourth and fifth dorsal is opposite the sternal angle in front

The ninth dorsal vertebra is opposite the xiphisternal joint in front

twelve thoracic vertebrae (kyphotic curve)

Disc between third and fourth lumbar vertebrae is opposite the umbilicus

five lumbar vertebrae (lordotic curve)

The fourth lumbar vertebra is opposite the crest of the ilium

sacrum (five fused vertebrae)

The second sacral segment is opposite the anterior superior spines of the ilia

coccyx (four-imcompletely fused vertebrae).

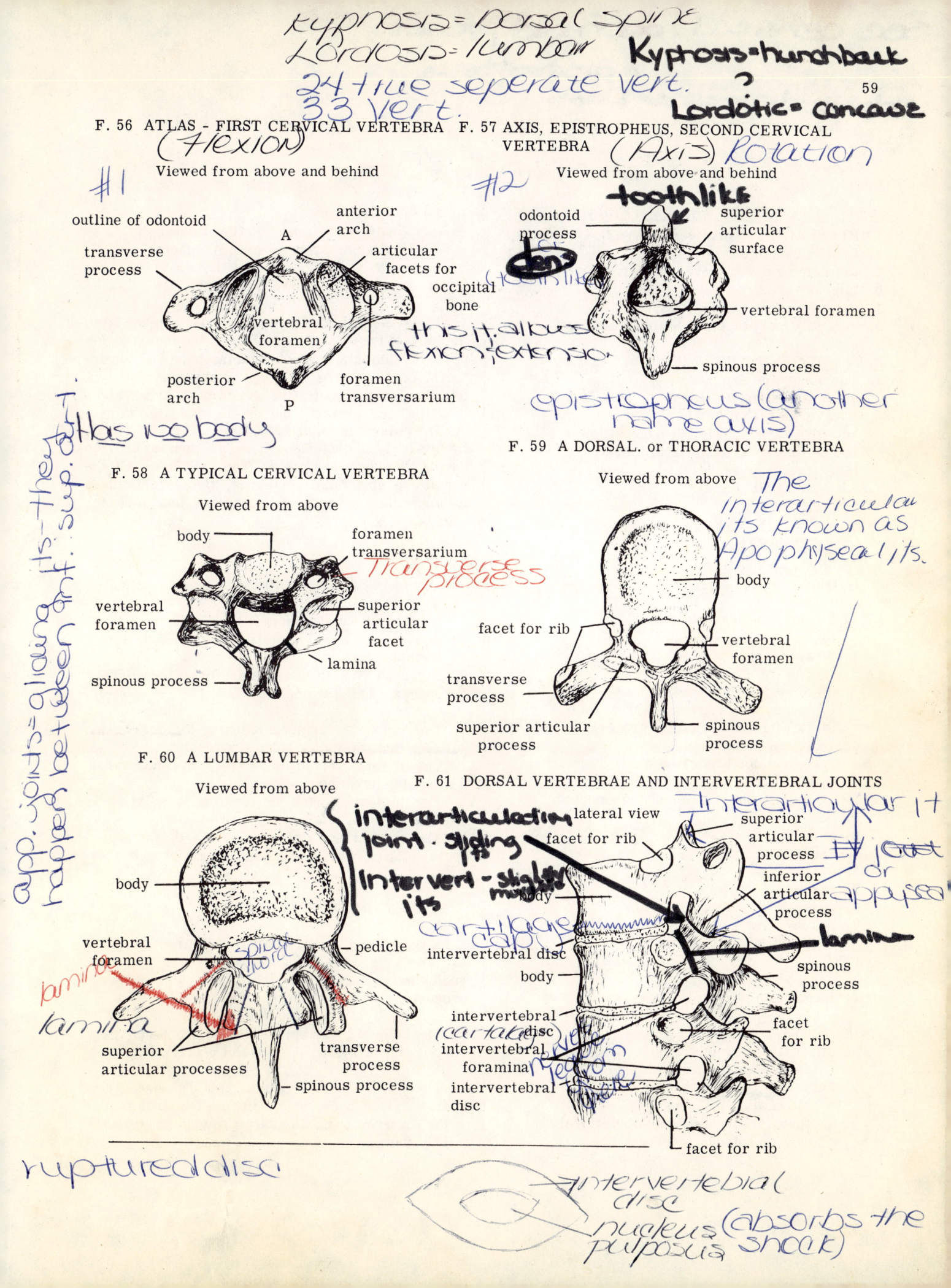

Handwritten annotations at top:
Kyphosis = Dorsal spine
Lordosis = lumbar   Kyphosis = hunchback
24 true seperate vert.
33 vert.   Lordotic = concave

59

F. 56 ATLAS - FIRST CERVICAL VERTEBRA
(flexion) #1
Viewed from above and behind

Labels: outline of odontoid, anterior arch, transverse process, articular facets for occipital bone, vertebral foramen, posterior arch, foramen transversarium

this jt. allows flexion, extension
Atlas has no body

F. 57 AXIS, EPISTROPHEUS, SECOND CERVICAL VERTEBRA
(Axis) Rotation #2
Viewed from above and behind

Labels: toothlike - odontoid process (dens), superior articular surface, vertebral foramen, spinous process

epistropheus (another name axis)

F. 58 A TYPICAL CERVICAL VERTEBRA
Viewed from above

Labels: body, foramen transversarium, transverse process, vertebral foramen, superior articular facet, lamina, spinous process

F. 59 A DORSAL or THORACIC VERTEBRA
Viewed from above

The interarticular jts known as Apophyseal jts.

Labels: body, vertebral foramen, facet for rib, transverse process, superior articular process, spinous process

F. 60 A LUMBAR VERTEBRA
Viewed from above

Labels: body, vertebral foramen, lamina, pedicle, superior articular processes, transverse process, spinous process

F. 61 DORSAL VERTEBRAE AND INTERVERTEBRAL JOINTS
lateral view

interarticulation joint - sliding
Intervert - slightly movable jts
cartilage caps

Labels: facet for rib, superior articular process, inferior articular process, intervertebral disc, body, intervertebral foramina, intervertebral disc, spinous process, lamina, facet for rib, facet for rib

Interarticular jt. — jt or apophyseal

app. joints = gliding jts - they happen between ant. & sup. of Tl

ruptured disc

intervertebral disc
nucleus pulposus (absorbs the shock)

sec cervical - odontoid process
epistropheus
odontoid process = Dens
the spinal chord goes down through the sacrum = sacral canal

CHAPTER VIII   THE VERTEBRAL COLUMN

S. 61 THE BONES OF THE VERTEBRAL COLUMN.

VERTEBRAE - 33 (sing. vertebra; adj. vertebral).
1. cervical vertebrae - seven
2. thoracic or dorsal vertebrae - twelve
3. lumbar vertebrae - five
4. sacrum - five fused bodies
5. coccyx - four; or three to five incomplete

S. 62 JOINTS OF THE VERTEBRAL COLUMN.
1. atlanto-occipital joints (two) *flexion*
2. atlanto-epistropheal joint *rotation*
3. intervertebral joints
4. accessory cervical intervertebral joints
5. interarticular or apophyseal joints
6. lumbosacral or sacrovertebral joint
7. sacrococcygeal joint

S. 63 PARTS OF A VERTEBRA; SPECIAL VERTEBRAE.

A TYPICAL VERTEBRA:
1. body
2. arch:
   (a) two pedicles or roots
   (b) two laminae or plates
3. processes:
   (a) two transverse processes
   (b) one spinous process
   (c) two superior articular processes
   (d) two inferior articular processes
4. vertebral foramen
5. vertebral notches - two

SACRUM (composed of five fused segments):
1. body
2. alae, lateral masses
3. sacral foramina, anterior and posterior
4. sacral canal
5. cornua
6. superior articular processes
7. promontory

COCCYX:
1. cornua
2. incomplete vertebrae

UNUSUAL VERTEBRAE:
1. atlas, first cervical:
      no body
2. axis, epistropheus, second cervical;
      odontoid process
3. vertebra prominens, seventh cervical:
      long spinous process

4. dorsal vertebrae:
      body - facets for joints with heads of ribs
      articular process - similar facets

S. 64 DETAILED STUDY OF VERTEBRAE.

The vertebral column or back bone extends from the base of the skull to the tail bone, and includes this bone. All animals, including human beings, with vertebral columns, are termed vertebrates. The vertebral column supports the weight of the trunk, gives it shape, and protects the spinal cord from injury.

The column is made up of thirty-three vertebrae, twenty-four of which remain as separate bones during life and are called true vertebrae. Of the remaining nine false vertebrae, five become fused to form the sacrum, and the other four form the coccyx.

DIVISIONS OF THE VERTEBRAL COLUMN.

1. cervical, seven in the neck
2. thoracic or dorsal - twelve behind the chest.
3. lumbar - five
4. sacrum - five fused - posterior wall of pelvis.
5. coccyx - four incomplete

The cervical vertebrae form a ~~forward curve~~, called a ~~lordotic curve~~ (noun - lordosis).

The thoracic vertebrae form a curve backwards, a kyphotic curve (noun - kyphosis).

The lumbar vertebrae form a forward curve like the cervical - lordotic.

The sacrum and coccyx, like the thoracic vertebrae, form a curve with concave anterior border.

STRUCTURE OF A VERTEBRA (pl. vertebrae)

A typical vertebra has a body, an arch (including two roots or pedicles, and two laminae or plates, enclosing a canal, the vertebral foramen) and seven processes, arising from the arch.

The body of a vertebra is the solid anterior part, shaped like a cylinder, with flat posterior surface.

The pedicles or roots are thick rounded extensions passing back, one from each lateral border of the flattened posterior surface of a body. (pedicle, a little foot).

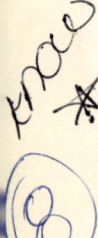

The two laminae (plates) are two flattened plates of bone, one passing towards the midline from the posterior end of each pedicle. These unite in the midline behind to form the spinous process, and complete the arch. (sing. lamina).

The vertebral foramen is the opening behind the body, enclosed by the arch. Along with similar openings in the other vertebrae it forms a canal for the spinal cord.

The vertebral notches are formed by the curved upper and lower borders of the pedicles. A similar curve of the pedicle above or below completes an opening, the intervertebral foramen. A spinal nerve leaves the cord through these openings on each side.

The transverse processes (two) one on each side, extend laterally (outward) from the junction of the pedicle and a lamina.

The superior articular processes (two) project upwards towards the head from the bases of the transverse processes. Their smooth articular surfaces are directed back and laterally.

The inferior articular processes (two) project downwards (caudally) from the bases of the transverse processes. Their smooth articular surfaces are directed to the front and medially, often obliquely. These processes form joints with the superior articular processes of the vertebra below. As they lie behind the superior processes, forward displacement cannot occur unless there is a defect in the arch, from a fracture or congenital defect.

The spinous process (one) extends posteriorly or back from the posterior border of the vertebral arch, at the junction of the laminae.

The cervical vertebrae have small bodies, and their spinous processes may be forked or double.

The first cervical vertebra, the atlas, has no body, but has a ring of bone, with hollow center. This ring of bone forms anterior and posterior arches. The lateral parts are thickened, and on the upper surface a concave articular facet is present on each side. These form joints with the condyles of the occipital bone. Flexion occurs at these joints.

The second cervical vertebra, the axis or epistropheus, has a process shaped like a large tooth projecting upward from its body. This odontoid process (dens, a tooth) fits into the arch of the atlas. Rotation of the head takes place at this joint.

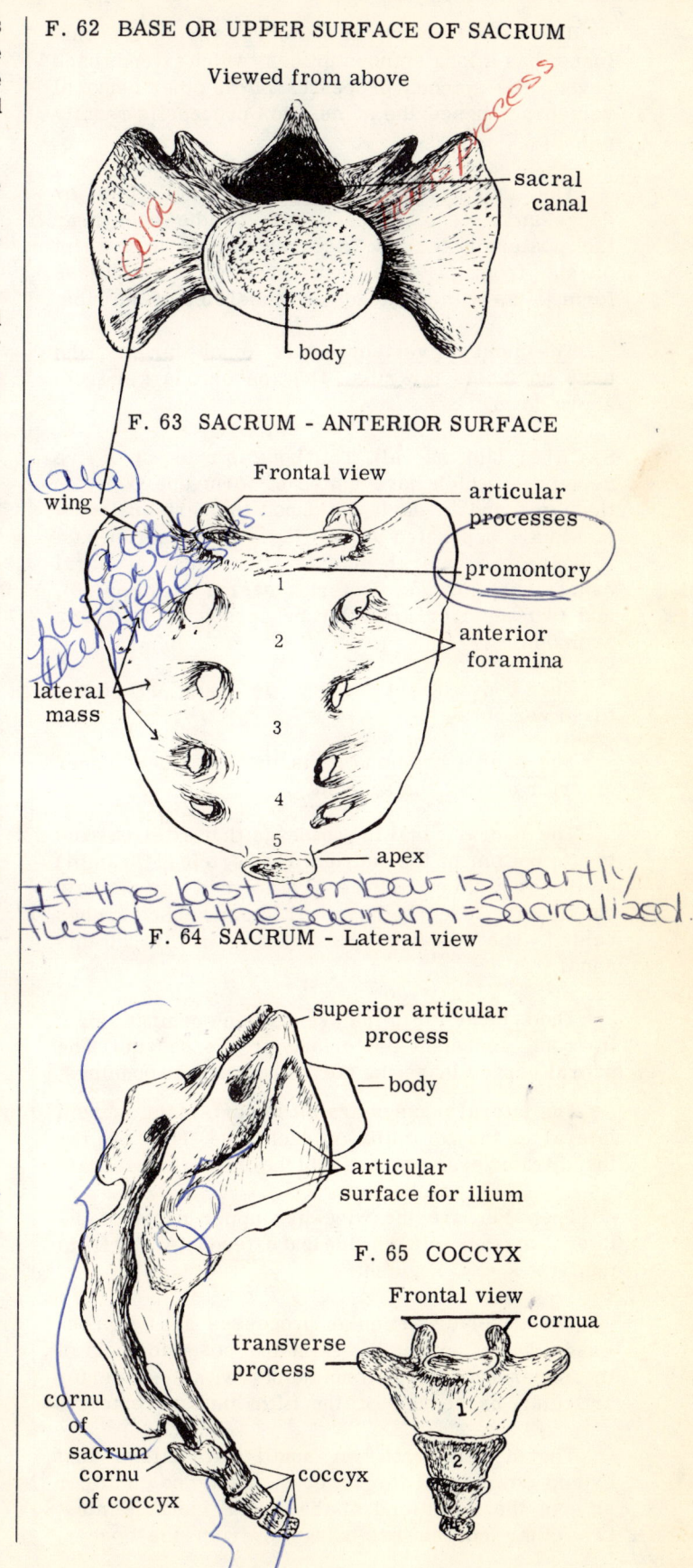

F. 62 BASE OR UPPER SURFACE OF SACRUM
Viewed from above

F. 63 SACRUM - ANTERIOR SURFACE
Frontal view

F. 64 SACRUM - Lateral view

F. 65 COCCYX
Frontal view

where does canal end?

The seventh cervical vertebra, vertebra prominens, has a long spinous process which extends back beyond the spinous processes of the other cervical vertebrae; hence the name. This process is readily palpated.

The thoracic vertebrae have small pits or depressions, one on each side of the body near the posterior border. A further facet is present on the front of each transverse process. These form joints with the heads and tubercles of the ribs.

The lumbar vertebrae are much larger, and have no facets for ribs. They become larger from above down.

SACRUM (adj. sacral). This bone is made up of five vertebrae which have united to form one bone. In the fetus and in early childhood the vertebral segments are separated by cartilages. The sacrum has: a body, two lateral masses, two alae, a sacral canal, anterior and posterior sacral foramina (16), and two superior articular processes, as well as a promontory.

The body of the sacrum is made up of five fused vertebrae.

The sacral promontory is the prominent upper anterior edge of the sacrum.

The sacral canal is a passage that extends from top to bottom of the sacrum. The vertebral foramina of the original vertebrae have formed into a single canal, with fused bodies in front and fused arches behind. The spinal cord extends down through this canal.

The sacral foramina are sixteen openings, eight in front, and eight posteriorly in the sacrum. The sacral nerves leave the cord through these openings.

The lateral masses are those parts of the sacrum lateral to the foramina on each side. They are the fused transverse processes of the original vertebrae.

The alae are the wing-like upper parts of the lateral masses on each side that extend laterally from the first sacral segment.

The superior articular processes are two processes which extend up from the posterior part of the upper sacrum to form joints with the inferior articular processes of the fifth lumbar vertebra.

The cornua are two small projections that extend down from the lower sacrum, one on either side of the lower end of the sacral canal, to meet two other cornua extending up from the coccyx.

F. 66 JOINTS OF UPPER CERVICAL VERTEBRAE
- condyle of occipital bone
- lateral mass of atlas
- odontoid process
- body of axis or second cervical vertebra

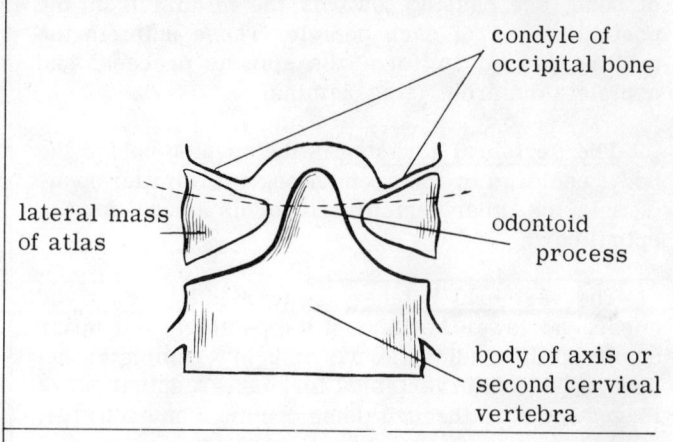

F. 67 INTERARTICULAR JOINTS - vertebrae -
- body of vertebra
- inferior articular process
- interarticular joint
- superior articular process

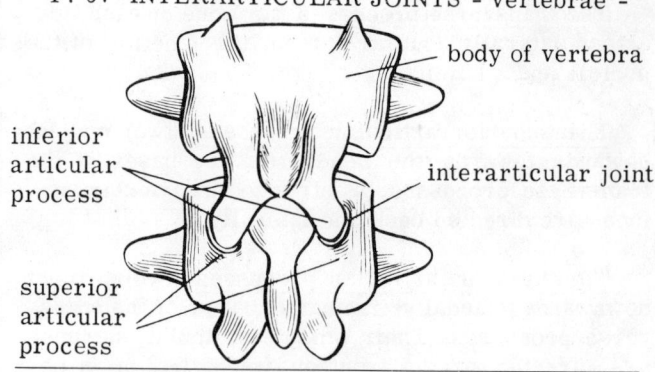

F. 68 INTERVERTEBRAL JOINTS - lateral view -
- body of a vertebra
- articular cartilage
- nucleus pulposus (shock)
- intervertebral joint
- annulus fibrosus
- body of a vertebra
- spinal cord
- intervertebral joint

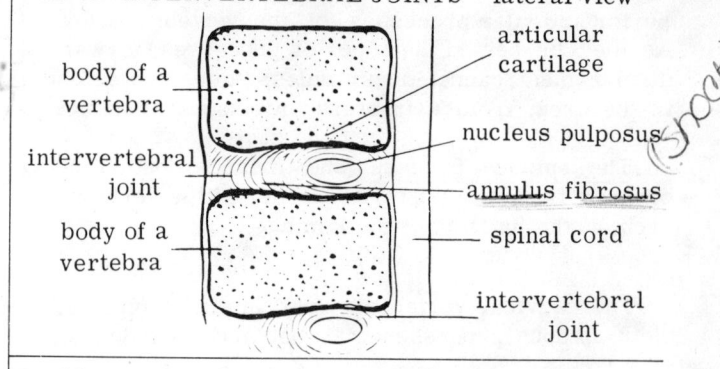

F. 69 LUMBO-SACRAL or SACRO-VERTEBRAL JOINT - lateral view -
- fifth lumbar vertebra
- lumbo-scral joint
- sacrum

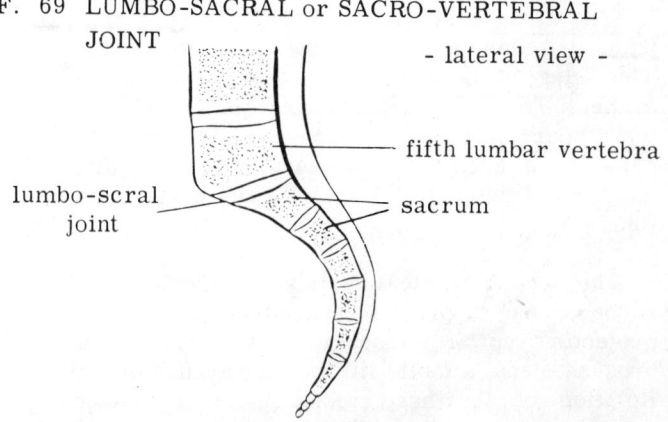

be able to tell if they're pathological or due to posture

COCCYX (adj. coccygeal). The coccyx includes four incompletely developed vertebrae. These may fuse in later life to form one bone. Occasionally there are three or five segments.

The cornua (horns) of the coccyx extend up from the posterior border of the proximal segment of the coccyx to meet the cornua of the sacrum.

S. 65 THE JOINTS OF THE VERTEBRAL COLUMN

Atlanto-occipital. There are two of these. The condyle of the occipital bone on each side rests upon the articular facet on the superior surface of the lateral part of the first cervical vertebra.

Atlanto-epistropheal joint. This joint is between the anterior surface of the odontoid process of the second cervical and the anterior arch of the atlas.

The intervertebral joints. These lie between the bodies of adjacent vertebrae, and form cushions. These structures help to form these joints:
   (a) articular cartilages - a layer of cartilage covers the upper and lower surface of each vertebral body;
   (b) annulus fibrosus - a layer of fibrous tissue and cartilage forms a pad between the articular cartilages on the adjacent vertebrae;
   (c) nucleus pulposus - the pulpy center of the annulus fibrosus.

Test

These structures form the intervertebral disc. Under pressure resulting from a strain on a disc, the nucleus pulposus may rupture, and the pulpy center may be forced out through the rupture in its fibrous capsule. If this occurs posteriorly, the extruded disc may press upon the spinal cord or one of the nerve roots, resulting in pain in the part supplied by that particular nerve.

Accessory cervical joints. In the cervical area there is a further small joint on each side of the intervertebral disc between the lateral margins of adjacent bodies.

Interarticular joints - apophyseal joints:
   (a) inferior articular process of one vertebra
   (b) superior articular process of vertebra below.

Lumbosacral or sacrovertebral joint:
   (a) inferior surface fifth lumbar body
   (b) superior surface of sacrum

Sacrococcygeal joints:
   (a) lower surface of body of sacrum
   (b) upper surface of first coccygeal segment

usually congenital

Spondylolisthesis is the forward displacement of one vertebra upon the upper surface of the vertebra beneath it. This usually occurs at the lumbosacral joint. There must be a defect in the arch of the upper vertebra to allow this slipping. This may be congenital or due to fracture. *the whole ver. is out of line - it slides forward*

S. 66 CONGENITAL ANOMALIES - VERTEBRAL COLUMN.

Fusion of vertebrae: two or more vertebrae may be united forming one bone with no joint between.

Hemivertebrae: the right or left half of a vertebrae may be absent, or one half of one vertebrae may fuse with the vertebra above or below, leaving the other half as a separate bone.

Spina bifida: the laminae of a vertebra may fail to unite with each other in the midline posteriorly. The vertebral arch will be incomplete with a gap in the midline. Several vertebrae may be involved, particulary the lower lumbar and upper sacral segments. The spinal cord may bulge or herniate out through this defect. This results in a swelling in the midline posteriorly - a meningocele.

spinous process is 2 pieces rather than one

Interarticular defect: a defect may be present between the superior and inferior articular processes of a vertebra, at the isthmus. This occurs most frequently at the fifth lumbar. See spondylolisthesis.

Absence of sacrum: the lower part of the sacrum may fail to develop; if so, the coccyx will be absent.

Sacralization: the last lumbar vertebra may be partly or completely fused with the first sacral segment. The reverse may also occur. The first sacral segment may form as a separate bone, resulting in six lumbar vertebrae.

Note: to locate any particular lumbar vertebra on a processed film it may be necessary to locate the twelfth dorsal body. The first lumbar will then be the vertebra below this. This applies particularly to lateral views wherein the lumbosacral joint is not included.

S. 67 LANDMARKS - PROMINENCES - VERTEBRAL COLUMN

Spinous processes: the spinous process of a true vertebra is the only part of it than can be seen or felt. The tips of these processes form a vertical chain of knob-like prominences in the midline

Intervertebral joints are part-movable.

behind. As stated above, the spinous process of the seventh cervical is quite prominent and is used as a landmark in counting the vertebrae on a patient.

The spinous processes all lie at a lower level than the corresponding vertebral body, especially in the thoracic region.

Sacrum and coccyx: these may be felt in the fold of skin between the buttocks, or with a finger in the rectum.

Anterior body surface markings for vertebrae.

Suprasternal notch: joint between 2nd & 3rd dorsal.

Sternal angle: joint between the 4th & 5th dorsal.

Xiphisternal junction: body of 9th dorsal.

Umbilicus: joint between 3rd & 4th lumbar.

Crest of ilium: 4th lumbar vertebra.

Anterior superior spine: second sacral segment.

S. 68 APPLICATION TO RADIOGRAPHY - VERTEBRAE.

In order to verify the statements made below the student should place a mounted skeleton supine on a table, or with a little more imagination the upright skeleton may be used. If the student will then view each region of the spine from above or in front, the eyes will then see what the focal spot of the x-ray tube must encounter.

Attention is again directed to the lordotic curves in the cervical and lumbar areas, and the kyphotic curves in the thoracic and sacral regions. Because of these curves it will be impossible to look directly through the intervertebral joints. There will be overlapping of adjacent vertebrae. This would apply to antero-posterior views. To get rid of these curves it would seem reasonable to position the subject so as to straighten out the curves.

In the cervical division flexing the head upon the chest will obliterate the curve but will throw the facial bones at a lower level to obscure even the lower cervical bodies. Flexion therefore does not help. However, the mouth may be opened to get the mandible off the upper cervical vertebrae and the odontoid process. The intervertebral foramina are not visible when viewed from the front. It is necessary to turn the subject into the oblique position in order to visualize them.

Because there is limited movement between the thoracic vertebrae, it is often impossible to get rid of the kyphotic curve. It is necessary to view a small area with the eye or tube at right angles to the part examined. Multiple small films should prove satisfactory if the tube be angulated towards the head for the upper dorsal area. The tube should be at right angles to the table top for the mid dorsal vertebrae, and directed towards the feet or the lower dorsal area.

In the lumbar region considerable movement is possible. The lordotic curve may be corrected. If the student will place a hand under the lumbar vertebrae, a definite curve may be felt. If the thighs and the knees are flexed, the curve will disappear and the vertebrae will touch the hand. This maneuver is used to obtain films of the lumbar division.

The student should examine the interarticular joints. It should be noted that they lie obliquely from front to back. They cannot be looked into without overlapping of the articular processes, with the subject in the antero-posterior position. Turning the skeleton into the oblique position will bring these joints at right angles to the eye or central ray.

Because the sacrum and coccyx form a kyphotic curve and the sacrum is directed posteriorly, they appear fore-shortened when viewed directly from in front. It is necessary to look up at them, or to angulate the tube towards the head end.

The lumbosacral joint also lies obliquely, and the same procedure is necessary to look directly through this joint.

In the lateral position it is possible to look directly through any joint, provided the eye is at the level of this joint. This is often complicated by the subject sagging so that the spine becomes curved to the side - a scoliotic curve. This is particulary true of the lumbosacral joint.

S. 69 TERMS USED TO DESCRIBE THE VERTEBRAL COLUMN.

annulus fibrosus
apophyseal joints
arch of vertebra
articular cartilage of a vertebra

articular cortex
atlas
atlanto-occipital joints
axis

body of a vertebra
cervical vertebra
coccyx
coccygeal (adj.)
congenital anomaly
cornu
cornua (pl.)
cornus of:
    sacrum
    coccyx
dens
dorsal vertebra
epistropheus
facets of vertebra
foramen
foramina (pl.)
foramina of vertebrae
hemivertebra
inferior articular process of a vertebra
interarticular isthmus
interarticular joints
intervertebral discs
intervertebral ligaments
intervertebral foramen
intervertebral joints
kyphosis
kyphotic (adj.)

lamina
laminae (pl.)
laminae of vertebra
lordosis
lordotic (adj.)
lumbar vertebra
lumbosacral joint
nucleus pulposus
odontoid process
pedicle of a vertebra
sacrum
sacrococcygeal joint
sacroiliac joint
sacro-vertebral joint
scoliosis
scoliotic (adj.)
spina bifida
spinous process of a vertebra
superior articular process of a vertebra
thoracic vertebra
vertebrae (pl.)
vertebral (adj.)
vertebral foramen
vertebral foramina (pl.)
vertebral notch
vertebra prominens

Suprasternal notch is at the level at ~~D6~~ D7
Extra rib is called a cervical rib

F. 70 STERNUM - RIBS - COSTAL CARTILAGES - frontal view -

- costovertebral joint
- first right rib
- third right rib
- sternum
- costal cartilages of 8th, 9th, 10th ribs join with 7th costal cartilage
- suprasternal or jugular notch
- sternal angle
- sternochondral (sternocostal) joints
- costochondral joint ✓
- costal cartilages
- left costal margin
- free or floating ribs

F. 71 STERNUM - frontal view -

- clavicular notch
- first costal notch
- sternal angle
- costal notches

F. 72 STERNUM - lateral view -

- manubrium of sternum
- sternal angle
- notches for costal cartilages
- body of sternum
- ensiform or xiphoid process

F. 73 A RIB - from above

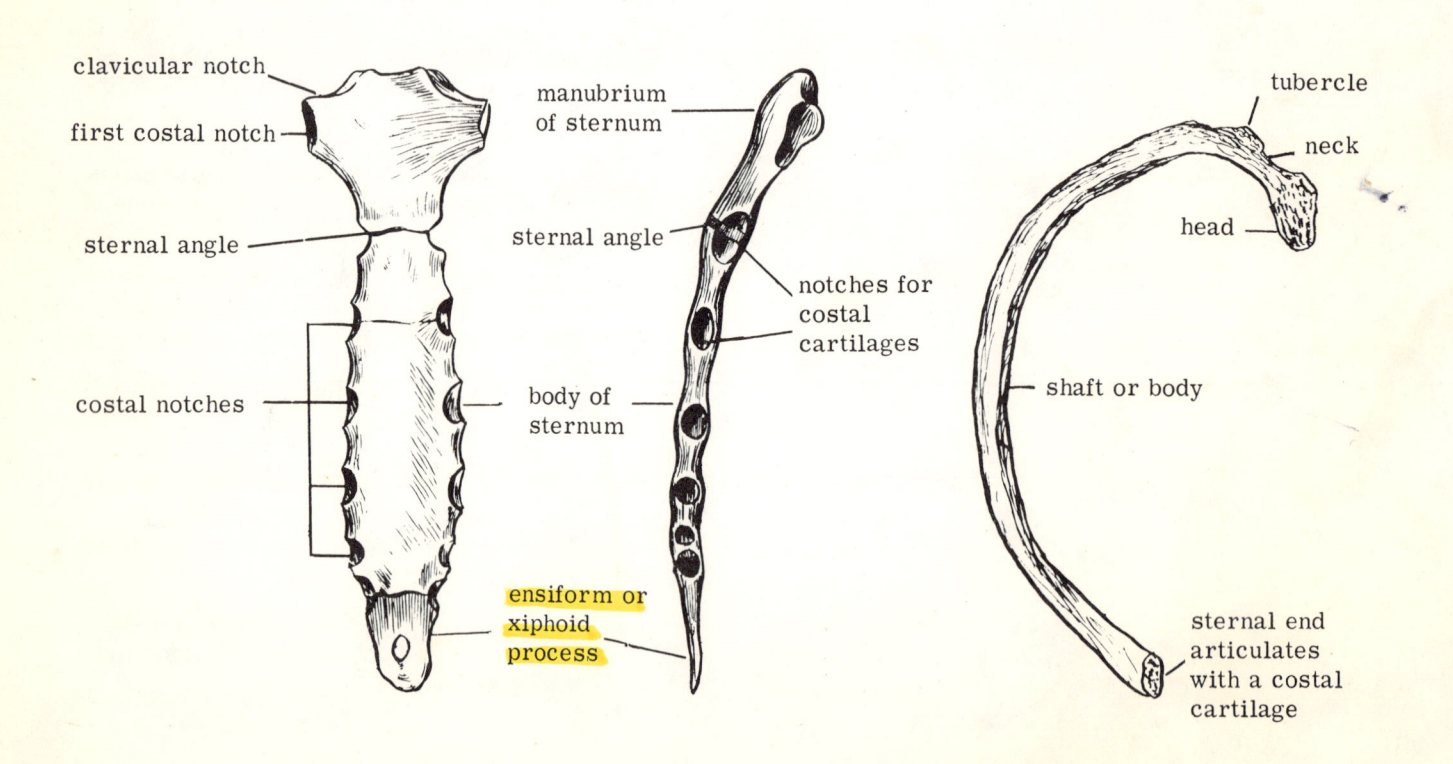

- tubercle
- neck
- head
- shaft or body
- sternal end articulates with a costal cartilage

gladiolus = body of sternum
depressed sternum = pectus excavatum (funnel chest)

Vertebrae
Ribs + sternum (not scapula)

CHAPTER IX. THE THORAX

S. 70 THE BONES OF THE THORAX.

1. Twelve thoracic vertebrae
2. Sternum, breast bone (pl. sterna; adj. sternal)
3. Ribs, twelve pairs (costa, pl. costae; adj. costal)

S. 71 THE JOINTS OF THE THORAX.

1. Costovertebral joints
2. Costochondral joints
3. Sternocostal or sternochondral joints
4. Xiphisternal joint

S. 72 IMPORTANT DETAILS - BONES OF THORAX.

THORACIC VERTEBRAE: see section 63 and 64.

STERNUM:

3 main parts
1. manubrium
2. body or corpus - four united segments
3. xiphoid or ensiform process
4. suprasternal or jugular notch
5. clavicular notches
6. costal notches
7. sternal angle

RIBS:

twelve pairs:
seven pairs of true ribs
five pairs false ribs (two pairs floating) *11,12*
structure of a rib:
1. posterior end:
   head
   neck
   tubercle
   articular facets
2. shaft or body:
   costal groove
3. anterior or sternal end:
   articular surface

COSTAL CARTILAGES:

twelve pairs:
upper seven pairs articulate with sternum;
8th, 9th, 10th articulate with cartilage above;
11th, and 12th have free anterior ends.

S. 73 DETAILED STUDY OF BONES OF THE THORAX.

The thoracic cage is formed in the midline behind by twelve thoracic vertebrae, in front by the sternum. Twelve pairs of ribs, and twelve pairs of costal cartilages complete the framework behind, laterally, and in front. It protects the heart, lungs, and great vessels from injury. The muscles of the neck and chest wall are attached in such a manner that, when they contract, the size of the chest is increased. This expansion takes place from front to back, from side to side, and from top to bottom. The thoracic vertebrae have already been studied in detail, and the student should see sections 63, 64.

protect heart + lungs

THE STERNUM

Sternum or breast bone (pl. sterna; adj. sternal).
The sternum is a long bone, flattened from front to back, and lies vertically in the anterior chest wall in the midline. This bone is shaped somewhat like a dagger or sword. Its upper end forms the handle and is called the manubrium. The part below this is the body or corpus (originally called the gladiolus or blade). The lower pointed end is the xiphoid or ensiform process. The sternum has: a suprasternal or jugular notch, clavicular notches, costal notches, and a sternal angle.

The manubrium of the sternum is the upper segment, which in early life is separated from the body by cartilage, but later fuses with the body.

The body of the sternum extends from the manubrium to the xiphoid process below. It consists of four fused segments in adult life.

The xiphoid or ensiform process is the lower pointed end below the body. It becomes ossified in later life and may unite with the body.

The suprasternal or jugular notch is the concave upper border of the manubrium.

The clavicular notches are depressions, one at each lateral border of the suprasternal notch. These with the medial ends of the clavicles form the sterno-calvicular joints.

The costal notches are depressions on each lateral margin of the sternum, which articulate with the costal cartilages.

Angle formed by the ribs + the diaphragm = costophrenic angle

The sternal angle is the prominent transverse ridge at the junction of the manubrium and body of the sternum. This ridge is readily felt. It lies opposite the second costal cartilages and is used as a landmark in counting ribs.

THE RIBS

Rib (L. costa; pl. costae; adj. costal).

There are twelve pairs of ribs. They are named from above downwards as the first, second, third, etc., and as right or left. They are flat, curved bones that form part of the posterior wall, the entire lateral wall, and part of the anterior wall of the thorax.

The upper seven pairs have separate costal cartilages, which in turn articulate with the costal notches on each side of the sternum. They are called true ribs.

The lower five pairs are called false ribs. The eighth, ninth, and tenth have costal cartilage which are joined together at their anterior ends, and to the seventh costal cartilages above. The eleventh and twelfth ribs have short costal cartilages which are unattached at their anterior ends - free floating ribs.

Each rib has a head, neck, tubercle, articular facets; a shaft or body; and an anterior end.

The head of a rib is the slightly expanded posterior end. It articulates with the pits on the adjacent borders of two vertebrae or a single vertebra.

The neck of a rib is the slightly constricted part lateral to the head.

The tubercle is a small prominence lateral to the neck. It forms a joint with the anterior surface of the adjacent transverse process of a vertebra.

The articular facets on the head of a rib are one or two pits that articulate with a facet on a single vertebral body, or facets on adjacent margins of two vertebrae. A similar pit on the tubercle articulates with the pit on the anterior surface of a transverse process.

The shaft of a rib is the long, flat, curved part that passes from the neck around the chest wall. Its lower border is grooved for an intercostal artery, vein, and nerve. The angle of a rib is the bend lateral to the tubercle.

The anterior or sternal end articulates with a costal cartilage.

COSTAL CARTILAGES

The costal cartilages are twelve pairs of cartilaginous flat plates on the anterior chest wall. The lateral end of each cartilage articulates with the anterior end of the adjacent rib. The medial ends of the upper seven cartilages articulate with the notches on the lateral borders of the sternum. The anterior parts of the eighth, ninth, and tenth cartilages are joined together and to the seventh costal cartilage above. The anterior ends of the eleventh and twelfth are free.

The costal margin on each side is formed by the curved border of the costal cartilages on each side of the ensiform process.

The upper costal cartilages are short, and the ribs end close to the sternum. Each cartilage below is longer than the one above, and each rib is farther from the sternum. Injury to the upper thorax near the midline might result in a fracture of a rib, but an injury the same distance from the sternum lower down would involve the cartilage, not a rib.

S. 74 ARTICULATIONS OF THE THORAX.

1. Costovertebral joints, two joints:
   (a) head of a rib with pit on vertebra, or vertebrae
   (b) tubercle of a rib with transverse process

2. Costochondral joints, (costa, rib; chondrus, a cartilage):
   (a) anterior end of rib
   (b) lateral end of costal cartilage

3. Sternocostal or sternochondral joints:
   (a) medial end of costal cartilage
   (b) costal notch on sternum

4. Xiphisternal joint:
   (a) body of sternum - lower end
   (b) upper end of xiphoid process

S. 75 CONGENITAL ANOMALIES - BONES OF THORAX.

Cervical rib: an extra rib may be present on one or both sides above the normal first rib. It arises from the seventh cervical vertebra. It may be long or short. It may press upon the large nerve trunk which passes from the neck out to the arm. This may be the cause of pain in the upper limb.

Lumbar rib: a short extra rib may be present below the twelfth, arising from the first lumbar body.

Absence of a rib: one or more ribs may be absent on one or both sides. This usually accompanies anomalies of adjacent vertebrae.

Forked rib: the anterior end of a rib may be forked.

Fused ribs: anterior ends of adjacent ribs are one.

Pectus excavatum: the sternum may be depressed and thus decrease the antero-posterior diameter of the chest. This may embarrass the heart.

S. 76 LANDMARKS - PROMINENCES - BONES OF THORAX.

The suprasternal notch can be felt as a depression above the sternum. It is often visible. It lies opposite the joint between the second and third thoracic vertebrae.

The sternal angle is often visible and can be felt as a ridge passing transversely across the upper sternum, at the junctions of manubrium and body.
It lies opposite the costal cartilages of the second ribs.
It lies opposite the joint between the fourth and fifth thoracic vertebrae.

The xiphisternal joint can be felt at the lower end of the body of the sternum.

The costal margins can be felt on each side curving up towards the lower end of the sternum. The gall bladder lies under the right costal margin, the spleen under the left.

S. 77 APPLICATION TO RADIOGRAPHY - THE THORAX

The student must imagine that his eye is the focal spot of an x-ray tube and visualize what the central ray would encounter.

The sternum lies directly in front of the thoracic vertebrae, and its image will be obscured by that of the more dense vertebral bodies. Its image may be separated from that of the vertebrae by rotating the subject to the right or left. In the lateral position the sternum is visible without superimposition, except for the anterior rib margins.

The sternoclavicular joints and medial ends of the clavicles are also obscured by vertebrae and become visible in the oblique positions.

Ribs: when viewed from the front or back, the lateral parts of the ribs are foreshortened as they are directed from front to back. The lateral borders can be satisfactorily outlined if the subject is placed in an oblique position.
In the lateral position the ribs on opposite sides overlap and obscure detail.
The lower ribs overlie the liver, which is dense and obscures rib detail. A different technic is therefore necessary.
The costal cartilages are radiolucent and are not visible in younger subjects. In the older age group they calcify and become visible in films.
It cannot be too strongly emphasized that chest technic is not satisfactory to show rib detail.

S. 78 TERMS USED IN CHAPTER IX - THORAX

angle of sternum	costosternal joint	manubrium sterni	sternocostal joint
angle of rib	costovertebral joints	neck of a rib	sternomanubrial joint
body of sternum	costal notch	retrosternal	substernal
cervical rib	ensiform process, sternum	rib	suprasternal
chondrosternal joint	facet	shaft of rib	thorax
corpus sterni	false rib	sternum	thoracic (adj.)
costa	gladiolus of sternum	sternal (adj.)	true rib
costae (pl.)	head of a rib	sternal angle	tubercle of a rib
costal (adj.)	intercostal space	sternochondral joint	xiphoid process sternum
costal cartilage	jugular notch	sternoclavicular joint	

70

F. 74 SKULL - vertex -   F. 75 SKULL - frontal view -   F. 76 SKULL - occipital view -

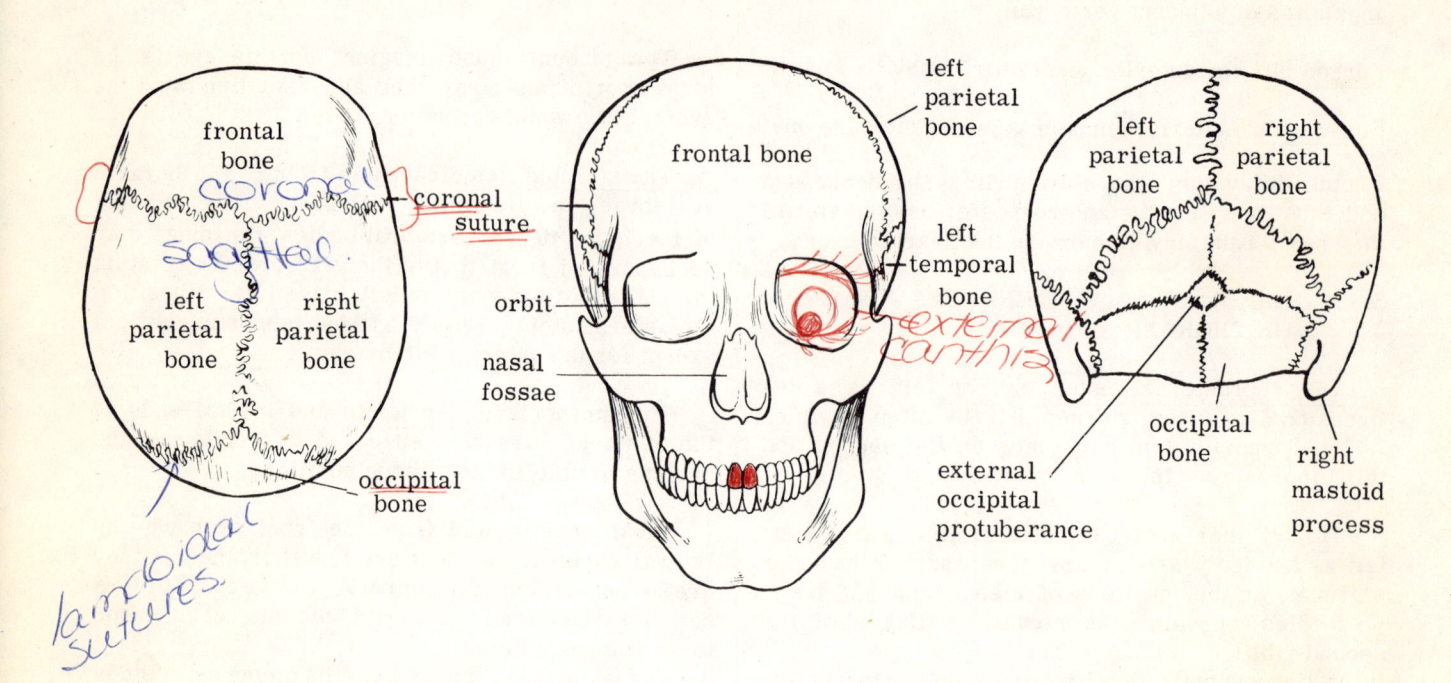

F. 77 SKULL - lateral view   F. 78 SKULL - basal view -

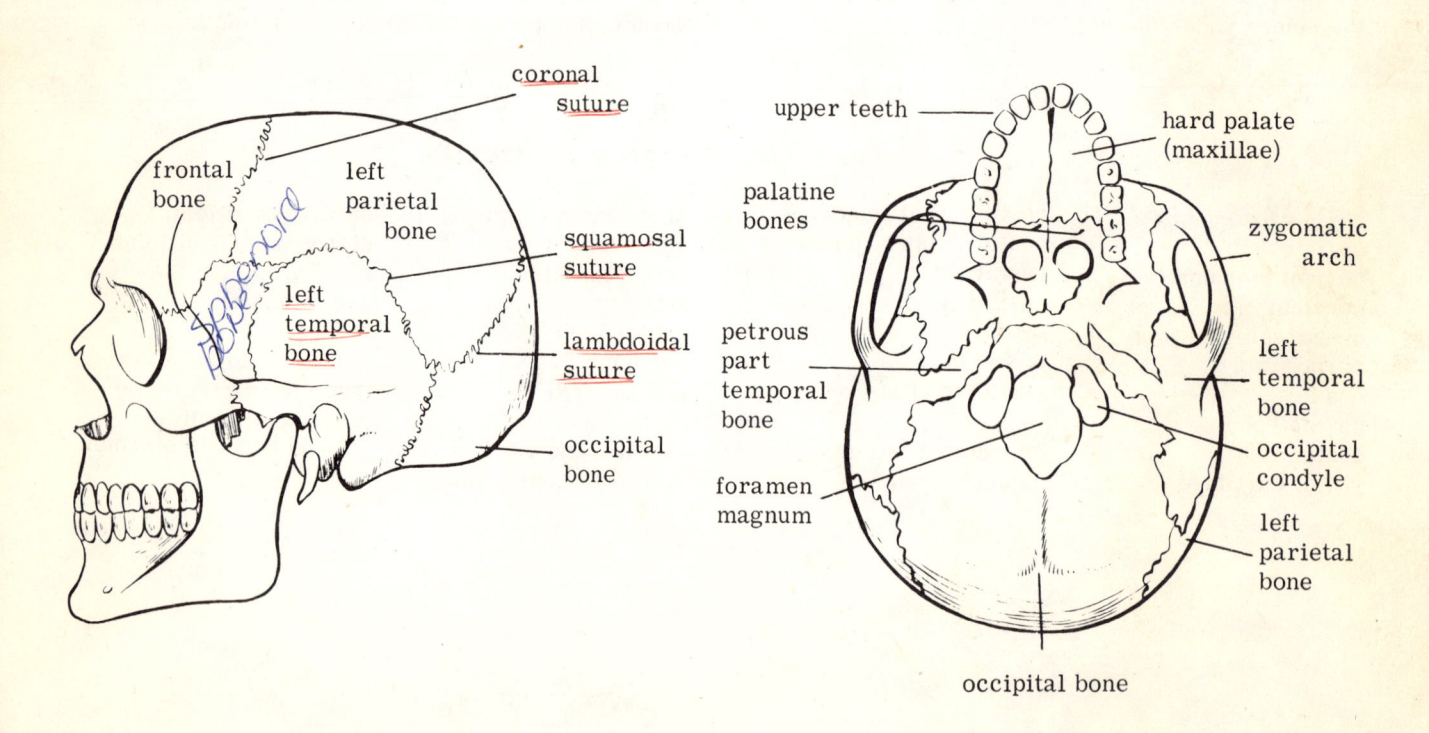

Fontanels—

71

F. 79 THE SKULL - left lateral view -

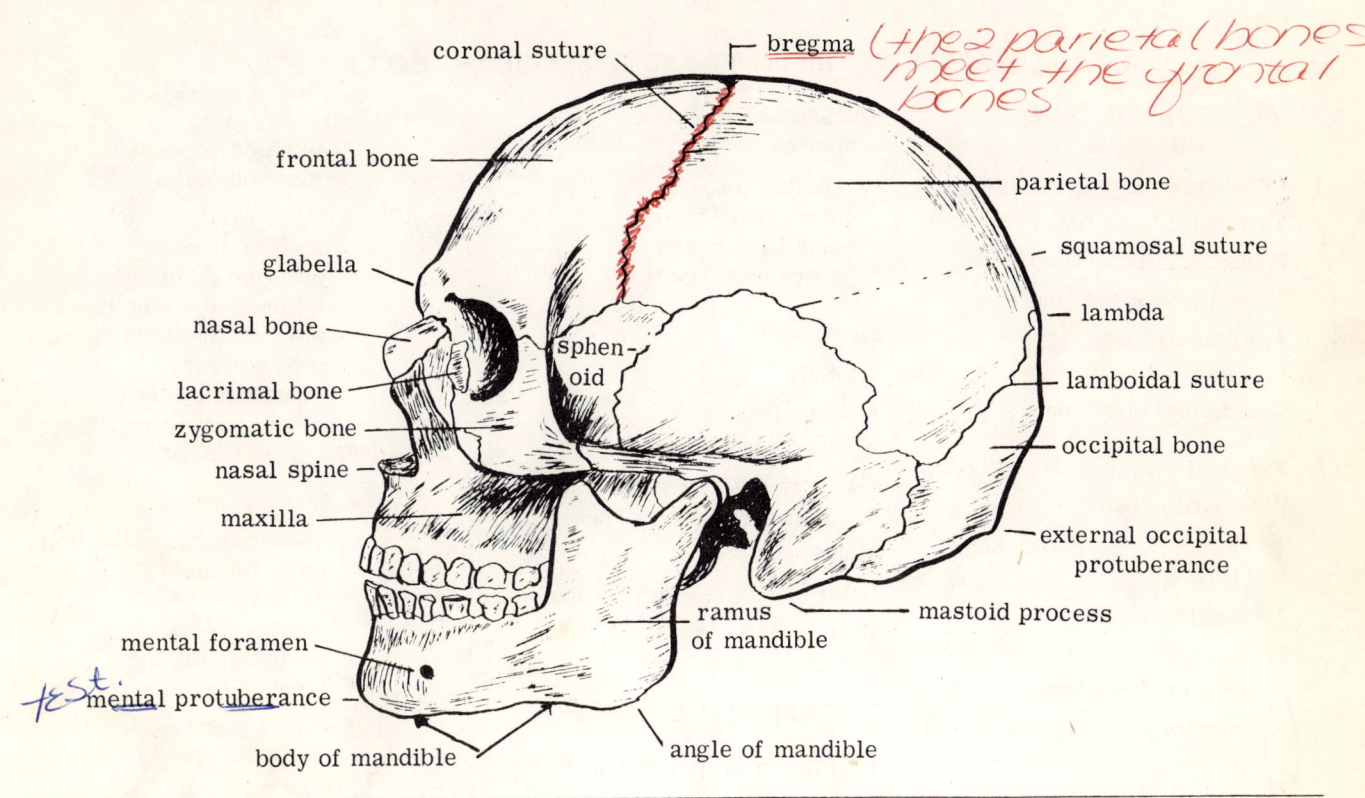

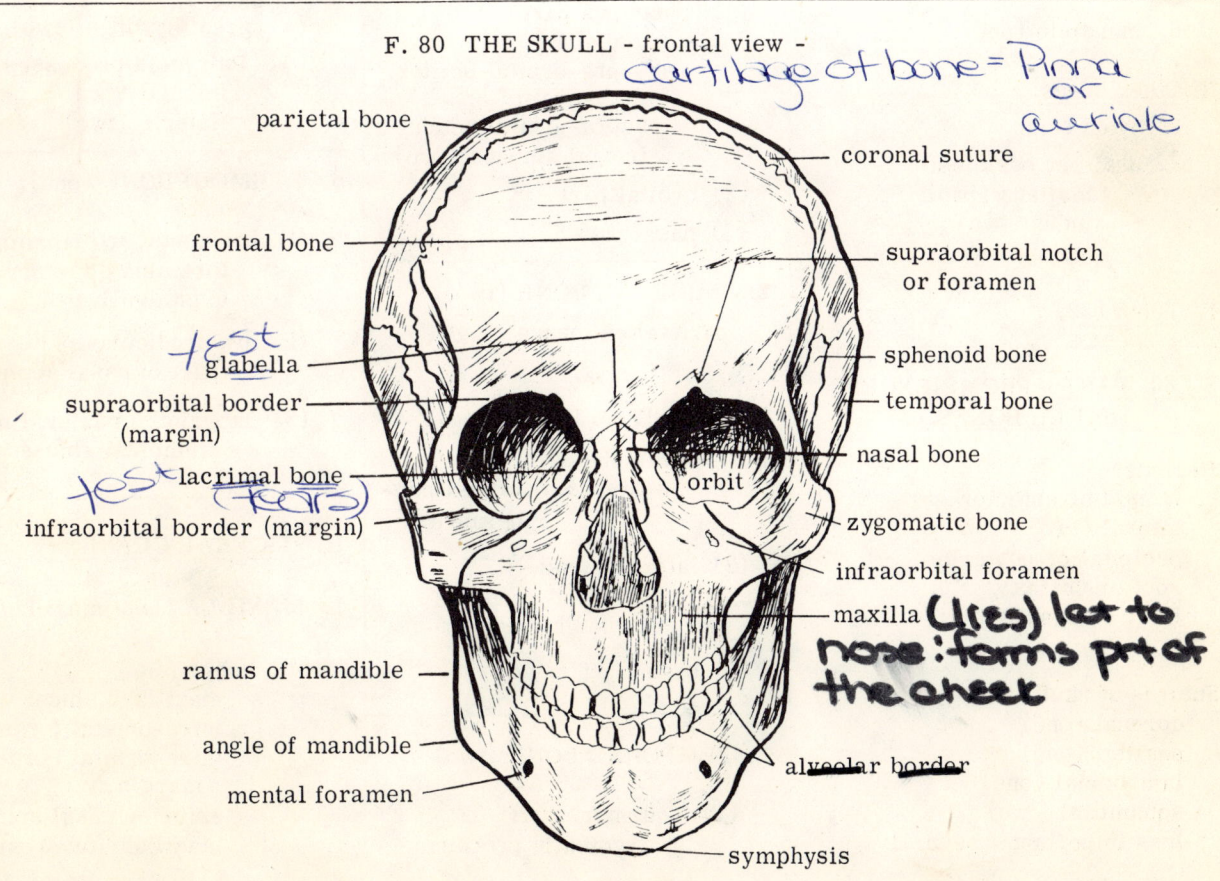

- coronal suture
- bregma — *the 2 parietal bones meet the frontal bones*
- frontal bone
- parietal bone
- squamosal suture
- glabella
- lambda
- nasal bone
- sphenoid
- lamboidal suture
- lacrimal bone
- zygomatic bone
- occipital bone
- nasal spine
- maxilla
- external occipital protuberance
- ramus of mandible
- mastoid process
- mental foramen
- *Test* mental protuberance
- body of mandible
- angle of mandible

F. 80 THE SKULL - frontal view -

cartilage of bone = Pinna or auricle

- parietal bone
- coronal suture
- frontal bone
- supraorbital notch or foramen
- sphenoid bone
- temporal bone
- *Test* glabella
- supraorbital border (margin)
- nasal bone
- *Test* lacrimal bone (tears)
- orbit
- infraorbital border (margin)
- zygomatic bone
- infraorbital foramen
- maxilla *(jes) lat to nose: forms prt of the cheek*
- ramus of mandible
- angle of mandible
- alveolar border
- mental foramen
- symphysis

Joints of skull = suture lines

CHAPTER X. THE BONES AND JOINTS OF THE SKULL.

S. 79 BONES OF SKULL - CRANIUM "*brain case*"

I. Cerebral cranium, calvarium:
1. frontal bone (one)
2. parietal bone (two)
3. occipital bone (one)
4. temporal bone (two)
5. sphenoid bone (one)
6. ethmoid bone (one)

(Test know) (8)

II. Visceral cranium, facial bones:
1. maxilla (two) pl. maxillae
2. zygomatic or malar bone (two)
3. nasal bone (two)
4. lacrimal bone (two)
5. palatine bone (two)
6. inferior concha, turbinate (two)
7. vomer (one)
8. mandible (one)

Test (14)

III. Other bones:
1. hyoid bone
2. auditory ossicles:
   malleus (two)
   incus (two)
   stapes (two)

IV. Teeth (32)

S. 80 PARTS - PROMINENCES - SKULL BONES.

Regions:
frontal or anterior
lateral (two)
occipital or posterior
roof or vertex
floor or basal

Sutures of skull:
coronal (one)
sagittal (one)
lambdoidal (one)
squamosal (two)
less important - several

Paranasal, accessory nasal sinuses
{ frontal (two)
  ethmoidal (two)
  maxillary (two)
  sphenoidal (two)

Bregma
Lambda
Orbits (two)
Nasal fossae (two)
Nasal septem (one)
Mouth or oral cavity (one)
Mentum
Lateral, outer, external canthus
Zygomatic arch

I. CEREBRAL CRANIUM.

1. FRONTAL BONE (one):
   (1) squamous part:
       glabella
       supra-orbital border, margin
       supra-orbital notch
       frontal sinuses (two)
   (2) orbital part
   (3) nasal part

2. PARIETAL BONE (two):
   parietal eminence

3. OCCIPITAL BONE (one):
   (1) squamous part:
       external occipital protuberance
   (2) lateral parts:
       occipital condyles
       foramen magnum
   (3) base

4. TEMPORAL BONE (two):
   (1) squamous part:
       zygomatic process

   (2) mastoid part:
       mastoid process
       mastoid cells
   (3) petrous part:
       styloid process
       external auditory meatus
       internal auditory meatus
       internal auditory opening
       internal ear
       mandibular fossa

---

5. SPHENOID BONE (one):
   (1) body:
       sphenoid sinus (two)
       optic foramen
       sella turcica
       dorsum sella
       posterior clinoid processes
   (2) lesser wings (two)
       anterior clinoid processes
   (3) greater wings (two)
   (4) Pterygoid processes
       medial (two)
       lateral (two)

---

6. ETHMOID BONE (one):
   (1) horizontal or cribriform plate
       foramina olfactory nerves
       crista galli
   (2) perpendicular plate:
       part of nasal septum
   (3) labyrinth or lateral mass
       ethmoidal sinuses

II; VISCERAL CRANIUM

1. MAXILLA (two maxillae):
   (1) body:
       maxillary sinus
       infra-orbital foramen
       infra-orbital border, margin
       anterior nasal spine
       maxillary tuberosity

(2) processes:
   frontal
   zygomatic
   alveolar
   palatine

---

2. ZYGOMATIC BONE (two):

   (1) temporal process
   (2) frontal process

---

3. PALATINE BONE (two):

   (1) horizontal plate
   (2) perpendicular plate

---

4. MANDIBLE (one):

   (1) body:
      symphysis
      mental protuberance
      mental foramen
      alveolar border

---

(2) ramus, rami (two):
   angle of jaw
   coronoid process
   condyloid process
   capitulum
   neck
   mandibular notch
   mandibular foramen

III; OTHER BONES.

1. HYOID BONE (one):

   (1) body
   (2) greater cornu (two, cornua)
   (3) lesser cornu (two, cornua)

---

2. TEETH - 20 deciduous;
         - 32 permanent

DECIDUOUD - left; right similar

	molar	pre-molar	canine	in-cisor
upper	2	0	1	2
lower	2/4	0/0	1/2	2/4

PERMANENT - left; right similar

	molar	pre-molar	canine	in-cisor
upper	3	2	1	2
lower	3/6	2/4	1/2	2/4

Parts   Structure
1. crown   1. pulp cavity
2. neck   2. dentine
3. root   3. enamel
                 4. cementum
                 5. peridental membrane
                 6. cusps

S. 81 DETAILED STUDY - THE BONES OF THE SKULL.

The skull or cranium includes all of the twenty-two bones forming the skeleton of the head.

The cerebral cranium is that part of the skull that encloses the brain. It is also referred to as the calvarium or brain case. It protects the brain from injury. It is made up of eight bones:

1. one frontal bone   4. two temporal bones
2. two parietal bones   5. one sphenoid bone
3. one occipital bone   6. one ethmoid bone

The visceral cranium or facial skeleton includes the fourteen bones of the face. It forms bony cavities for the protection of the eyes, nasal passages, and mouth; hence, visceral (viscus, an organ):

1. two maxillae   5. two palatine bones
2. two zygomatic bones   6. two inferior conchae or
3. two nasal bones   7. one vomer (turbinates)
4. two lacrimal bones   8. one mandible

Some authorities restrict the term cranium to include only the eight bones of the brain case or calvarium, and call the remainder the facial bones.

Because the following terms are used in describing the individual bones of the skull, they are defined below. They will be described in detail later.

Regions. The skull is described as having:

1. an anterior or frontal region
2. two lateral regions or walls
3. a posterior or occipital region
4. a roof, vertex or superior region
5. a base, floor or inferior region

Sutures. These are the special interlocking joints between the various bones of the cerebral cranium. The more important are:

1. one coronal suture   3. one lambdoidal suture
2. one saggital suture   4. two squamosal sutures

The bregma is that point on the roof of the skull where the two parietal bones meet the frontal bone.

The lambda is that point on the posterior surface where the two parietal bones meet the occipital bone.

Paranasal sinuses or accessory nasal sinuses. These are cavities within certain cranial bones. They

BONES OF THE CEREBRAL CRANIUM

F. 81 THE FRONTAL BONE - viewed from the front -   **F. 82 LEFT PARIETAL BONE** - from lateral side -

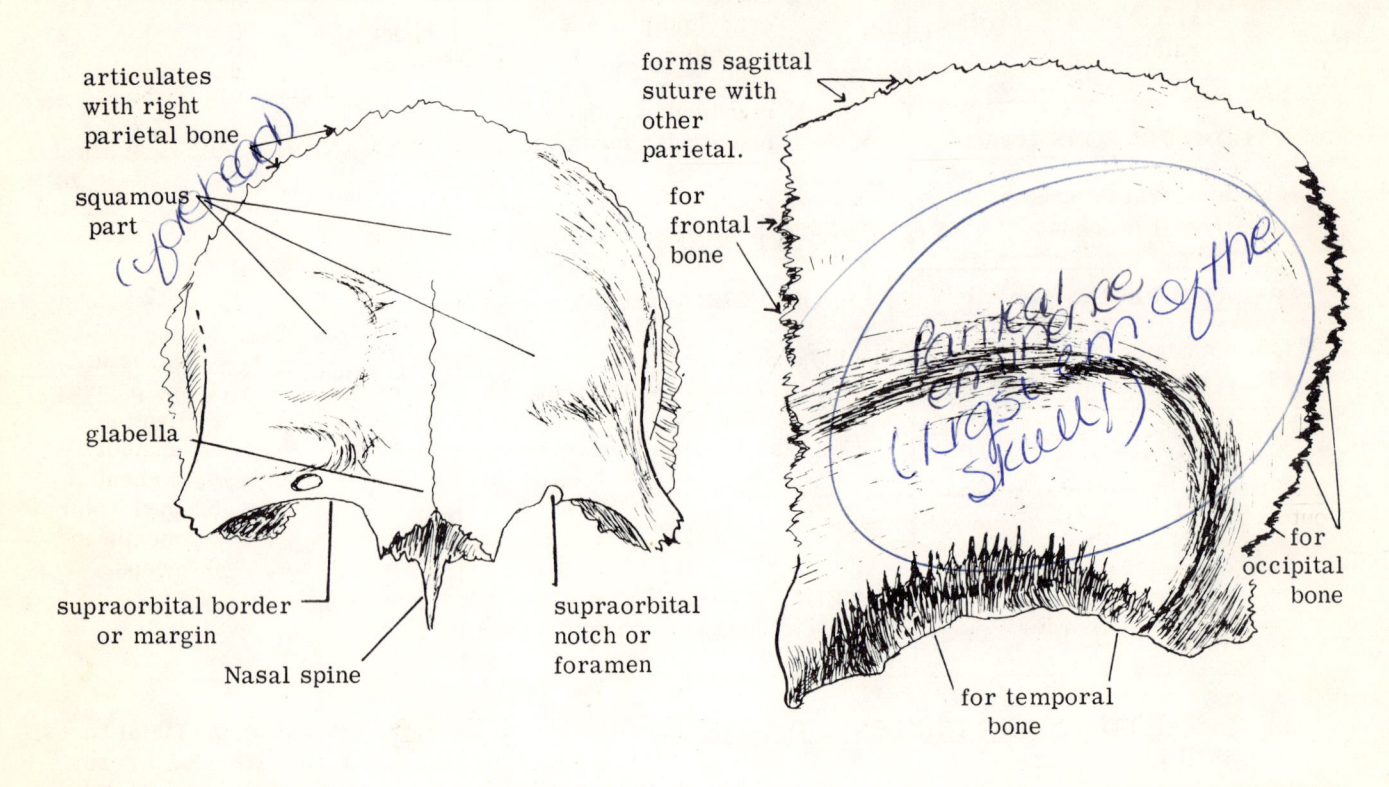

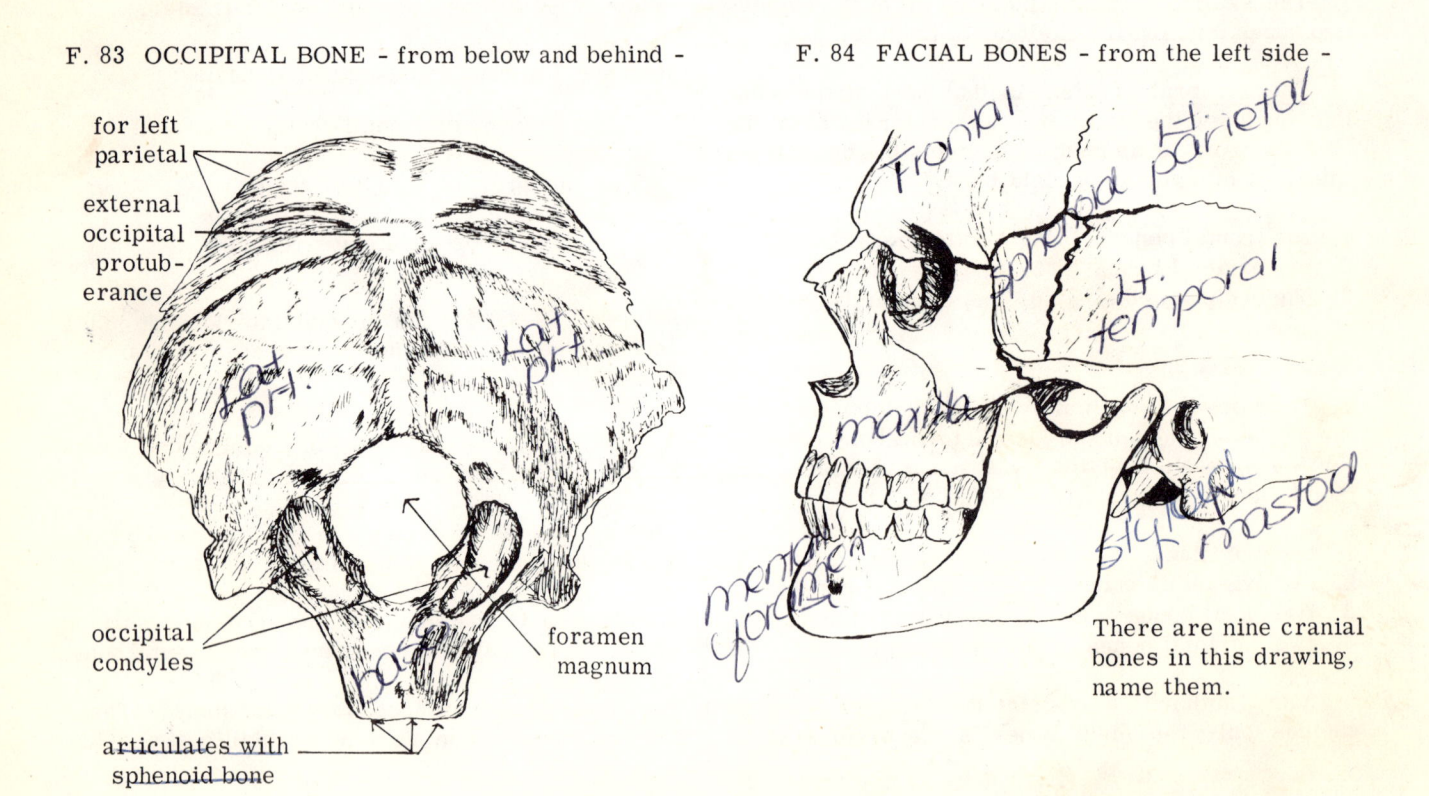

- articulates with right parietal bone
- squamous part
- glabella
- supraorbital border or margin
- Nasal spine
- supraorbital notch or foramen

- forms sagittal suture with other parietal.
- for frontal bone
- for occipital bone
- for temporal bone

F. 83 OCCIPITAL BONE - from below and behind -   **F. 84 FACIAL BONES** - from the left side -

- for left parietal
- external occipital protuberance
- occipital condyles
- foramen magnum
- articulates with sphenoid bone

There are nine cranial bones in this drawing, name them.

hammer
stapis

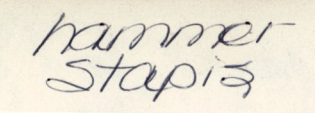

75

communicate with the nasal cavities, and are paired thus:

1. two frontal sinuses in the frontal bone
2. two ethmoidal sinuses in the ethmoid bone
3. two maxillary sinuses (antra); each maxilla has one
4. two sphenoidal sinuses in the sphenoid bone.

The orbits are the cavities for the eyeballs.

The nasal fossae or cavities are the two chambers of the nose; these end behind the nasal part of the throat, the nasopharynx.

The nasal septum is the vertical partition between the two nasal fossae.

The mouth or oral cavity opens behind into the lower part of the throat, the oropharynx. (L. os - opening)

The lateral or external canthus is the point at the outer border of the eye where the upper and lower eyelids meet; a landmark in radiography.

I. CEREBRIAL CRANIUM. *8 bones*

(1.) THE FRONTAL BONE.
forehead

This single bone, which in the fetus is two separate bones, forms the forehead and part of the roof of the skull. Its squamous part forms the forehead; its orbital parts form the roofs of the orbits; and its nasal parts help to form the nasal cavities.

The supra-orbital borders or margins are the ridges xorming the upper margins of the circular openings of the orbits. They are covered by the eyebrows.

The glabella is a smooth, rounded, bony prominence above the root of the nose. It lies between the supra-orbital borders of the frontal bone.

The frontal sinuses are paired cavities in the squamous or forehead part of the frontal bone, one on each side of the midline. They communicate with the nose. They vary in size and may be absent.

The supra-orbital notch or foramen lies towards the medial end of each supra-orbital border.

(2.) THE PARIETAL BONES.

There are two parietal (L. paries, - a wall) bones, one on each side of the cerebral cranium. Each forms most of the lateral wall and part of the roof of the skull. They meet in the midline of the roof to form the saggital suture. Their anterior (front) borders meet the frontal bone to form the coronal suture.

The parietal eminence is a bony prominence on the outer surface of each parietal bone. The distance between the two eminences is the greatest transverse diameter of the skull; important in childbirth.
("knobs" of the head)

(3.) THE OCCIPITAL BONE.

(Occiput, L. posterior or back part) This single bone forms the posterior part, as well as the part of the base or floor, of the cerebral cranium. The upper posterior border, along with the posterior borders of the two parietal bones form the lambdoidal suture.

The squamosal part is the flat posterior part.

The foramen magnum (large opening) is an opening in the lower part of the occipital bone through which the medulla of the brain leaves the skull. It is formed entirely by the occipital bone.
(only opening in brain case)

The lateral parts of the occipital bone lie one on each side of the foramen magnum.

The occipital condyles are two oval prominences on the under surface of the lateral parts, one on each side of the foramen magnum. They form joints with the superior articular surfaces of the first cervical vertebra, the atlas. The head, therefore, rests upon the atlas at these joints.

The base of the occipital bone is that part in front of the foramen magnum. It unites with the sphenoid bone in front and forms part of the floor of the skull.

The external occipital protuberance is the bony prominence on the outer surface of the squamous part of the occipital bone. It lies in the midline where this bone curves forward. It is readily palpated.
(knob at base of neck)

(4.) THE TEMPORAL BONES. (2)

(Tempus, L. time). The two temporal bones form part of the lateral walls and base of the skull. The hair over this area often becomes grey early - tempus. Each temporal bone consists of a flat or squamous part above the ear, a mastoid portion behind the ear, and a petrous (hard) part that forms part of the base of the skull.

The zygomatic process is a slender bony process that extends forward from the squamous part of the
malar bone →

temporal bone to meet a similar process of the zygomatic bone forming the zygomatic arch.

The mastoid process is a large rounded bony prominence extending down behind the ear as part of the mastoid portion.

The mastoid cells are small cavities in the mastoid process and adjacent part. These cells communicate with the middle ear. Infection in the middle ear may spread into these cells - mastoiditis.

The petrous part of the temporal bone is shaped like a pyramid. It extends from the ear medially and forward in the base of the skull. Its inner end is pointed. It contains the organ of hearing. "houses the ear"

The styloid process is a sharp pointed process that extends down from the base of the petrous part. In lateral views of the skull it will be outlined behind the ramus of the mandible.

The external auditory meatus is a tube-like passage extending into the petrous part of the temporal bone. It ends at the ear drum (tympanic membrane). This membrane separates it from the middle ear. This passage conveys sound vibrations to the drum.

The internal auditoy meatus or canal lies in the middle or inner part of the petrous part, medial to the middle ear. At its inner end is an opening by which the facial and auditory nerves leave the cranial cavity, and enter the internal meatus. This opening lies on the posterior surface of the petrous temporal. (meatus - a canal)

The internal ear lies in the petrous part. It is the organ of hearing.

The mandibular or articular fossa is a depression on the temporal bone in front of the external auditoy meatus. With the capitulum of the mandible it forms the temporo-mandibular joint. Only movable jt in the skull tmj joints

5. THE SPHENOID BONE.

(Sphenoid - wedge-like). This single bone helps form a small part of the lateral wall of the skull on each side as well as part of the base. It is a difficult one to visualize as it lies behind the facial bones. The frontal bone lies in front, and the anterior end of the base of the occipital bone lies behind it. It has been compared to a bat with two pairs of extended wings. It has a body, the two pairs of wings, and two pterygoid processes.

The body is the central part and lies in the midline of the floor of the skull, in front of the occipital bone. The student should procure a skull with skull cap or vertex removed to study it.

The wings extend laterally from the body. There are two pairs, the greater and lesser, with one of each on either side of the body.

The pytergoid processes extend down from the under surface of the body. There are two medial and two lateral, one on either side of the body.

The spenoid sinuses are two cavities within the body of the bone, one on each side of the midline. They lie behind the nasal fossae and open into them.

The optic foramen is an opening at the front on each side of the body of the sphenoid. The optic nerves (nerves of sight) leave the cranial cavity by these openings to enter the orbits.

The sella turcica is a depression hollowed out on the upper surface of the body of the sphenoid. It is shaped like a saddle; hence the name Turkish saddle. The pituitary gland lies in this depression.

The dorsum sella (back of saddle) is the posterior wall of the sella turcica. It is curved upwards like the back of a saddle.

The posterior clinoid processes are two small rounded bony processes that extend up and forward from the top of the dorsum sella.

The anterior clinoid processes are two similar processes that extend back from the lesser wings of the sphenoid over the sella turcica. With the posterior they form an incomplete roof for the pituitary gland.

6. THE ETHMOID BONE.

(Ethmoid - sieve-like). This single bone lies in the anterior part of the base of the skull. Like the sphenoid it is difficult to visualize. It has a cribriform or horizontal plate, a perpendicular plate, and two lateral masses or labyrinths.

The cribriform plate (L. cribrum - sieve) should be studied with the skull cap removed. It fills in a small gap between the orbital parts of the frontal bone in the midline. It contains several small openings for the exit of the olfactory nerves (nerves of smell) from the cranial cavity to the nasal cavities. These openings will serve to identify it.

The crista galli is a sharp flat pointed process that extends up from the cribriform plate in the midline. In the cavity

Test sphenoid bone forms part of the skull
2 long Ap. under the lesser wing of the sphenoid; Sup. Orbital fossa
know for test

77

BONES OF THE CEREBRAL CRANIUM.

F. 85 TEMPORAL BONE - lateral view -

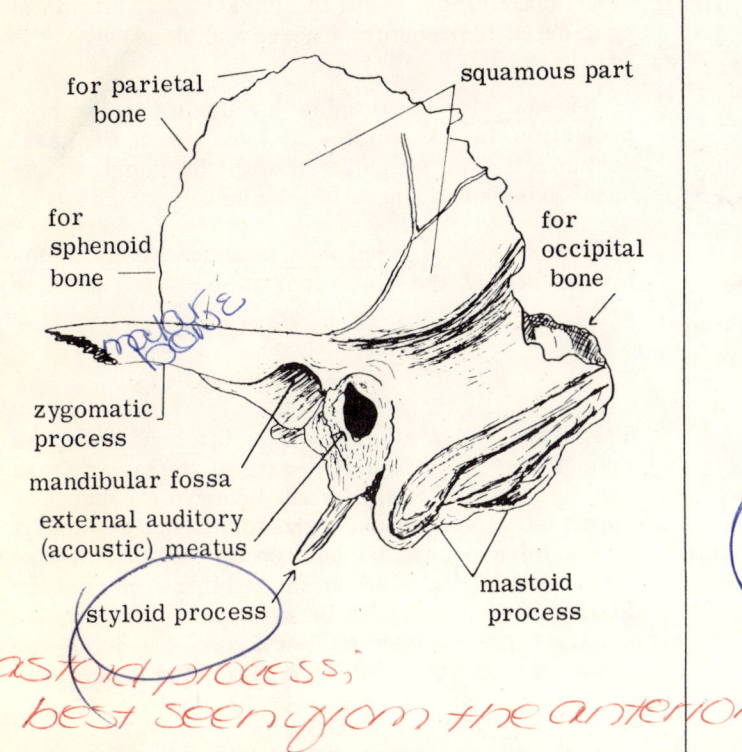

- for parietal bone
- squamous part
- for sphenoid bone
- for occipital bone
- zygomatic process
- mandibular fossa
- external auditory (acoustic) meatus
- styloid process
- mastoid process

F. 86 TEMPORAL BONE - showing petrous part -

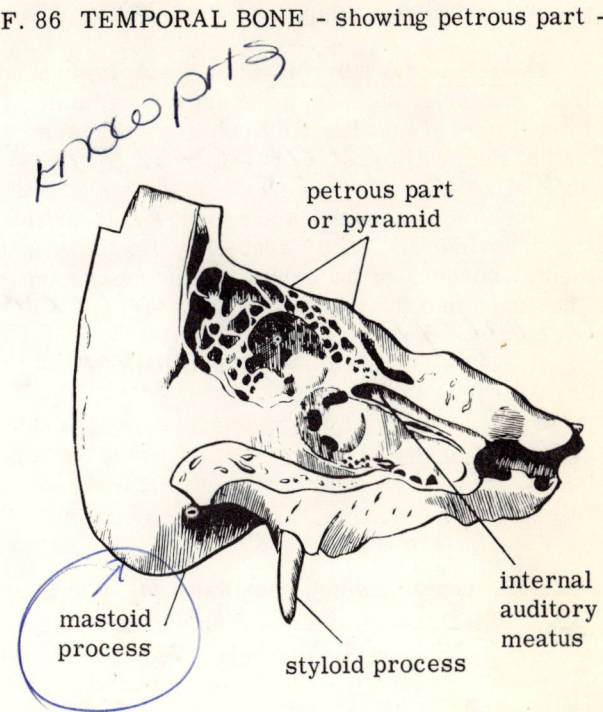

know parts

- petrous part or pyramid
- mastoid process
- styloid process
- internal auditory meatus

mastoid process; best seen from the anterior

It lies midline of the floor of skull
optic foramen here

F. 87 SPHENOID BONE
- viewed from behind and above -

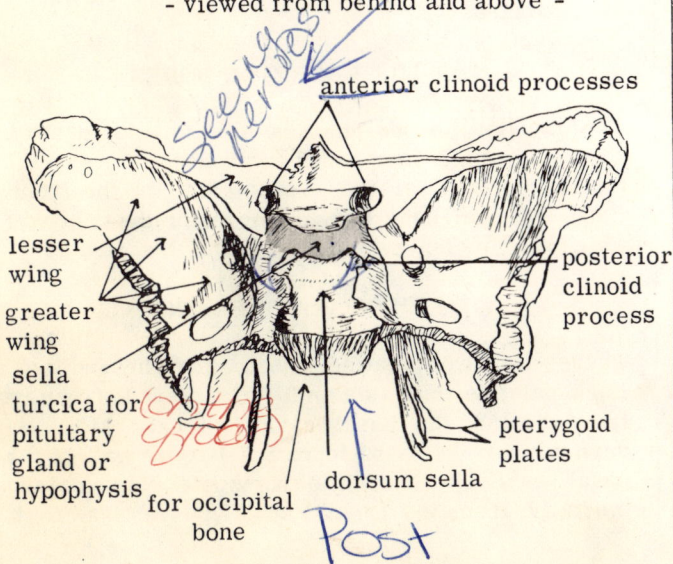

seeing nerves

- anterior clinoid processes
- lesser wing
- greater wing
- sella turcica for pituitary gland or hypophysis
- posterior clinoid process
- dorsum sella
- for occipital bone
- pterygoid plates

Post

Test cribriform is found in the ethmoid bone.
ethmoid = smell nerves pass through here

F. 88 ETHMOID BONE
ant part of skull
- viewed from above -   - viewed from behind -

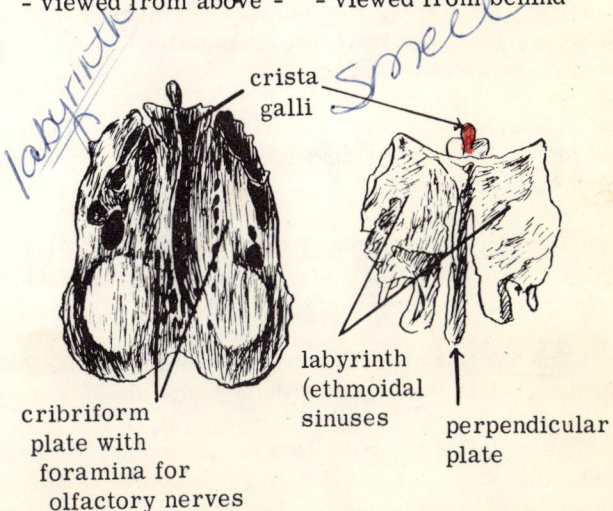

labyrinth   *smell*

- crista galli
- cribriform plate with foramina for olfactory nerves
- labyrinth (ethmoidal sinuses)
- perpendicular plate

(looks a little spongy)

Forms part of orbit

The perpendicular plate is a thin, flat, downward extension from the cribriform plate that forms a part of the nasal septum. (inside nose)

The ethmoidal labyrinth on each side is suspended from the under surface of the cribriform plate. The lateral part of each labyrinth helps to form the medial wall of the orbit. plates on both sides inside nose

The ethmoidal sinuses are many small cavities in the labyrinth on each side. They lie between the medial borders of the orbits and the nasal cavities. They open into the nose and contain air. (holes in labyrinth)

II. THE VISCERAL CRANIUM.

The visceral cranium or facial skeleton is made up of fourteen bones. There are six pairs and two single bones.

1. THE MAXILLA.

Maxilla - upper jaw (pl. maxillae; adj. maxillary). There are two maxillary bones, a right and a left. Together they make up a large part of the facial skeleton. They are solidly united at the midline. They extend from the medial borders of the orbits to the upper teeth. They form:
- the floor of the orbits,
- the medial parts of the infra-orbital borders,
- the lateral walls of the nasal fossae,
- the floor of the nasal cavities,
- part of the roof of the mouth, the anterior part,
- most of the cheek.

Each maxilla has a body and four processes, so that the descriptions given below apply to each maxilla. There are, therefore, two of most of these structures.

The body of the maxilla is large, forms part of the cheek and lies lateral to the nose.

The maxillary sinus (antrum of Highmore) [know] is a large cavity in the body of each maxilla. Each opens into the nose and contains air.

The frontal process extends up along the lateral border of the nose and inner part of each infra-orbital margin.

The zygomatic process extends laterally from the body to meet the maxillary process of the zygomatic bone.

The aveolar process extends down from the body to accommodate the upper teeth on each side.

The palatine process is a flat plate that extends medially above the mouth to meet its mate and form the anterior part of the hard palate.

The infra-orbital border is a ridge of bone forming the inner part of the lower border of the opening of the orbit.

The infra-orbital foramen is an opening in the body of the maxilla just below the infra-orbital margin of each orbit. It transmits a nerve and blood vessels to the cheek.

The anterior nasal spine is a single small pointed projection in the midline at the base of the nasal septum. It can be palpated with the thumb in one nasal fossa and a finger in the other.

The maxillary tuberosity is a small bony prominence behind the last upper molar tooth on each side.

2. THE ZYGOMATIC BONES.

There are two zygomatic or malar bones. Each of them forms the prominent part of the upper cheek and can be felt immediately below the orbit. The upper border is concave and forms the outer part of the infra orbital border, on its own side. It also forms the lateral wall of the orbit, and part of the floor. It articulates with the zygomatic process of the maxilla. Its slender temporal process joins the zygomatic process of the temporal bone to form the zygomatic arch.

3. THE NASAL BONES.

The two nasal bones form the bridge of the nose. They are thin plates of bone that articulate with the frontal bones above and extend down to end in the nasal cartilages. They meet in the midline and extend laterally to joint the maxillary bones. The septum of the nose lies under the junction of the two nasal bones. The movable part of the nose is composed of cartilages.

4. THE LACRIMAL BONES.

The lacrimal bones may be difficult to identify. They are small four-sided flat bones and lie on the medial borders of the orbits close to the front. Each lacrimal bone has a groove for the tear duct which carries tears to the nasal cavities.

5. THE PALATINE BONES.

There are two palatine bones, a right and left. Each palatine bone is a small "L" shaped structure lying behind the nasal cavity on each side. Its vertical part helps to form the lateral wall of the nasal cavity behind. The horizontal part passes medially from the lower end of the vertical part.

ant. of Highmore

FACIAL BONES

F. 89 LEFT MAXILLA - lateral view -

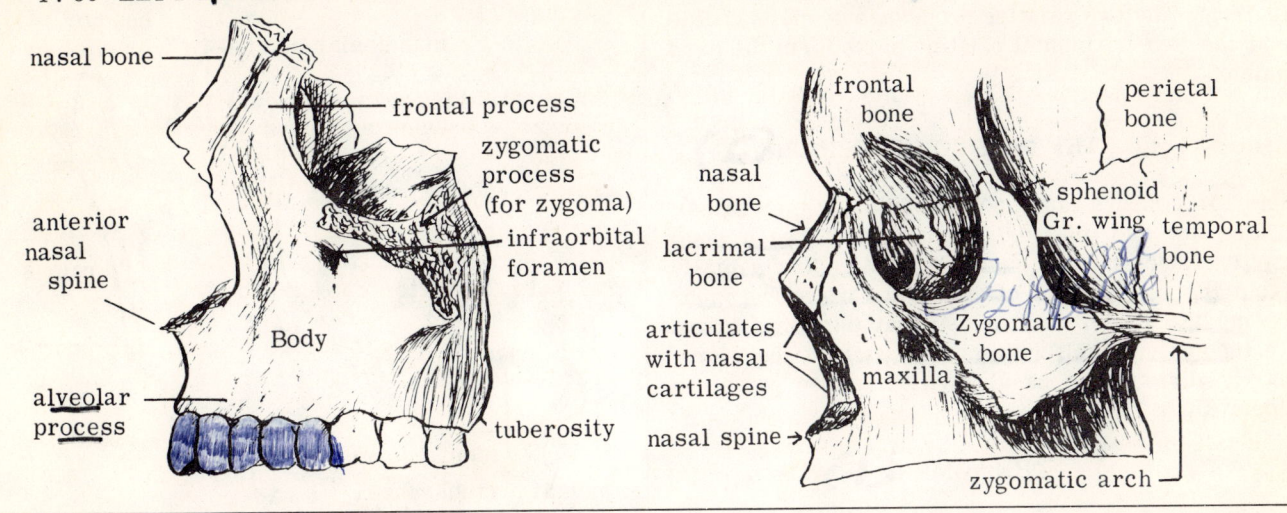

- nasal bone
- frontal process
- zygomatic process (for zygoma)
- infraorbital foramen
- anterior nasal spine
- Body
- alveolar process
- tuberosity

F. 90 LEFT ZYGOMATIC BONE (ZYGOMA - lateral view -

- frontal bone
- parietal bone
- nasal bone
- lacrimal bone
- sphenoid Gr. wing
- temporal bone
- articulates with nasal cartilages
- maxilla
- Zygomatic bone
- nasal spine
- zygomatic arch

F. 91 HARD OR BONY PALATE - viewed from below -

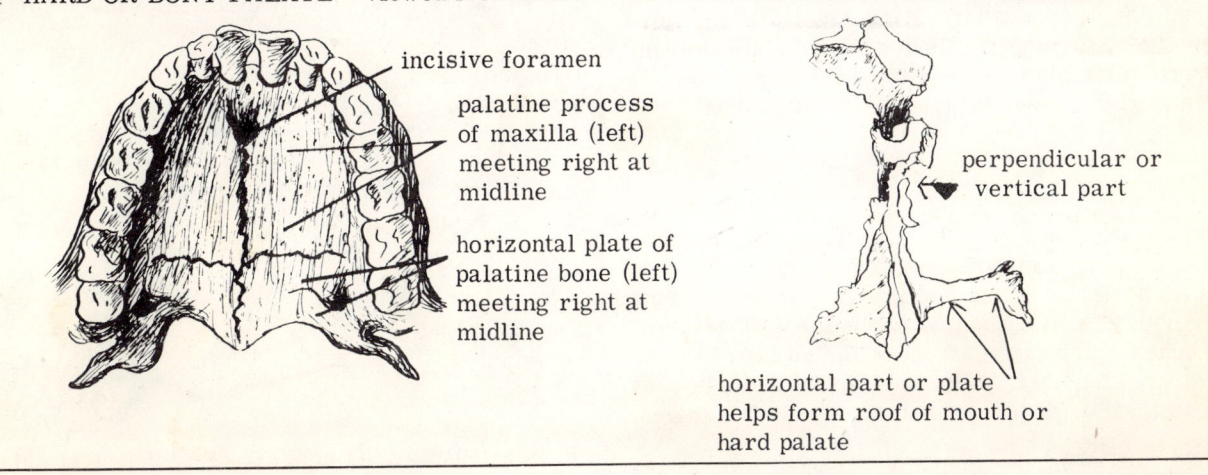

- incisive foramen
- palatine process of maxilla (left) meeting right at midline
- horizontal plate of palatine bone (left) meeting right at midline

F. 92 PALATINE BONE - viewed from behind -

- perpendicular or vertical part
- horizontal part or plate helps form roof of mouth or hard palate

F. 93 NASAL SEPTUM - lateral view to left of nasal septum -

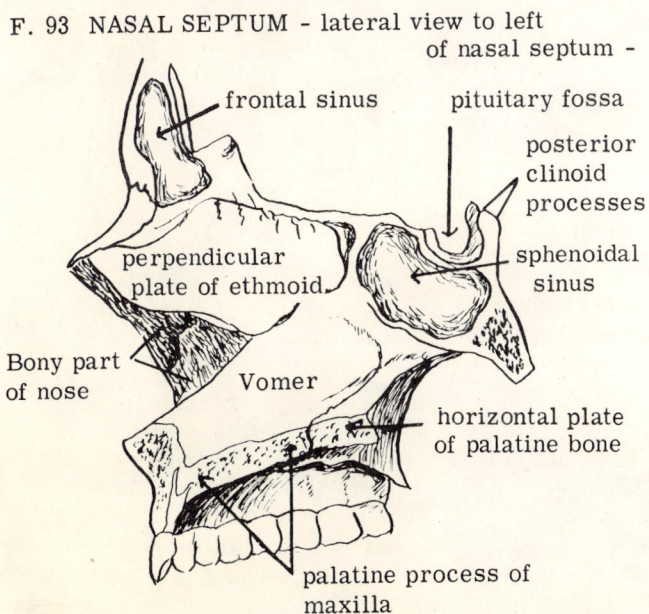

- frontal sinus
- pituitary fossa
- posterior clinoid processes
- perpendicular plate of ethmoid
- sphenoidal sinus
- Bony part of nose
- Vomer
- horizontal plate of palatine bone
- palatine process of maxilla

F. 94 LATERAL WALL OF RIGHT NASAL CAVITY - viewed from the left side -

Note: concha and turbinate bone the same.

- superior concha
- middle concha
- Inferior nasal concha

thin curved bone extending into the nasal cavity forming an incomplete shelf

79

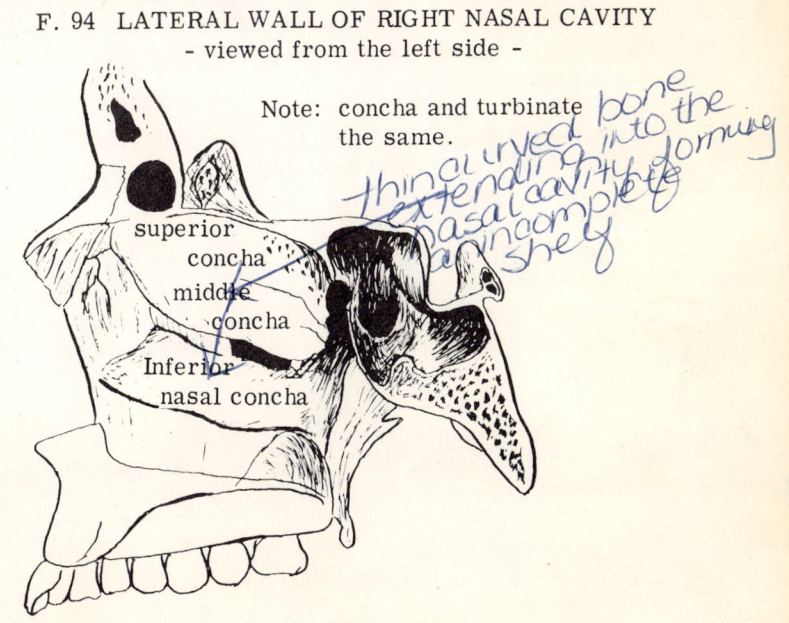

It meets the other palatine bone in the midline, and joins with the palatine process of the maxilla in front. The two palatine processes of the maxillae and the two horizontal palatine parts form the hard palate.

6. THE INFERIOR CONCHAE.

Inferior conchae (sing. concha, inferior turbinates). There are two inferior conchae, one in each nasal cavity. Each is a thin curved bone extending medially from the lateral wall of the nasal cavity. The inner or medial border is free, so that this bone forms an incomplete shelf within the nostril. It, therefore, partly divides the nasal cavity into two parts, an upper and a lower.

7. THE VOMER

(Vomer - ploughshare). This single bone is flat and shaped like a ploughshare. It lies vertically and helps form the nasal septum. It lies behind and below the perpendicular plate of the ethmoid. Its lower border rests upon the upper surface of the hard palate.

8. MANDIBLE.

Mandible or lower jaw (L. mandibula; adj. mandibular). The single mandible is shaped like a horseshoe with its posterior (hinder) ends turned up on each side to articulate with the temporal bone. This bone forms two bones which fuse in front at the midline to form the single mandible. The mandible has a single body and two rami, which meet the body at the angles.

The angle of the mandible on each side is the prominent rounded part where the horizontal part turns up to become the vertical part. It lies in front of and below the ear.

The body is the horizontal part extending from the angle on one side around the midline and back to the angle on the other side.

The rami (sing. ramus, a branch) are the flattened parts extending from the angles up to the joints with the temporal bone on each side. Each ramus has a coronoid process, a mandibular notch and a condyloid process.

The symphysis is a faint ridge running vertically in the midline where the two halves of the mandible have fused to form a single bone.

The mental protuberance is the prominence at the lower border of the symphysis of the mandible, and is called the chin.

F. 95 LEFT HALF OF MANDIBLE - lateral view -

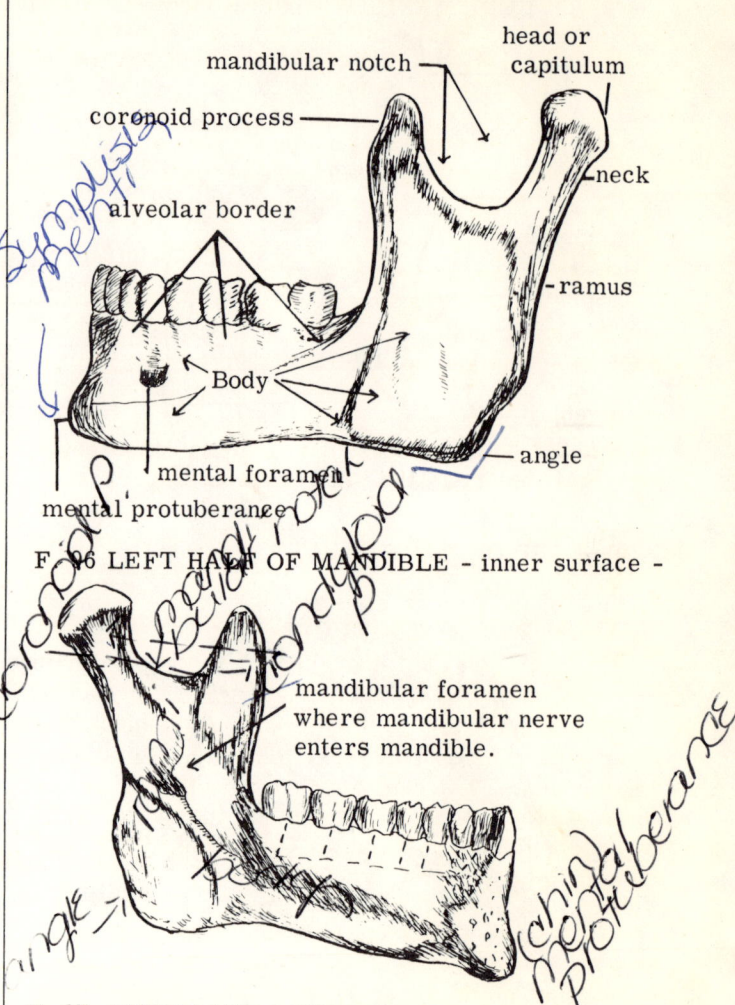

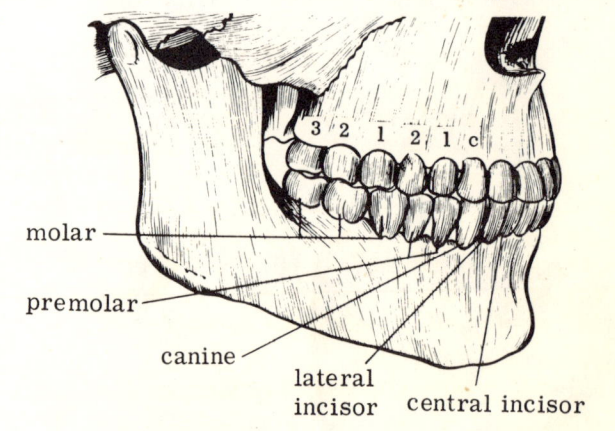

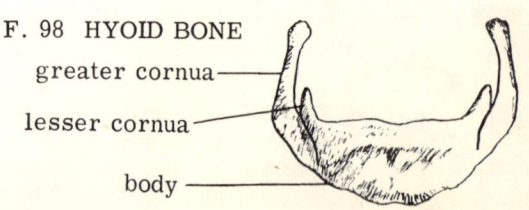

F. 96 LEFT HALF OF MANDIBLE - inner surface -

mandibular foramen where mandibular nerve enters mandible.

F. 97 UPPER AND LOWER TEETH - right side -

F. 98 HYOID BONE
greater cornua
lesser cornua
body

[handwritten at top: The thin flattened process extending up in the ant portion of ramus of the mandible = ___]

[handwritten: aud oss connect the internal ear c̄ ear drum]

The mental foramen is a small opening on the outer suface of the body below the second premolar tooth on each side. The mandibular nerve passes out to the face through this opening.

The aveolar border is the upper part of the body with cavities for the roots of the lower teeth.

The coronoid process on each side is a thin, flattened, pointed process extending up from the front of the ramus.

The condyloid process is the posterior part of each ramus extending up from the angle to the joint.

The capitulum is the slightly expanded upper end of the condyloid process. It articulates with the temporal bone at the temporo-mandibular joint.

The neck is the constricted part between the capitulum and remainder of the condyloid process.

The mandibular notch is a half-moon shaped notch between the coronoid and condyloid processes, on each side.

The mandibular foramen is an opening on the inner side of each ramus. It leads into the mandibular canal. This canal for the mandibular nerve ends at the mental foramen on the body. This nerve supplies a branch to each lower tooth and ends in the skin about the chin.

The mandible is palpable throughout its length. The angles are visible and palpable. The protuberance is readily felt at the front. The temporo-mandibular joints lie in front of the ears and may be felt with the subject opening the mouth.

1. THE HYOID BONE.

[handwritten: tongue is attached here!]

This is a single horseshoe-shaped bone that lies in front of the neck. It is placed about half way between the mandible and Adams's apple or thyroid cartilage. It has a body and a greater and lesser cornu (horn) on either side. The body is the broad front part. The cornua extend back from either end of the body. This bone is visible in lateral views of the cervical spine, below the mandible.

2. THE AUDITORY OSSICLES.

(Ossicle - a little bone). These are three very small bones which lie in the middle ear (tympanic cavity) in the petrous part of each temporal bone. They are the malleus (little hammer), incus (anvil), and the stapes (stirrup). The malleus is attached at one end to the inner surface of the ear drum (tympanic membrane). Between its other end and the stapes, the incus is placed, and in contact with one end of each. The other end of the stapes is in contact with the labyrinth of the interal ear. Vibrations of the ear drum, due to sound waves, are thus transmitted by these ossicles to the internal ear.

S. 82 THE TEETH.

(L. dens, adj. dental). The average subject has two sets of teeth during lifetime. T~~wenty~~ baby or deciduous teeth develop and are replaced by thirty-two permanent teeth.

[handwritten circled: 32]

NUMBER AND ARRANGEMENT OF THE TEETH ON EACH SIDE:

molar; premolar; canine; incisor

		molar	premolar	canine	incisor
Deciduous: - 20 -	upper	2	-	1	2
	lower	2	-	1	2
		4	-	2	4
Permanent: - 32 -	upper	3	2	1	2
	lower	3	2	1	2
		6	4	2	4

[handwritten: important]

[handwritten: 12 8 4 8 = 32]

The teeth develop in the alveolar processes of the upper jaw (maxillae) and the lower jaw (mandible). They erupt or break through the gums at varying ages. The approximate time of eruption of any one tooth is fairly constant. Usually there are an equal number of teeth in the upper and lower jaws, and in the right and left halves of each jaw.

The t~~wenty~~ deciduous teeth develop during infancy and childhood.

Thirty-two permanent teeth replace the baby teeth, and are noted below.

The incisor or biting teeth are in the front of the mouth. There are four in the upper and four in the lower jaws, two on each side of the midline. The incisor adjacent to the midline on each side is termed the central incisor; that lateral to the central incisor is termed the lateral incisor tooth. *[handwritten: (8)]*

The canine teeth (L. caninus - a dog). The dog teeth are pointed and in animals are longer that the incisor teeth. These animals use them to grasp and hold their prey. There are two upper and two lower, one lateral to each lateral incisor tooth. *[handwritten: 4]*

The premolar (pre - in front of) or bicuspid teeth lie behind the canine teeth, in front of the molars, hence pre-molar. There are two on each side in both upper and lower jaws. The anterior one is called the first premolar, the hinder one the second premolar.

The molar or chewing teeth lie three on each side in both upper and lower jaws, and behind the premolars. They are called, from front to back, the first, second and third molars, upper or lower, and left or right. The first molar is the first permanent tooth to erupt. It comes in behind the last deciduous tooth. Often it is neglected and allowed to decay as it is thought to be a deciduous tooth. The third molars or wisdom teeth are the last to erupt. They may be absent. Impaction of a tooth means that it grows at an angle so that its crown lodges against an adjacent tooth. It cannot erupt. The third molars are prone to develop thus.

S. 83   THE PARTS AND STRUCTURE OF A TOOTH.

Each tooth has:
(a) a crown or exposed part, visible in the mouth,
(b) a root, imbedded in a socket of an aveolar process,
(c) a neck, or constricted part, where the crown and root meet.

F. 99   PARTS AND STRUCTURES OF A TOOTH

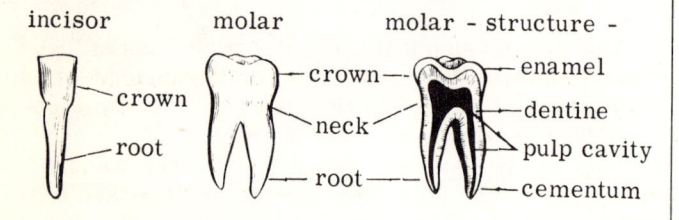

incisor — crown, root
molar — crown, neck, root
molar - structure - enamel, dentine, pulp cavity, cementum

Structure of a tooth.

1. The pulp cavity is the central cavity extending from the crown down through the root, and ending in a small opening at the apex of the root, the foramen.

2. The dentine is modified bone that surrounds the pulp cavity in the crown and root.

3. The enamel is the hard thin covering of the crown, the hardest substance in the whole body. It lies outside of the dentine.

4. The cementum is a layer of modified bone that covers the dentine of the root.

5. The peridental membrane is a fibrous membrane which lies between the cementum of the root and the adjacent bone which surrounds the tooth socket.

ROOTS. The incisors, canine and premolar teeth have usually only one root. The upper molars usually have three roots, the lower molars two. The roots of the third molars are often compressed together and fused to form a single root.

CUSPS. These are the prominences on the flattened surfaces of the crowns, seperated by shallow grooves. The premolars have two cusps - hence the name bicuspid. The molars have three to five cusps.

OCCLUSION. This refers to the position of opposing upper and lower teeth when the mouth is closed. The upper incisors usually project in front of the lower incisors and overlap them. The cusps of the upper molar and premolar teeth fit into the grooves between the cusps of the opposing lower teeth or the gaps between these teeth. In malocclusion the teeth lying opposite each other on each side do not touch; this may occur following a fracture of the jaw.

FUNCTION.   Incisors bite, premolar and molar grind.

S. 84   THE CRANIAL FOSSAE.

The base of the skull when viewed from above presents three levels from front to back. These are the anterior, middle, and posterior cranial fossae. Certain definite parts of the brain occupy each fossa. Several paired foramina (openings) allow exit of the nerves and the entrance of blood vessels to the cranial cavity.

The anterior cranial fossa lies above the orbits, and ends behind at the shelf formed by the lesser wings of the sphenoid bone, on each side. The frontal lobes of the cerebrum lie in this fossa.

The middle cranial fossa extends back from the lesser wings of the sphenoid to the ridges of the petrous parts of the temporal bones. The body of the sphenoid lies under the central part. The temporal lobes of the brain lie there.

The posterior cranial fossa is at the lowest level. It lies behind the petrous ridges and reaches back to the squamous part of the occipital bone. This is the largest of the three. The hindbrain lies within it.

S. 85   THE BASAL FORAMINA.

Optic foramen (two): a circular opening medial to the anterior clinoid process on each side; the optic nerve leaves the cranial cavity to reach the orbit through this opening; special views are required for it.

enamel - hardest substance in body.

Superior orbital fossa (two): a long slit under the lesser wing of the sphenoid bone on each side, and opening into the orbit. Special views are required to show it.

Foramen rotundum (two) (rotundum - round): a small opening below the medial end of the superior orbital fissure on each side, and lateral to the body of the sphenoid bone. The maxillary division of the fifth cranial nerve passes out through this opening to reach the posterior surface of the maxilla.

Foramen ovale (two): a large oval opening about one half inch behind the foramen rotundum on each side, lateral to the posterior part of the body of the sphenoid. It transmits the mandibular branch of the trigeminal (fifth cranial) nerve to the space in front of the ramus of the mandible.

Foramen spinosum (two): a small circular opening lateral to the posterior part of the body of the sphenoid bone. It transmits the middle meningeal artery to the cranial cavity.

Foramen lacerum (two): a large irregular opening lateral to the dorsum sella on each side, at the apex of the petrous temporal. The interal carotid artery enters the skull through this, after it has entered the carotid foramen on the under surface and has passed through the carotid canal.

Internal auditory foramen (two): an opening on the posterior surface of the petrous part of the temporal bone forming the entrance to the internal auditory meatus. The facial and auditory nerves enter through this opening. Special views necessary.

Jugular foramen (two): a large irregular opening between the petrous temporal and adjacent lateral border of the occipital bone, and behind the internal auditory meatus. The internal jugular vein leaves the cranium here on each side.

Foramen magnum (one): a large oval opening in the basal part of the occipital bone through which the medulla of the brain leaves to become the spinal cord. Special basal views necessary.

S. 86 INTRACRANIAL GROOVES.

(a) Many small grooves radiate up from the foramen spinosum to accommodate the branches of the middle meningeal artery on the inner surface of the parietal bone on each side. This artery branches at acute angles, and the grooves are slightly hazy and wavy unlike most fracture lines in the skull.
(b) Large grooves lie on the inner surface of the sagittal suture, the occipital bone, the mastoid parts of the temporal bones, and the petrous temporals. These accommodate the large venous sinuses (veins) that drain blood from the cranial cavity and empty it into the jugular vein at the foramen lacerum on each side.

S. 87 JOINTS OF THE SKULL.

(a) The temporo-mandibular joints are the only movable joints of the skull. There are two, right and left. The capitulum of the condyloid process of the mandible articulates with the mandibular fossa of the temporal bone on each side.
(b) The sutures of the skull are described on page 67.

S. 88 DEVELOPMENT OF THE CRANIAL BONES.

The flat ones of the skull, including all except those of the base, are formed first as membranes. At birth these membranous bones have become ossified. The membrane persists between their adjacent margins. During childbirth the cranial bones may overlap - moulding - so that the fetal hand becomes smaller. The membrane between the cranial bones later becomes the sutures of the skull. The bones of the base, like the bones of the body, form first as cartilage, which is replaced by bone tissue.

The fontanels (fontanelles) are the gaps at the angles where bones meet and where membrane has persisted after birth. They gradually become ossified.

The anterior or frontal fontanel lies in the midline of the roof of the skull where the frontal bone meets the two parietals. It can be felt as a soft spot in infants. It becomes closed by bone at about eighteen months of age. It is then called the bregma.

The posterior or occipital fontanel lies in the midline on the posterior surface where the occipital bone meets the two parietal bones. It closed at about six months of ages and is called the lambda.

There are four other fontanels about the angles of the parietal bones which close soon after birth.

When an infant is not getting enough fluid, or, as a result of vomiting or diarrhoea, is not retaining its fluid, the fontanels become sunken.

When there is an increased pressure within the cranium, the fontanels bulge out.

S. 89 CONGENITAL ANOMALIES - THE SKULL.

Kephale (cephale) G. head; hence, cephalic.
acephalic - without a head,
dicephalic, bicephalic - two heads

macrocephalic - large head,
microcephalic - small head,

Occasionally monsters of one of the above types are demonstrated in films taken for pregnancy. Cleft palate: the front of the palate, including the two central incisor teeth, forms from a separate epiphysis which eventually fuses with the right and left maxillae. The two maxillae should also unite at the midline of the roof of the mouth. Failure of union in the above results in an opening between the roof of the mouth and the nasal cavities, cleft palate.

S. 90 SUMMARY OF STRUCTURES AND LANDMARKS - THE SKULL.

Most of the structures covered in the following summary have already been studied in connection with the bones of the skull. They are summarized below to complete the study, and for quick reference.

1. ACCESSORY OR PARNASAL SINUSES. These are paired cavities within some of the cranial and facial bones. They have openings into the nasal cavities and are filled with air. Their lining membranes are continuous with those of the nasal cavities. Because of their air content they show as dark (translucent) shadows in films of the skull. Infection in the nasal cavities may spread into these sinuses through the openings.

The frontal sinuses are cavities within the frontal bone, one on each side above the orbits. They extend up into the squamosal part forming the forehead, and may pass back in the roofs of the orbits. They may be absent or very small (rudimentary) or quite large. One may be larger than the other. They are called right or left.

The two maxillary sinuses (antra of Highmore) are large cavities, one in each maxilla. They lie behind the soft tissues of the cheek, and lateral to the nasal cavities. The roots of the upper teeth are often separated from them by a very thin sheet of bone. These sinuses are designated as right and left.

The ethmoidal sinuses are groups of small cavities lying in the lateral wall of the nasal cavities on each side. There is an anterior and a posterior group. The labyrinth of the ethmoid bone forms most of their walls. In films they appear as multiple translucencies between the nasal fossae and orbits (right - left).

The sphenoid sinuses are two cavities, one on each side of the midline, in the body of the sphenoid bone. They lie under the sella turcica, behind the nasal fossae, and are visible in open mouth or lateral views.

2. SUTURES OF THE SKULL. These are special interlocking, immovable joints between the cranial bones. Tiny projections like saw teeth of one bone fit into small indentations of the adjacent bone. Their appearance is much like that of a seam made by a seamstress, when the two pieces of cloth are pulled upon.

The sagittal suture. (L. sagitta - an arrow) is the joint between the upper adjacent borders of the two parietal bones. It extends from front to back along the midline of the roof or vertex of the skull.

The coronal suture crosses the roof of the skull transversely, above and behind the forehead. It is the joint between the posterior border of the frontal bone and the anterior borders of the parietal bones. It meets the sagittal suture at right angles, at the midline of the vertex or roof.

The lambdoidal suture (Greek letter Lambda) is the joint between the posterior borders of the two parietal bones and the upper border of the occipital bone. It forms a curved line on the posterior surface of the skull. It meets the posterior end of the sagittal suture in the midline. The sagittal suture, along with the two legs of the lambdoidal suture form a stem with two legs like the Greek letter "λ".

The squamosal suture forms the joint between the lateral border of the parietal bone and upper border of the squamosal part of the temporal bone on each side. This suture lies on the lateral wall of the skull above and behind the ear. Other short, less important, sutures are present between other cranial bones.

3. FONTANELS or fontanelles. These are gaps in the skulls of infants between the angles formed at the junctions of the parietal, frontal, and occipital bones. The membrane which formed the fetal cranium has not been replaced by bone at these points. They show as translucent areas because of the lack of bone.

The anterior or frontal fontanel lies at the junction of the two parietal bones with the frontal bone at the midline of the roof or vertex. This is a large, soft area that becomes filled in with bone at about eighteen months of age. This is at the junction of the coronal and sagittal sutures, the bregma.

The posterior or occipital fontanel is the small gap on the posterior surface of the skull at the junction of the two parietal bones with the occipital. It is the point where the sagittal suture meets the lambdoidal suture. It becomes filled in with bone at about six months of age, the lambda.

4. BONY PROMINENCES.

The bregma is the point on the roof or vertex of the skull where the coronal and sagittal sutures meet and where the anterior fontanel was originally. There may be a small prominence here.

The lambda is that point on the posterior surface of the skull where the posterior end of the sagittal suture meets the lambdoidal suture, the posterior fontanel in the infant.

The glabella is a smooth prominence in the midline on the forehead, above the bridge of the nose. It lies between and above the supra-orbital margins of the orbits.

5. THE ORBITS. These are two large cone-shaped cavities in the upper anterior part of the cranium. Their walls are formed by some facial and other cranial bones. Their anterior ends are circular; their posterior ends form the apex of cones. They contain the eyeball, eye muscles, nerves and blood vessels of the eyes. They afford protection to these structures. In the film their circular anterior ends show as translucent circles lateral to the nasal fossae.

The optic foramina are two small openings, one at the posterior end of each orbit. The optic nerves pass through these openings to get from the cranial cavity to the orbits (sing. foramen).

The supra-orbital margin or border is the prominent ridge of bone forming the upper border of the circular opening of the orbit on each side. It separates this cavity from the forehead and is covered by the eyebrow.

The infra-orbital margin or border is the bony ridge forming the lower border of the circular opening of each orbit, separating it from the cheek.

6. THE NASAL CAVITIES are the chambers of the nose, extending from the nostrils (nares) or openings on the face of the nasopharynx (throat) behind. These are also called the nasal fossae.

The nasal septum is the partition between the two nasal cavities or fossae. This is formed by several bones.

The anterior nasal spine is a sharp bony process extending forward at the base of the nasal septum in the midline, above the upper lip. It can be felt with the thumb and a finger in the nasal fossae.

7. MAXILLAE. The aveolar process of the maxilla is the bony ridge extending down from each maxilla to accommodate the roots of the upper teeth. There are eight tooth sockets on each side.

The maxillary tuberosity is the prominent posterior end of the alveolar process of each maxilla, behind the last molar tooth.

8. TEMPORAL BONE. The petrous part of each temporal bone is the dense pyramid-shaped part extending medially in the base of the cranium. It contains the essential part of the ear, the organ of hearing.

The ear consists of three parts: the external ear (external auditory meatus), the middle ear (tympanic cavity), and the internal ear, where the organ of hearing is located.

The pinna or auricle is the prominent cartilage which projects from the side of the face.

The external auditory meatus or canal is the passage extending from the opening in the cartilage of the ear into the petrous part of each temporal bone as far as the ear drum (tympanic membrane).

The middle ear is a cavity in the petrous part medial to the ear drum. It contains the auditory ossicles, the malleus, incus, and stapes, which transmit sound vibrations to the internal ear.

The inner ear lies medially to the middle ear and within the petrous part. It contains three semicircular canals concerned with equilibrium, as well as the end organs of the auditory nerve, which is concerned with hearing. These end organs are contained within a complicated system of bone canals, the labyrinth.

The internal auditory foramen is an opening on the posterior or back surface of the petrous part of the temporal bone near its inner end. The auditory and facial nerves leave the cranial cavity through this opening, and enter the internal auditory meatus. The auditory nerve (eighth cranial) is concerned with hearing.

The internal auditory meatus or canal is a passage in the petrous part extending from the internal auditory opening to the internal ear and organ of hearing. The auditory nerve traverses this canal.

The auditory or Eustachian tube is a canal passing from the nasopharynx (throat) to the middle ear. It opens into the throat above the tonsil on each side. Infection in the throat may therefore travel up through the auditory tube into the middle ear. The subject develops an earache - otitis media.

The mastoid process of the temporal bone is a large bony prominence extending down from the temporal bone behind the ear. It is readily palpable.

The mastoid cells are several small cavities within the mastoid part of the temporal bone. These communicate with each other and with the middle ear. Infection may pass into them from the middle ear - mastoiditis. These cells are designated as right or left.

9. RADIOGRAPHIC LANDMARKS. The outer, lateral or external canthus of each eye is that point at the outer border where the upper and lower eyelids meet, a landmark in radiography.

The orbito-meatal or radiographic base line is a line drawn from the outer canthus of the eye to the opening of the external auditory meatus on the same side. It is used for positioning of the head for films of the skull, sinuses, etc.

The interpupillary or interorbital line is a line drawn horizontally between the pupils of the eyes.

10. MENTUM. This refers to the chin. The adjective mental refers to the chin, or (the mind, mens; adj. mental).

The mental protuberance is the prominence at the lower border of the mandible in the midline at the front.

The mental foramen is a small opening on the outer surface of the body of the mandible on each side below the second lower premolar tooth. The mandibular nerve passes out to the face through this opening.

Submental means under the chin, and is used to describe positioning in radiography of the skull, e.g., submento-vertical, submento-occipital, etc.

11. OCCIPITAL BONE. The external occipital protuberance is a definite bony prominence on the posterior surface of the skull in the midline. It lies at the point where the occipital bone bends forward to help form the base of the skull.

The foramen magnum is a large opening in the occipital bone between its two lateral parts. The medulla of the brain leaves the cranial cavity here and enters the spinal canal.

The occiptial condyles are two knuckle-like processes on the lower surface of the occipital bone, one on either side of the foramen magnum. They form joints with the articular surfaces of the first cervical.

The zygomatic arches. Each is a slender rod of bone that extends forward from the temporal bone in front of the ear to the corresponding zygomatic bone. It is readily palpated and lies just below where the ear piece of eye glasses would run, from the eyeglass to the ear.

12. THE SPHENOID BONE. See skull with skull cap removed.

The sella turcica (Turkish saddle) is a depression hollowed out on the upper part of the body of the sphenoid bone in the midline. It has the shape of a saddle; hence, sella turcica. The pituitary gland, hypophysis cerebri, lies in this cavity.

The dorsum sella is the curved posterior wall of the sella turcica (dorsum - back; sella, saddle).

The anterior clinoid processes are two small bony projections that extend back over the sella on each side.

The posterior clinoid processes are two small processes that extend up and forward from the dorsum sella, one on each side to form, with the anterior, an incomplete roof for the sella turcica.

13. MANDIBLE. The angle of the mandible is the prominent bony prominence on each side of the mandible at the point where it turns upwards towards the base of the skull.

The body of the mandible is the horseshoe shaped part extending from the angle on one side around to the front and back to the angle on the other side.

The ramus of the mandible is that part above and behind the angle of each side - two rami.

The coronoid process of the mandible is the thin flattened process extending up from the front of the ramus.

The condyloid process is the posterior part of the ramus of each side. It consists of a constricted neck, and an expanded upper end, the head or capitulum. This articulates with the temporal bone at the mandibular fossa.

The mandibular notch is the half-moon shaped hollow between the coronoid and condyloid processes of the mandible.

14. CRANIAL FOSSAE are the three levels of the floor of the skull when viewed from above (split levels): the anterior, middle, and posterior cranial fossae.

15. BASAL FORAMINA are openings in the base of the skull, usually paired, through which the cranial nerves and veins leave the cranium, and arteries enter the cranium.

16. INTRACRANIAL GROOVES are the small grooves on the inner surface of the skull for intracranial arteries, and the larger grooves for the venous sinuses.

88

F. 100 SKULL OF AN INFANT
- viewed from above to show fontanels -

- lambdoidal suture
- occipital bone
- posterior fontanel
- parietal bone
- sagittal suture
- anterior fontanel
- coronal suture
- frontal bone

F. 101 LANDMARKS OF THE SKULL

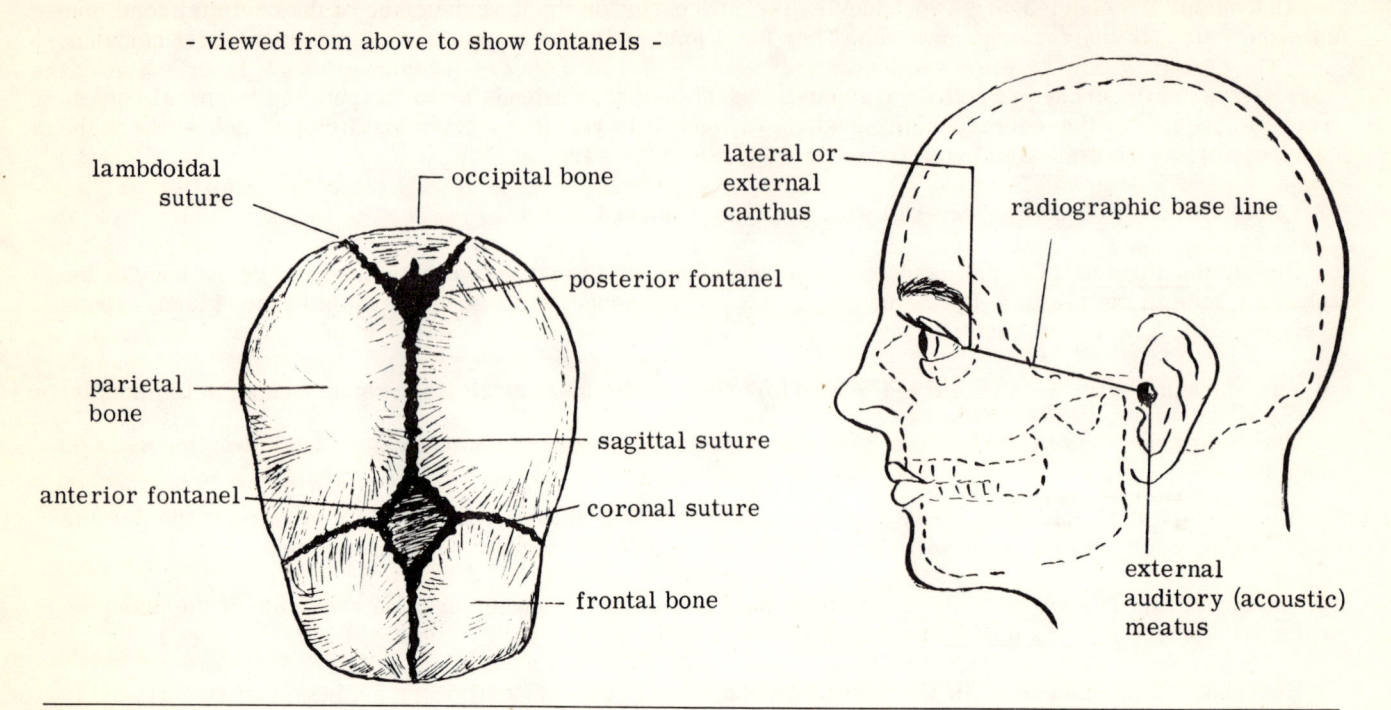

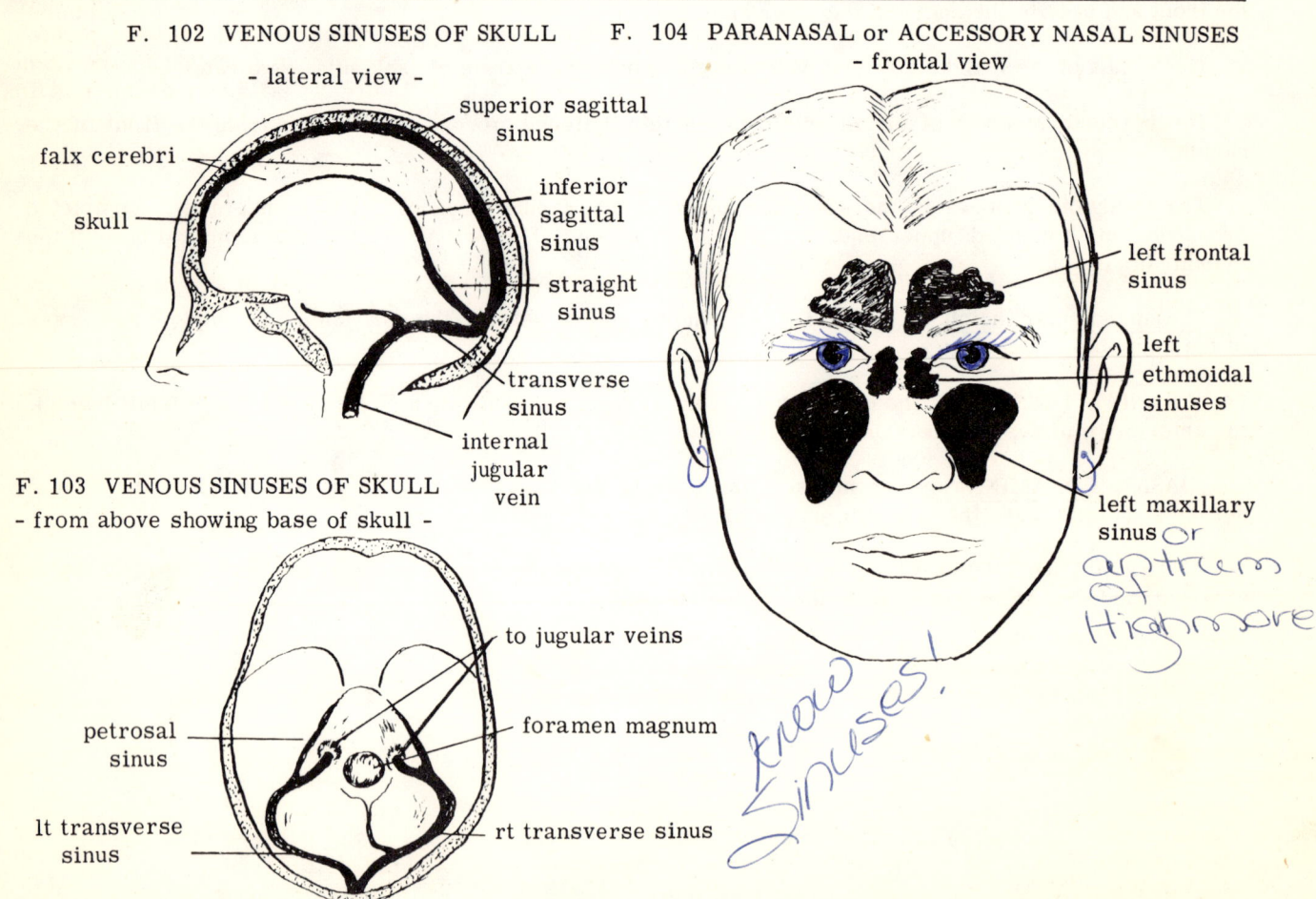

- lateral or external canthus
- radiographic base line
- external auditory (acoustic) meatus

F. 102 VENOUS SINUSES OF SKULL
- lateral view -

- falx cerebri
- skull
- superior sagittal sinus
- inferior sagittal sinus
- straight sinus
- transverse sinus
- internal jugular vein

F. 103 VENOUS SINUSES OF SKULL
- from above showing base of skull -

- petrosal sinus
- lt transverse sinus
- to jugular veins
- foramen magnum
- rt transverse sinus

F. 104 PARANASAL or ACCESSORY NASAL SINUSES
- frontal view

- left frontal sinus
- left ethmoidal sinuses
- left maxillary sinus or antrum of Highmore.

know sinuses!

S. 91 APPLICATION TO RADIOGRAPHY - THE SKULL.

The student should obtain a skull with detachable skull cap to verify the following observations.

The skull is like a hollow globe, so that it is impossible to obtain films of most bones without superimposition of other bones. The mandible, mastoid cells, and zygomatic arches may be viewed without overlapping.

It is necessary to devise positions by which this superimposition of other parts will cause the least possible interference.

Lateral views of the skull, with bones on opposite sides accurately superimposed, can only be obtained if the following details are carefully attended to:
(a) the interpupillary or interorbital line must be perpendicular to the film holder;
(b) the median line of the face must be parallel to the film holder;
(c) the sagittal suture of the skull, viewed from the end of the table, must be parallel to the holder.

True postero-anterior or antero-posterior views of the skull may be obtained:
(a) if the sagittal suture, corresponding to a continuation of the median line back over the top of the head, is perpendicular to the film holder;
(b) if the orbito-mental (radiograph base) line is also perpendicular to the film holder.

Two parts of the skull cause considerable difficulty in obtaining satisfactory views of the facial bones:
(a) the petrous part of the temporal bone because of its density and position in the base of the skull;
(b) the external occipital protuberance and ridge of bone on either side of it.

Remove the skull cap. Place the skull with the forehead and nose resting on the film holder. Note that in this position the frontal and ethmoidal sinuses can be viewed without overlapping of the petrous temporal and occipital protuberance. Place the nose and chin on the holder. Note that the petrous temporal and occipital protuberance lie below the maxillary sinuses, which show clearly as well as most of the facial bones.

In this position, with the mouth open, the maxillary and sphenoidal sinuses show clearly. From the above it is obvious that several views must be taken to show all the paranasal sinuses.

Every examination of facial bones should include a view in the nose chin position - imperative.

The foramen magnum and occipital bone are shown to advantage with the head hyper-extended, i.e., bent backward.

Other views have been devised to show the mastoid cells, optic foramina, and internal auditory meatuses. In a difficult case a skull should be examined in order to figure out the best possible position for any special examination. Ingenuity may be required.

S. 92 TERMS USED IN CHAPTER X. - THE SKULL.

aveolar process
angle of mandible
antrum
antra (pl.)
anterior clinoid process
accessory nasal sinuses
auditory canal
auditory ossicles
anterior fontanelle
base of skull
bregma
capitulum of mandible
cerebral cranium
cheek bone
clinoid process
condyloid process of mandible
cribriform plate of ethmoid bone
cornua of hyoid bone
coronoid process of mandible
coronal suture
cranial fossae
borsum sella
ethmoid bone
ethmoidal sinuses

ethmoidal labyrinth
external auditory meatus
external ear
external occipital protuberance
facial bones
fontanel or fontanelle
foramen magnum
frontal bone
frontal sinus
glabella
greater wing of sphenoid
hydrocephalus
hyoid bone
incus
infra-orbital border, margin
infra-orbital foramen
internal auditory foramen
internal auditory meatus
internal ear
interorbital line
interpupillary line
inferior concha or turbinate
labyrinth of ethmoid bone
lacrimal bone

lambda
lambdoidal (adj.)
lambdoidal suture
lateral canthus of eye
lesser wing of sphenoid bone
malar bone
malleus
mandible
mandibular (adj.)
mandibular notch
mastoid process
mastoid cells
maxilla
maxillae (pl.)
maxillary (adj.)
maxillary sinus
maxillary tuberosity
median line
mentum - chin
mental (adj.)
mental foramen
mental protuberance
middle ear
midsagittal plane & section

nasal bones
nasal fossae & septum
occipital bone
optic foramen
orbit
orbital (adj.)
orbito-meatal line
palatine bones
paranasal sinuses
parietal bones
parietal eminence
perpendicular plate of ethmoid
petrous part of temporal bone

pituitary fossa
pituitary gland
posterior clinoid processes
posterior fontanel
sagittal suture
sella turcica
sphenoid bone
sphenoidal (adj.)
sphenoidal sinuses
squamous part of:
    frontal bone
    occipital bone
    temporal bone

squamosal suture
submental
supra-orbital border, margin
symphysis of mandible
temporo-mandibular joint
temporal bone
vertex of skull
visceral cranium
vomer
zygomatic bone
zygomatic arch
zygomatic process
tooth - deciduous - permanent

Jts = Freely movable = diarthroses
arthritis - inflammation of jts.

91

F. 105 SUTURE OF SKULL
- immovable joint -

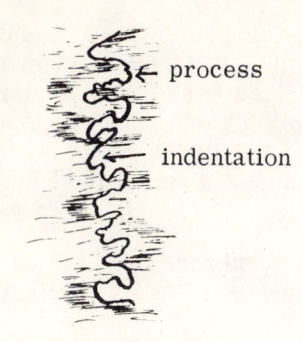

- process
- indentation

F. 106 SYMPHYSIS PUBIS
- slightly movable joint -

- Rt. pubic bone
- Lt. pubic bone
- pubic arch
- symphysis pubis (articular cartilage)

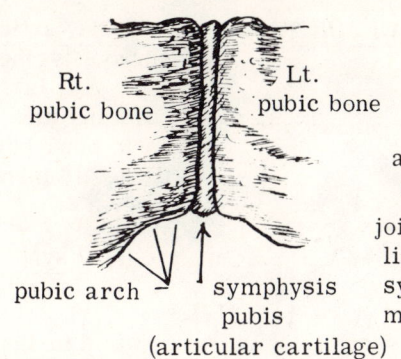

F. 107 A MOVABLE JOINT
- with joint cavity -

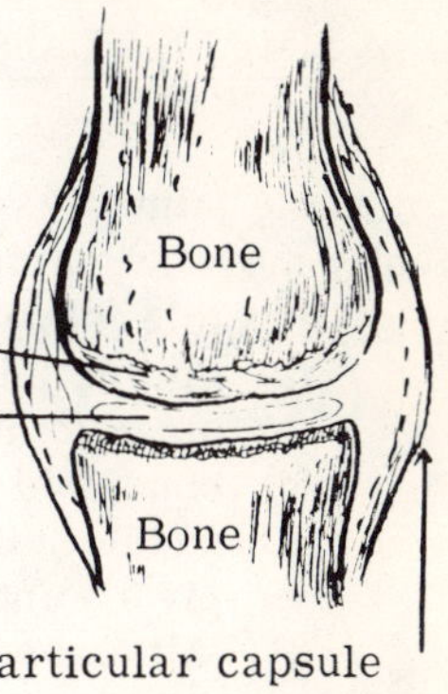

- Bone
- articular cartilage
- joint cavity lined by synovial membrane
- Bone
- articular capsule

F. 108 INTERVERTEBRAL JOINT
- slightly movable joint -

- intervertebral disc
- articular cartilage
- annulus fibrosus
- nucleus polposus
- body of vertebra
- intervertebral disc
- cartilage

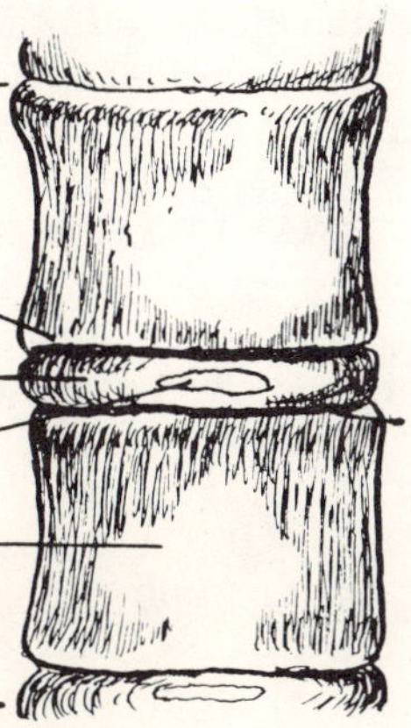

F. 109 INTERARTICULAR (APOPHYSEAL) JOINTS
- gliding joints -
between superior and inferior articular processes

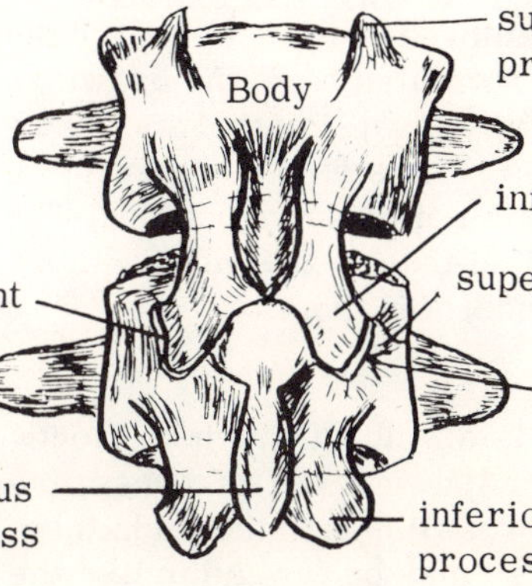

- Body
- superior articular process
- inferior articular pr.
- joint
- superior articular process
- interarticular joint
- spinous process
- inferior articular process

F. 110 HIP JOINT
- ball and socket joint -

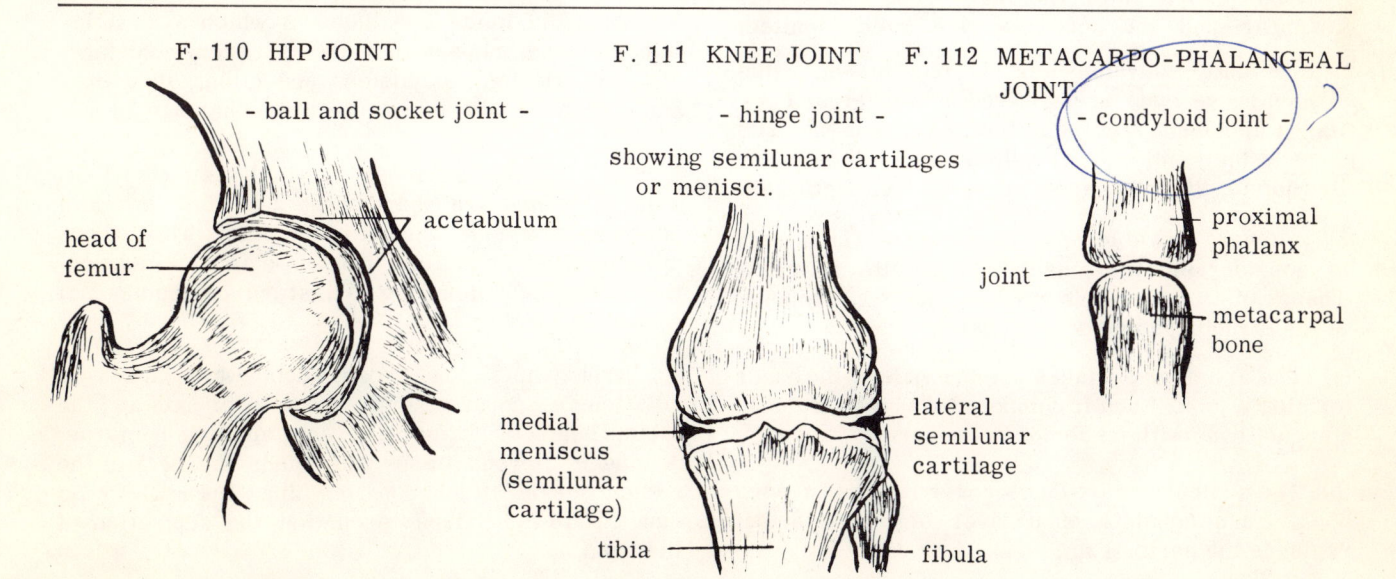

- acetabulum
- head of femur

F. 111 KNEE JOINT
- hinge joint -
showing semilunar cartilages or menisci.

- medial meniscus (semilunar cartilage)
- lateral semilunar cartilage
- tibia
- fibula

F. 112 METACARPO-PHALANGEAL JOINT
- condyloid joint -

- proximal phalanx
- joint
- metacarpal bone

CHAPTER XI. JOINTS - ARTICULATIONS.

S. 93 A SIMPLE CLASSIFICATION OF JOINTS.

1. Immovable joints.
2. Slightly movable joints.
3. Freely movable joints:
   (a) gliding joints
   (b) hinge joints
   (c) condyloid joints
   (d) saddle joints
   (e) pivot joints
   (f) ball and socket joints.

The joints of each part of the skeleton have been listed along with the bones. A brief study of the structure of the different types of joints is given below. It must be emphasized that in the living subject each joint is surrounded by strong ligaments and muscles. These give support to, and strengthen, the joint. They have been removed from specimens of the skeleton. They have been omitted from the drawings in this handbook. Radiographs of joints do not show them as separate images. Films of joints, therefore, give no direct information of these structures. The student should consult other texts in anatomy for more detailed information concerning them.

1. An immovable joint is one about which no movement takes place. The adjacent ends of bones are covered by a layer of fibrous tissue which holds them together. The bone edges may be irregular like the teeth of a saw (sutures of skull) or may be bevelled or roughened. In later life the fibrous tissue may disappear and the bones become solidly united.

2. A slightly movable joint is one in which the adjacent bone ends are covered by a layer of cartilage which separates them. Limited movement takes place at the joint, e.g., symphysis pubis, the sacro-iliac joints, the intervertebral joints. See section 65.

3. A freely movable joint is one about which there is considerable movement in a definite direction. These joints have joint cavities and are composed of the structures enumerated below.

(a) The articular surfaces are the ends of the bones forming a joint. Each is composed of a layer of dense compact bone with no periosteal covering.

(b) The articular cartilages cover the end of each bone. Each consists of a layer of cartilage that replaces the periosteum.

(c) The articular capsule is a membrane that surrounds the joint. It forms a sleeve about the joint and is reflected over the articular cartilage covering the end of each bone. It is attached to each bone beyond the limits of the articular cartilage. It forms a closed sac. It is composed of two layers:

(1) a synovial membrane lines the joint capsule; (it is thin and secrets a lubricating fluid).

(2) a further layer of fibrous tissue lies outside of the synovial membrane.

(d) The joint cavity is the space within the synovial membrane, and, as stated above, is a closed sac.

Bursae (sing. bursa) are extensions of the synovial sac under adjacent ligaments or muscles. These usually communicate with the joint cavity.
Other bursae are closed sacs which occur at points where a muscle or its tendon passes over a bone.

TYPES OF FREELY MOVABLE JOINTS

1. Gliding joints are those where there is a sliding movement, and the adjacent bones slide over each other during movement, e.g., intercarpal joints of the wrist, interarticular joints of the vertebrae.

2. Hinge joints allow angular movement like a hinge, with flexion and extension, e.g., elbow, interphalangeal joints of the fingers.

3. Condyloid joints are those at which a knuckle-like rounded surface fits into a concave surface, allowing flexion, extension, adduction, abduction, and circumduction, e.g., metacarpo-phalangeal joint.

4. Saddle joints are those at which the ends of the adjacent bones are shaped like a saddle, convex in one direction, and concave in the other. This allows motion in two directions, flexion, extension, adducttion, and abduction, e.g., first carpo-metacarpal joint.

5. Pivot joints are those about which there is rotation in one axis, e.g., odontoid of axis and the atlas, head of radius and capitulum of humerus. A ring of fibrous tissue surrounds the neck of the radius and is attached to the ulna. The radial head can rotate to produce pronation and supination of the hand.

6. Ball and socket joints have a rounded head fitting into a concave socket, allowing many movements, e.g., the shoulder and hip joints.

S. 94 APPLICATION TO RADIOGRAPHY - JOINTS.

The attention of the student is again directed to the clear space between the ends of bones as seen in radiographs. These are not actual gaps, but the space is occupied by the articular cartilages on the ends of bones which hold them apart. They are translucent. The same applies to epiphyseal lines in radiographs of bones of children.

Arthrography is the procedure of injecting some opaque or translucent material into a joint cavity, taking and processing of films of this joint, and the interpretation. Arthrogram - the resulting film.

Pneumoarthrography is the term applied when air is used for the injection. The bursae connected with the joint may also be outlined with this injection.

The above procedures are used frequently in the knee joint. Here, in addition to the articular cartilages, there is a semilunar-shaped piece of cartilage between the femoral and tibial condyles of the medial and lateral halves. These may become torn during injury. Arthrography may demonstrate the tear. These semilunar cartilages are called menisci.

Arthron (G. joint;) arthritis - an inflammation;
         arthrography - as above
Articulation - L. joint.

In radiography of joints the central beam must be directed at right angles to the articular surfaces of the bones so as to pass directly through the joint.

muscle sheath is called a fascia - sep. muscles from other muscles and bones

CHAPTER XII. THE MUSCULAR SYSTEM.

S. 95 CLASSIFICATION OF MUSCLES.

1. Skeletal, voluntary or striated muscles; attached to the skeleton.
2. Visceral, involuntary or non-striated (Visceral) muscles; in the walls of hollow organs, e.g., the stomach. *intestian - hair - vessels*
3. Cardiac muscle; in the walls of the heart.

S. 96 MUSCLES IMPORTANT TO THE TECHNICIAN.

1. The neck:
   sternomastoid or sternocleidomastoid muscles.
2. The thorax:
   pectoralis major muscles (two)
   intercostal muscles
   diaphragm
3. The abdomen:
   ilopsoas major (psoas) (two)
   iliopsoas minor (two)
4. The back:
   erector spinae or sacrospinalis (two)
5. The upper extermity:
   supraspinatus (two)
   infraspinatus (two)
   biceps brachii (two)
   brachialis (two)
   deltoid (two)
6. The lower extremity:
   quadriceps femoris (two)

S. 97 SKELETAL MUSCLES DEFINED.

A skeletal muscle is attached directly or indirectly to the skeleton - hence skeletal.

Most of these muscles are under the control of the conscious part of the brain. Nerves pass from the cerebrum through the spinal cord and out to them. *Front Brain* By messages from the cerebrum they may be made to contract at will - so voluntary (voluntas - will).

When examined under a microscope, alternating light and dark bands can be seen passing across the fibers; hence the name striated (stria - a band or line).

F.113 SKELETAL MUSCLE FIBERS

1. longitudinal view
   - fiber
   - nuclei
   - connective tissue

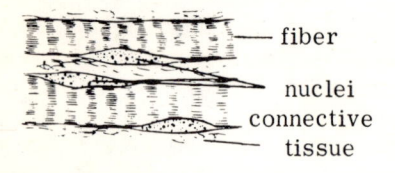

2. cross section
   - fibers
   - nuclei

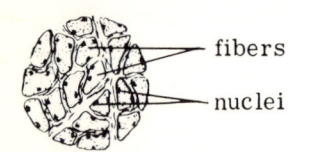

F. 114 MUSCULAR LEVERS - ELBOW

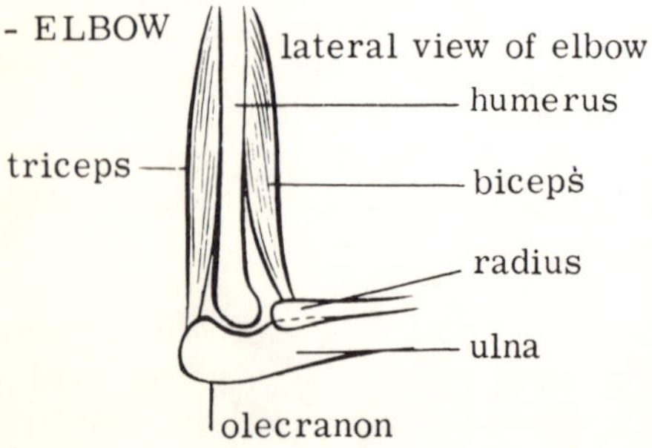

lateral view of elbow
- humerus
- triceps
- biceps
- radius
- ulna
- olecranon

F. 115 TENDONS OF THE BACK OF THE HAND

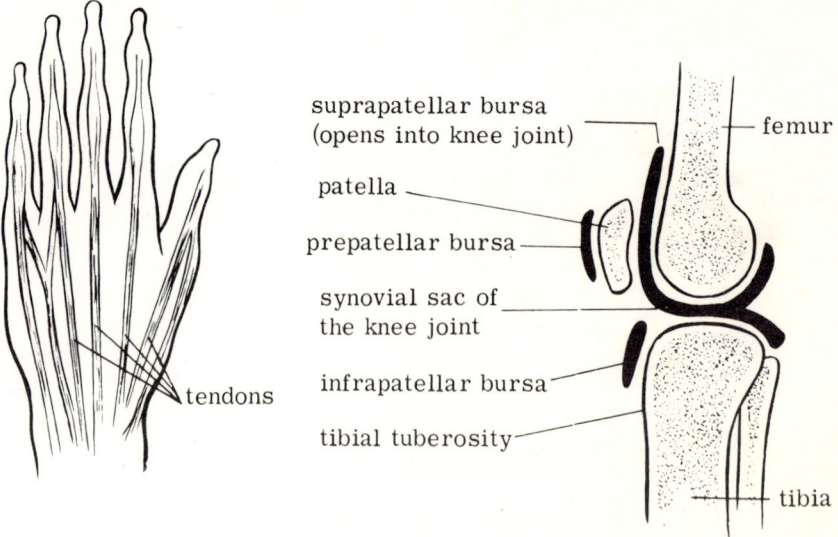

tendons

F. 116 BURSAE AT THE KNEE
- lateral view -

- suprapatellar bursa (opens into knee joint)
- femur
- patella
- prepatellar bursa
- synovial sac of the knee joint
- infrapatellar bursa
- tibial tuberosity
- tibia

Grt Tub of humerus - Spinatus
Rad " " radius - biceps
Delt. Tub of humerus - Deltoid

Skeletal muscles = cyl. shaped called fibers
extend the length of the muscle
involuntary = spindle

95

S. 98 THE STRUCTURE OF SKELETAL MUSCLES.

(involuntary)

While the cells of visceral muscles are spindle-shaped, the cells of skeletal muscles, called fibers, are cylindrical in shape and extend the entire length of the muscle. Their lengths depend upon the the length of the individual muscle.

Each fiber or muscle cell has a cell membrane (the sarcolemma) surrounding it.

Each cell has many nuclei which lie along the inner surface of the cell membrane.

Many fine thread-like structures called fibrils run lengthwise within each fiber or cell.

The muscle fibers are separated from each other by fine connective tissue (the epimysium; mys, muscle).

The fibers are arranged in bundles or fasciculi running parallel to each other like sticks in an armful of stove wood. Each bundle of fibers is also surrounded by a connective sheath. This separates yet binds the bundles together (the perimysium).

The whole muscle consisting of many bundles or fasciculi, depending upon the size of the muscle, is also surrounded by a further layer of connective tissue, the muscle sheath, often called fascia. This muscle sheath separates the muscle from other adjacent muscles and bones, etc.

If a piece of raw beefsteak be pulled apart, the fine white glistening connective tissue fibers will be seen tearing apart. Slices of a beef roast should be cut at right angles to the length of the muscle bundles, so that they do not have to be chewed into short lengths.

Muscles vary in size and shape in different parts of the body.

They may be very short like those in the face; they may be long as those in the thigh.

They may be flat and strap-shaped, or spindle-shaped, or flat sheets like those in the abdominal wall, or large masses like those in the buttocks.

They may be three-sided or four-sided, etc.

Skeletal muscles are attached to each end to bone, cartilage, ligaments, to other muscles, or the skin. Often they cross a joint, and being attached to a bone on either side of the joint, their contraction causes movement of that joint.

The origin of a muscle is more fixed, less movable attachment, usually at its proximal end.

The insertion of a muscle is its more movable point of attachment, and usually its more distal end.

An aponeurosis is a sheet of fibrous tissue, which is attached at one end of the muscle sheath and at the other end to a bone, cartilage, ligament or some other muscle. (See muscles anterior abdomen).

A tendon, sinew, cord or leader is a cord-like fibrous tissue structure, extending from one end of a muscle to a bone, cartilage or ligament. If the fingers are flexed and extended, the tendons on the back of the hand can be made to stand out.

Tendons and aponeuroses are actually attached to the muscle sheath of a muscle rather than to the muscle fibers themselves. Some muscles have a tendon at one end and an aponeurosis at the other end. Other muscles have a tendon at each end. Others are attached directly by their sheaths to a bone or ligament.

Tendon sheath: this is a closed sac forming a sleeve about a tendon.

Tenosynovitis is an inflammation in a tendon sheath.

A bursa is a sac-like structure lying between a muscle or tendon and a bone or organ over which the muscle or tendon must move. Bursae about a joint are usually continuous with the adjacent joint cavity.

Bursitis is an inflammation of a bursa.

Calcification may occur in a bursa or tendon sheath.

S. 99 FUNCTIONS OF MUSCLES.

1. To contract and cause movement.
2. To maintain position when standing upright, etc.
3. To give support to joints by maintaining a state of partial contraction.

Muscle tone. Muscles do not completely relax when at rest, but remain partly contracted. This partial contraction helps support joints, and hastens muscular contraction and movement when movement is required.

Contraction. The main function of muscles is to contract and cause movement. When contraction occurs, the muscle fibers become shorter and thicker. The contracted muscle becomes hard and stands out. To demonstrate muscular contraction the part must be moved against resistance. Place the wrist under a table top and attempt to bend the elbow. The muscles on the front of the arm will become firm and can be palpated. In this case the biceps muscle can be felt.

Opposing groups of muscles. Muscles are arranged in opposing groups so that if one group causes flexion (bending), another group on the opposite side of the limb or trunk will cause extension (straightening). Similarly there are adductors opposing abductors, supinators opposing pronators, and internal rotators opposing external rotators.

When one group of muscles contracts, the opposing group relaxes gradually so that the movement is smooth and not jerky.

The maintenance of the upright position of the body consists of a balanced contraction of some groups of muscles and a partial relaxation of opposing groups. The spine must be extended and held rigid, the femora extended at the hips, and the legs extended at the knees.

Many muscular movements are complex and must be acquired by trying over and over to accomplish the motion. The infant learns to crawl, to walk, to talk, and to feed himself by repeated attempts until these actions are mastered. Then they become automatic and can be done without conscious effort. The x-ray technician at first must concentrate on exposing and processing films. Later he or she can accomplish these without conscious effort.

S. 100 MUSCLE SPASM.

Spasm is a contraction of muscles which may persist for a long period of time without relaxation. Spasm of the muscles of a limb or part of the trunk often accompanies injury to the part. This may be a simple sprain, a dislocation or a fracture. The spasm or muscular contraction holds the limb in a fixed position usually in partial flexion. This is nature's method of preventing further injury. Every technician has seen elbows, wrists, hips, and knees held rigid and partly flexed following injury. When there is a definite history of injury, the technician must not attempt to force the limb into the usual positions for routine views. This may produce further injury and is painful. The technic must be adapted to the case in hand.

Frequently also spasm and often partial flexion is present when there is an inflammation about a joint. Without a history of injury the technician may attempt to position the limb, provided this is not too painful. Often pressure exerted gradually will overcome the spasm. In conditions like appendicitis, and peritonitis from a ruptured duodenal ulcer the abdominal muscles become rigid and board-like.

S. 101 PARALYSIS OF MUSCLES.

Paralysis of muscles follows injury to, or destruction of, the nerves supplying that muscle. Poliomyelitis (infantile paralysis) may cause death of the motor nerves to muscles. The muscles will become flaccid and will not contract. The opposing group, if not affected, then have no opposition and will pull the limb permanently into the position usually assumed by their contraction. In other types of paralysis the paralyzed muscles become contracted and rigid, deforming the limb by their own contraction.

Paralysis due to nerve injury or destruction of a nerve must be distinguished from inability to move a part following an injury in which a muscle or tendon is cut in two. If the muscle or tendon be repaired, function will be restored. It is often stated by the untrained that there is no fracture present, as the patient can move his fingers, etc. This is wrong.

S. 102 DISTRIBUTION OF MUSCLES.

The student should compare the appearance of a mounted skeleton to that of a well developed athletic living subject. It becomes apparent at once that there must be a great deal of soft tissue filling in the spaces and rounding out the body and limbs. Some of this is due to the subcutaneous fat (under the skin). Most of it is due to the muscles of the part. In the face alone there are more than forty muscles. These are responsible for movements of the eyes, eyelids, ears, nose, mouth and jaws.

Frequently there are two or more layers of muscles; those close to the skin (superficial muscles), and those at a deeper level (deep muscles). On the sole of the foot, for example, there are four layers of these muscles, each layer including several muscles.

The student has already learned that the right and left halves of the body have identical bones except for such bones as the sternum and vertebrae. There is a similar arrangement of muscles. Each side of the head, neck, trunk, each upper limb, and each lower limb has similar muscles. There are a few exceptions such as the diaphragm, tongue, etc.

Fractures following any one type of injury result in a certain definite deformity, depending upon the location of the injury. In fractures of the upper femur the upper fragment will be abducted because of the pull of the abductors of the hip on the upper fragment. In fractures of the lower femur the lower fragment will be displaced backward due to the pull of the flexor muscles behind the knee. The surgeon must have a thorough knowledge of the location and action of the various muscles of the body in order to use the proper maneuver to reduce the fracture or dislocation.

The student technician is concerned with only a few muscles related to radiography. These will be studied later. The section following is included to provide some general knowledge of the muscles of the body. No student should be expected to learn this classification. Muscles may be grouped or listed according to their function or action, as flexors, extensors, etc. But a muscle may be a flexor under certain conditions and may be an adductor or something else under other conditions. This method is not too satisfactory. On the other hand muscles may be grouped according to their location in the body, as listed below.

S. 103 MUSCLE GROUPING BY LOCATION.

1. Muscles of the head:
   (1) scalp muscles
   (2) muscles of the eyelids
   (3) muscles of the eyes
   (4) muscles of the nose
   (5) muscles of the mouth
   (6) muscles of mastication (chewing)

2. Muscles of the neck:
   (1) superficial cervical muscles
   (2) lateral cervical muscles
   (3) supra and infrahyoid muscles
   (4) anterior vertebral muscles
   (5) lateral vertebral muscles

3. Muscles of the trunk:
   (1) deep muscles of the the back
   (2) suboccipital group
   (3) muscles of the thorax or chest
   (4) muscles of the abdomen:
       (a) anterior lateral abdomen
       (b) posterior abdominal muscles
   (5) muscles of the pelvis
   (6) muscles of the perineum

4. Muscles of the upper extremity:
   (1) connecting the extremity to vertebral column
   (2) connecting the extremity to the chest wall
   (3) muscles of the shoulder
   (4) muscles of the arm (brachial, adj. of brachium)
   (5) muscles of the forearm (antibrachial)
   (6) muscles of the hand

5. Muscles of the lower extremity:
   (1) muscles of the iliac region
   (2) muscles of the thigh
       (a) anterior femoral
       (b) medial femoral
       (c) gluteal muscles
       (d) posterior femoral
   (3) muscles of the leg (crural, adj. of crux)
       (a) anterior crural
       (b) lateral crural
       (c) posterior crural, superficial, deep
   (4) muscles of the foot
       (a) dorsal muscles of the foot
       (b) plantar muscles of the foot:
           first, second, third and fourth layers.

The head. As stated above there are over forty muscles in the head. These are responsible for movements of the eyelids, eyes, nose, ears, mouth, jaws.

The neck. The rounded cylindrical appearance of the neck is due to the muscles here. Those in front control forward bending of the head and neck, as well as movements of the tongue and of the trachea during respiration and swallowing. The lateral cervical groups control lateral movements of the head and the cervical vertebrae. The posterior or sub-occipital group cause backward bending or hyper-extension of the head and neck.

The thorax. Several of the muscles on the front and back of the chest pass outward to the shoulder girdle or upper arm. These provide for movements of the shoulder and arm. Other muscles, the intercostals, fill in the gaps between adjacent ribs. These elevate the ribs during inspiration (breathing in).

The abdomen. The abdominal cavity, unlike the thorax, has no bony wall except at the back where the lumbar vertebrae and their transverse processes protect the organs. The remainder of the wall at the front and laterally is formed by muscles. The upper abdomen receives some support from the ribs or sternum and cartilages. The posterior wall on each side of the vertebrae is formed by psoas and quadratus lumborum muscles. These latter extend vertically from the last rib and transverse processes of the lumbar vertebrae to the iliac crests on each side.

The lateral and antero-lateral part is formed by three layers of flat, sheet-like muscles and their aponeuroses. The fibers of each layer are directed in opposite direction to those of the adjacent layers to give strength. These are the external oblique, the internal oblique, and the transversus muscles.

The anterior wall on each side of the midline is formed by the rectus (straight) muscles. These pass vertically from the xiphoid and adjacent costal cartilages down to the pubic bones.

The pelvis. The muscles of the pelvis form a sling across the floor of the pelvic cavity, with openings for the rectum and urinary passage.

The perineum. This space lies between the ischial tuberosities laterally and the coccyx and pubic arch. This area is occupied by the perineal muscles.

The upper extremity. The muscles extending from the chest to the shoulder girdle and arm have been noted. Most of the muscles of the upper extremity lie on the front and back of the bones of the extremity. On the front of the arm are the flexors of the elbow, the biceps brachii, and brachialis muscles. On the back is the triceps.

F. 117 OUTER LAYER OF SKELETAL MUSCLES
- frontal view -

F. 118 OUTER LAYER OF SKELETAL MUSCLES
- dorsal view -

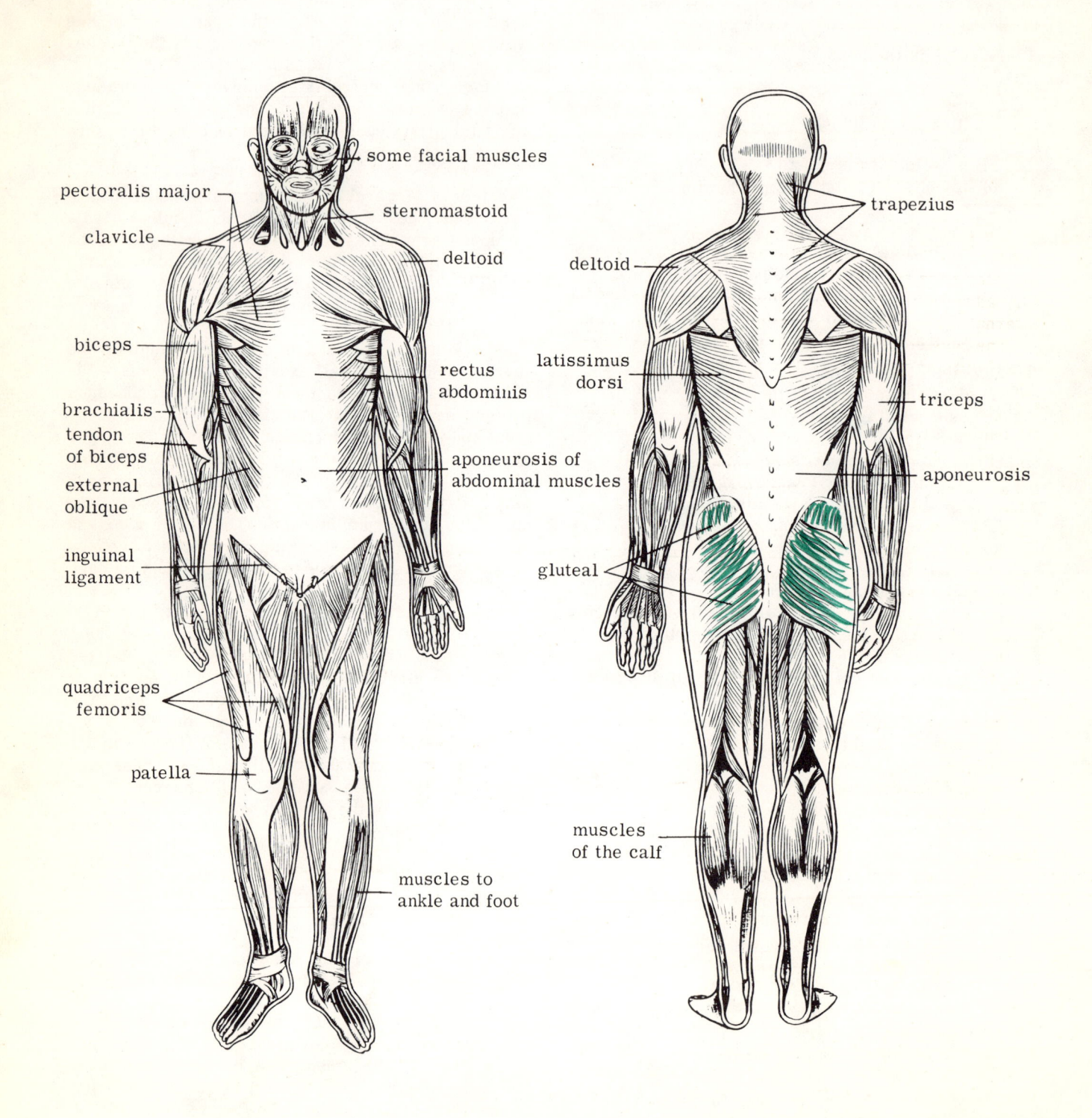

The flexors of the wrist and fingers pass down from the medial epicondyle of the humerus, over the front of the forearm. They end in tendons which pass to their insertions in the bones of the hands. The tendons to the fingers are long, and extend from the wrist, through the palm of the hand, to the digits. They are enclosed in tendon sheaths.

The extensor muscles of the wrist and digits pass from the lateral epicondyle of the humerus along the posterior surface (back) of the forearm to end in the tendons. These insert into the digits and straighten the fingers. There are also the supinators and pronators of the forearm, and adductors and abductors of the wrist and digits. Many small muscles are also present in the hand.

Lower extremity. As in the upper extremity, muscles connect the lower extremity with the trunk. These muscles pass from the pelvis to the femur to provide for adduction, abduction, flexion, extension, and internal and external rotation at the hip joint.

The adductors pass from the pubic bone to the inner side of the femur. The abductors, the gluteal group, lie on the lateral or outer side, and form the buttock. The flexors are in front. The extensors lie behind the hip joint.

The knee. Because flexion of the knee is backward not forward as at the elbow, the flexor muscles of the knee lie at the back of the thigh. They pass over the pack of the knee to the tibia and fibula. The extensor muscles lie in front of the femur and pass over the front of the knee as a tendon to reach the tibial tuberosity. These extensors form the quadriceps group (four heads). The patella is a sesamoid bone in the tendon of the quadriceps.

The foot. The foot is placed at right angles to the leg, a very different arrangement to that present in the hand. This has resulted in much confusion as to what is flexion and extension at the ankle. Bending the foot downward is termed plantar flexion or extension. Raising the forefoot off the floor is termed dorsiflexion, as the upper surface of the foot is its dorsal surface. The plantar flexors of the ankle lie behind the tibia and fibula, helping to form the calf of the leg. They end in a tendon that inserts into the calcaneal tuberosity, the tendo Achilles. The long flexor muscles of the feet and toes also lie behind the tibia and fibula. They pass down behind the medial malleolus to the sole of the foot. Their tendons pass forward to insert into the digits. There are four layers of muscles on the sole. The dorsiflexor muscles of the ankle, and the extensor muscles of the toes lie in front of the tibia and fibula, and ankle joint. The tendons of the dorsiflexors of the ankle end in the tarsal bones. The tendons of the extensors of the toes pass along the dorsum of the foot to the toes.

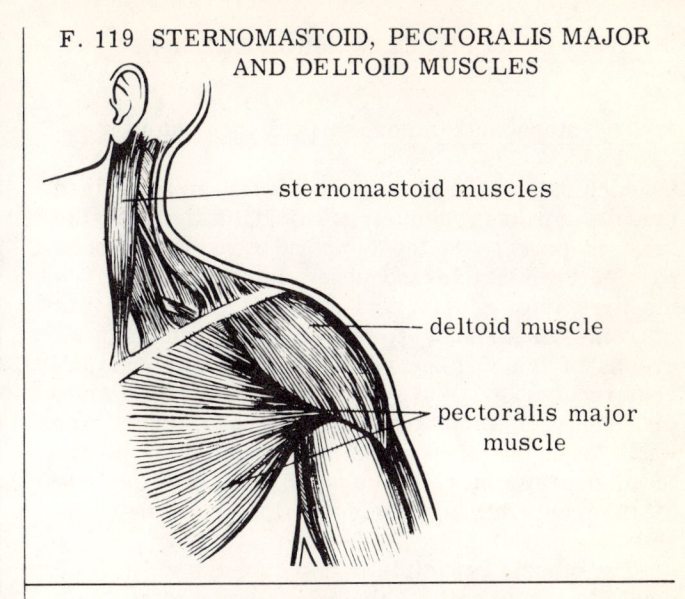

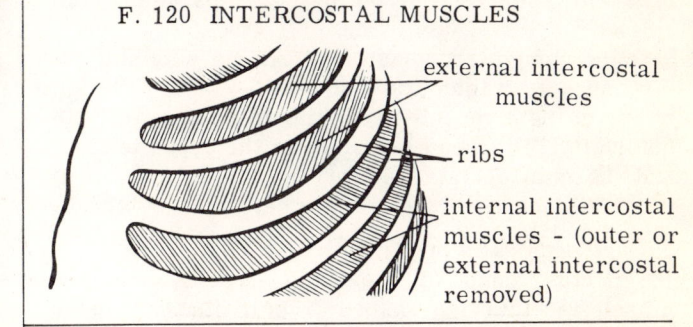

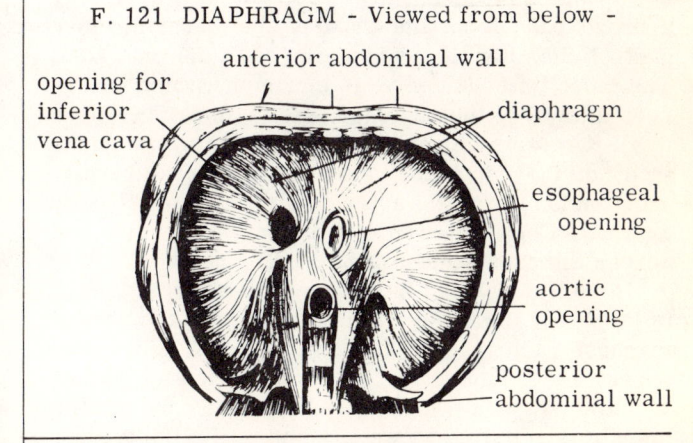

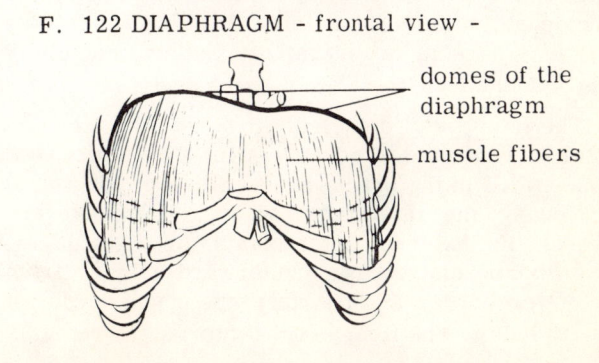

F. 119 STERNOMASTOID, PECTORALIS MAJOR AND DELTOID MUSCLES
- sternomastoid muscles
- deltoid muscle
- pectoralis major muscle

F. 120 INTERCOSTAL MUSCLES
- external intercostal muscles
- ribs
- internal intercostal muscles - (outer or external intercostal removed)

F. 121 DIAPHRAGM - Viewed from below -
- anterior abdominal wall
- opening for inferior vena cava
- diaphragm
- esophageal opening
- aortic opening
- posterior abdominal wall

F. 122 DIAPHRAGM - frontal view -
- domes of the diaphragm
- muscle fibers

S. 104. SOME MUSCLES IMPORTANT IN RADIOGRAPHY.

1. The sternomastoid or sternocleidomastoid muscle.

On each side of the neck there is a flat strap-shaped muscle. It passes obliquely down and forward from the mastoid process of the temporal bone to the inner part of the clavicle and upper sternum. It divides the neck into anterior and posterior triangles. It is of some importance to the therapy technician as groups of lymph glands lie in these areas and may require therapy. When the two sternomastoid muscles contract simultaneously, the head is bent forward. When one of them contracts, the head is turned to the opposite side. The mastoid process on the side of the contracting muscle is tipped towards the shoulder on this side.

The muscle is visible in thin subjects and may be made to stand out, if the head is turned and chin raised.

Note the name sternomastoid; sternum, mastoid.

Wry neck is a temporary or permanent contraction of one of these muscles resulting in a characteristic deformity. The head is turned to the opposite side, and the chin elevated. In wry neck it is difficult to get satisfactory views of the cervical vertebrae.

2. The pectoralis major muscle.

(L. pectus, chest or breast; major, larger). This muscle is a thick fan-shaped structure that covers the upper anterior chest wall on each side. It arises by a broad base from the front of the sternum, inner part of the clavicle, and cartilages of the true ribs. The muscle fibers converge in a tendon which is directed towards the shoulder. After folding over upon itself it inserts into the intertubercular groove on the front of the humerus, below the greater tubercle. This tendon forms the anterior border of the axilla or arm pit. Contraction brings the arm to the side and across the chest, adducting it.

In well developed muscular subjects this muscle is large and thick. It will obstruct some of the x-rays in chest radiography, causing the chest under it to appear grey. Lung detail may be obscured somewhat.

Often when a breast is removed for cancer, this muscle is removed as well. A chest film taken after this operation will show this half of the chest to be darker. There is no breast nor pectoral muscle to obstruct the x-rays.

3. The intercostal muscles.

(inter - between; and costa - a rib). The intercostal muscles fill in the spaces between the ribs and costal cartilages, the intercostal spaces. There are two layers: the external intercostals, or outer layer, have fibers passing down and forward obliquely from the lower border of one rib to the upper border of the rib below. The fibers of the internal intercostals forming the inner layer pass down and back. These muscles elevate the ribs during inspiration and thus increase the size of the chest cavity. The elevation of the ribs is aided by some of the muscles of the neck which are attached to the upper ribs.

4. The diaphragm.

(G. diaphragma, a partition or wall; G. phren, meaning the diaphragm; hence the adjective phrenic).

The diaphragm is a dome-shaped muscular partition which separates the thorax and the abdomen. This muscle is attached along its base or lower margin to the inner surfaces of the bones forming the chest wall, i.e., the sternum, costal cartilages, ribs, and behind, to the vertebrae. The muscle fibers pass up from their origins towards the center of the dome. They end in a central tendon of fibrous tissue which forms the top of the dome. The right hemidiaphragm reaches a higher level than the left. It may extend up to the fourth or fifth rib in front. The central part of the left hemidiaphragm is flattened to accommodate the lower border of the heart (hemi - half)

Three openings are present in the diaphragm:
(a) the vena caval foramen - for the inferior vena cava to pass up out of the abdomen;
(b) the aortic hiatus for the aorta to pass down;
(c) the esophageal hiatus for the esophagus to pass down to the stomach.

The convex upper surface of the diaphragm forms the floor of the chest. The concave under surface forms the roof of the abdomen. The base or margin of the diaphragm at their attachment to the ribs, etc., lie at a definitely lower level than the top of the dome. The angles formed between the inner surface of the chest wall and the curved upper border of the diaphragm laterally and behind are the costophrenic sinuses or sulci. Free fluid in the chest cavity will fill these angles first, as fluid seeks the lowest possible level.

Contraction of the diaphragm occurs with each inspiration. As the base is fixed to the bones, the fibers pull the dome down and flatten it. This pushes the contents of the abdomen down and increases the depth of the chest cavity. When the diaphragm relaxes, its dome again rises, and the depth of the chest is thus decreased.

The positions assumed by the diaphragm are of particular importance to the technician. The following points should be kept constantly in mind:
(a) the top of the dome lies well above the costal margin and may reach the fourth rib;
(b) following inspiration or breathing in, it lies at a lower level than at expiration. Chest films taken at inspiration must include the diaphragm;
(c) when the subject is lying down, the diaphragm lies at a higher level than when he is upright;

F. 123 THE SACROSPINALIS MUSCLE

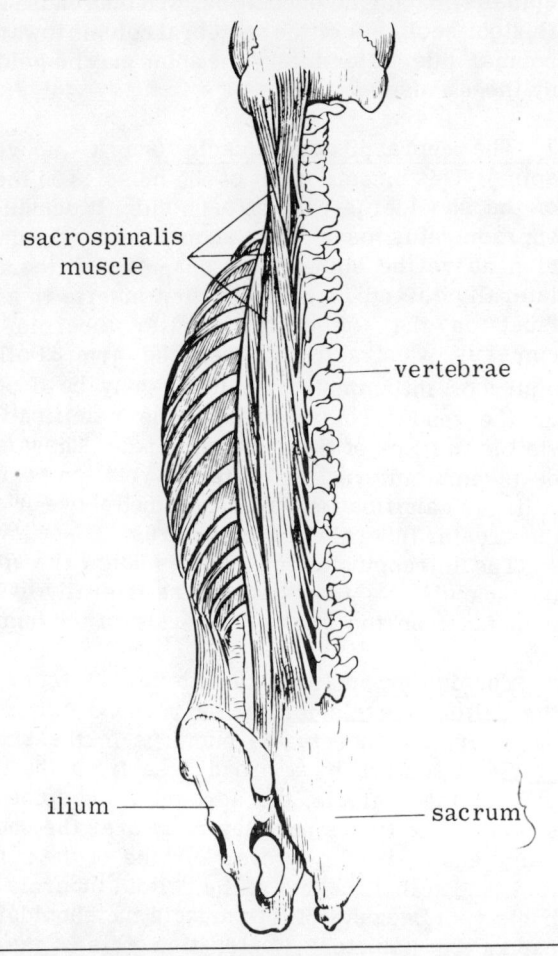

- sacrospinalis muscle
- vertebrae
- ilium
- sacrum

F. 124 THE PSOAS MAJOR MUSCLES
- posterior wall of abdomen -

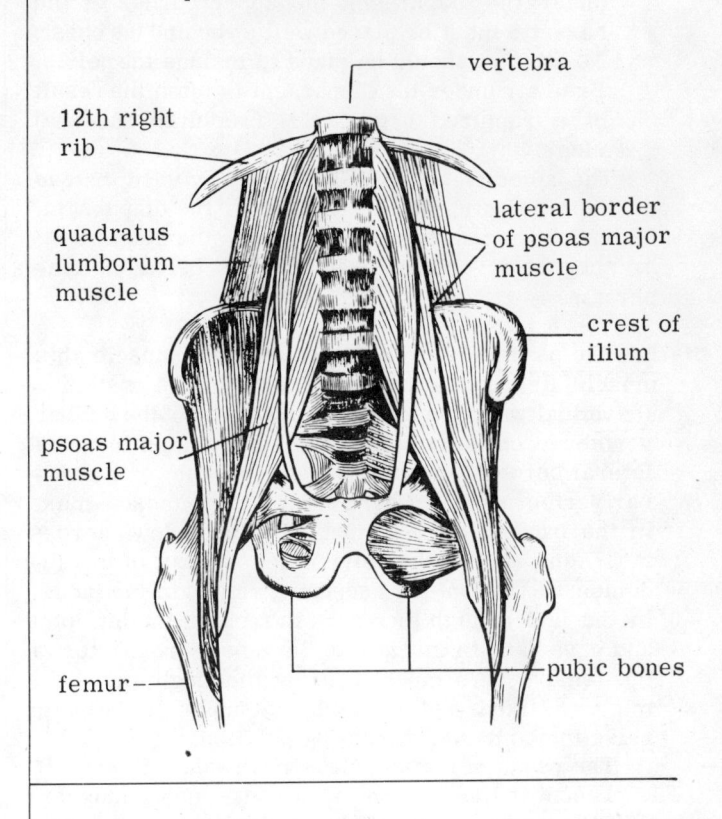

- vertebra
- 12th right rib
- quadratus lumborum muscle
- lateral border of psoas major muscle
- crest of ilium
- psoas major muscle
- femur
- pubic bones

F. 125 DELTOID, BICEPS, BRACHIALIS MUSCLES

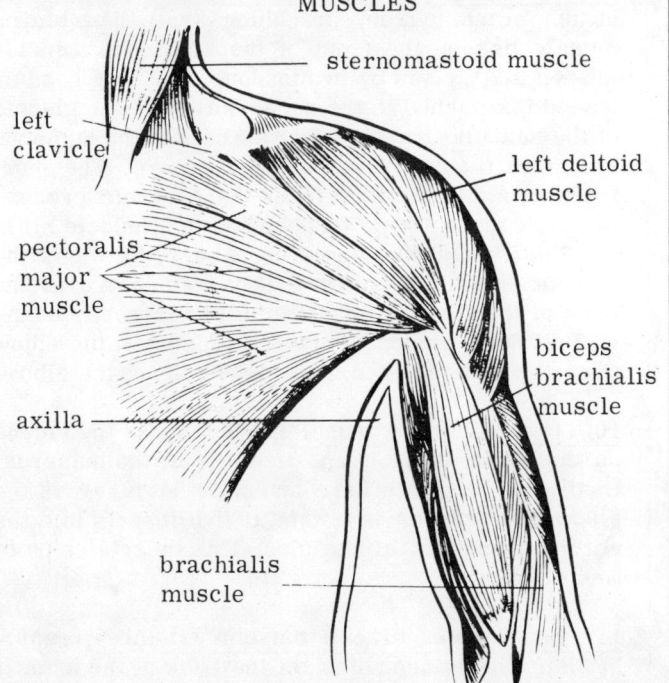

- sternomastoid muscle
- left clavicle
- left deltoid muscle
- pectoralis major muscle
- axilla
- biceps brachialis muscle
- brachialis muscle

F. 126 QUADRICEPS MUSCLE - anterior thigh -

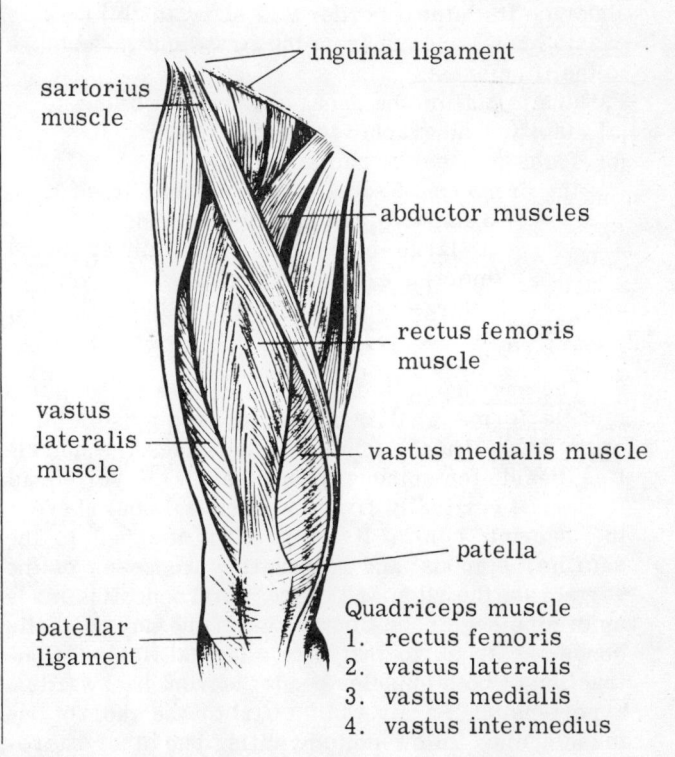

- inguinal ligament
- sartorius muscle
- abductor muscles
- rectus femoris muscle
- vastus lateralis muscle
- vastus medialis muscle
- patella
- patellar ligament

Quadriceps muscle
1. rectus femoris
2. vastus lateralis
3. vastus medialis
4. vastus intermedius

(d) for films of the abdomen taken to show air under the diaphragm, the upper border of the cassette must be placed well up behind the chest. No attempt should be made to include the pelvis. Free air under the diaphragm is often the result of a ruptured organ, e.g., ruptured duodenal ulcer.

The adjective phrenic is frequently used instead of diaphragmatic with reference to the diaphragm. Hence phrenic nerve - the nerve to the diaphragm; or subphrenic abscess - an abscess below the diaphragm.

5. The psoas major or iliopsoas major muscle; this muscle lies on the inner surface of the posterior abdominal wall along the lateral borders of the lumbar vertebrae on each side. It arises by slips from the lateral borders and transverse processes of the lumbar vertebrae. The fibers form a thick muscle mass in the back of the abdomen. They pass down across the ilium, around the pelvis inlet, and out of the abdomen in front of the ascending ramus of the pubis. In the upper thigh they pass in front of the hip joint and pass back to insert into the lesser trochanter of the femur. This muscle flexes the thigh, or if the thigh is fixed and the subject supine, it helps to raise the body into the sitting position.

The psoas minor muscle is much smaller, and if it is present it lies in front of the psoas major muscle.

The psoas muscle has sufficient thickness and density to obstruct some of the x-rays from passing through it to the film. In antero-posterior views of the abdomen its lateral border will show an oblique line passing down and out from the first lumbar vertebra to the iliac crest.

Failure to outline the psoas shadow may be due to:
(a) faulty radiographic technic;
(b) feces (faeces) or gas in the bowel;
(c) the presence of some mass obscuring it, such as:
 a tumor of the kidney or glands,
 a large blood clot from kidney hemmorrhage,
 a large hydronephrosis of a kidney pelvis, etc.

6. The sacrospinalis or erector spinae muscle: this muscle forms what is called the deep muscle layer of the back. There is one on either side. The muscle lies beside the spinous processes of the vertebrae. It extends vertically from the occipital bone above to the sacrum below. Its slips are attached to the sacrum, spinous and transverse processes of the vertebrae, the ribs, and the occipital bone. It is made up of nine segments. Contraction of one sacrospinalis bends the trunk to that side - lateral flexion. Contraction of both muscles bends the trunk backwards - hypertension. Paralysis of a part or the whole of one muscle may follow poliomyelitis. The other sacrospinalis, having no opposition, will then cause lateral flexion: scoliosis of the vertebral column towards the normal side. After injury the spine may be held rigid by these muscles.

7. The supraspinatus muscle (supra - above, and spine): This muscle is one of the muscles on the back of the shoulder girdle on each side. It occupies the supraspinatus fossa of the scapula, i.e., the depression above the spine of the scapula. Its fibers pass laterally to end in a tendon that inserts in a pit or facet on the top of the greater tubercle of the humerus. Contraction raises the arm. Following injury or inflammation, calcium may be deposited in the tendon. This supraspinatus calcification is visible in films of the shoulder girdle. These should be taken in internal and external rotation positions. A linear calcification will be outlined above or behind the greater tubercle of the humerus.

The infraspinatus muscle lies below the spine of the scapula. Its fibers also pass laterally to insert in a facet on the greater tubercle of the humerus.

8. The deltoid muscle (Greek letter D - triangular): the deltoid muscle forms the rounded curve of the shoulder. It connects the humerus to the shoulder girdle. It arises by a broad base from the lateral part of the clavicle, the acromion and spine of the scapula. The fibers pass laterally over the shoulder joint, and down the lateral surface of the humerus to a tendon that inserts at the deltoid tubercle of the humerus. Because of this muscle the shoulder joint cannot be palpated. Contraction raises the arm.

9. The biceps brachii muscle (bi - two, ceps - heads, brachii, from brachium, arm). The biceps muscle lies on the front of the arm. It is spindle-shaped and arises by two tendons. The long head or tendon is attached to the upper border of the glenoid of the scapula. It passes over the head of the humerus and down in the intertubercular groove. The short tendon or head arises from the coracoid process of the scapula. These tendons end in a muscle mass on the front of the humerus. Above the elbow the muscle ends in a tendon that passes down over the front of the elbow to insert into the tuberosity of the radius. This tendon can be felt in front of the elbow when the joint is flexed. This muscle flexes the elbow.

10. The brachialis muscle: it lies under the biceps on the lower half of, and in front of, the humerus. Its fibers originate here and pass down across the elbow joint to end in a tendon that inserts into the coronoid process of the ulna. This muscle helps to flex the elbow.

11. The triceps brachii muscle (tri three; ceps - heads). The triceps lies on the back of the arm. It

arises by three heads, hence tri, and forms a muscle mass on the back of the humerus. It ends in a tendon that inserts into the olecranon of the ulna. This muscle is an extensor and straightens the elbow. It opposes the biceps and brachialis muscles.

12. The quadriceps femoris muscle (quad - four). The quadriceps muscle of the thigh is actually four muscles forming a large muscle mass on the front of the thigh. One, the rectus femoris, arises from the ilium; the other three, from the shaft of the femur. All four end in a common tendon above the knee joint. This tendon encloses within it the patella, a sesamoid bone. It passes in front of the knee joint to insert into the tibial tuberostiy. This muscle is an extensor of the knee.

Three bursae are usually present about this tendon. The suprapatellar (supra - above) bursa lies between the upper part of the tendon and the femur behind it. The second or prepatellar bursa (pre - in front of) lies in front of the patella. The third, the infrapatellar bursa (infra - below) lies between the lower part of the tendon and upper tibia.

The suprapatellar bursa usually is continuous with the cavity of the knee joint. Air or opaque substances injected into the knee joint will also outline this bursa. (arthrogram)

S. 105   TERMS USED IN CHAPTER XII.

voluntary - involuntary	psoas (iliopsoas)
skeletal - visceral	erector spinae
striated - non-striated	sacrospinalis
sternomastoid	supraspinatus
pectoralis major	infraspinatus
intercostal	biceps (brachii)
diaphragm	triceps
diaphragmatic	quadriceps (femoris)
aortic hiatus	tendon
esophageal hiatus	tendon sheath
vena caval foramen	aponeurosis

[Handwritten notes at top:]
normal = 6 qts blood (? pints)
Plasma = 90% H₂O
most of blood is plasma
Protein is next in line (growth + repair)
main sub in red blood cells is hemoglobin (red color)
The more oxy - the redder

CHAPTER XIII. THE BLOOD.

S. 106 CONSTITUENTS OF THE BLOOD.

1. Blood plasma or fluid.
    (1) Water
    (2) Salts in solution:
        sodium   calcium
        potassium   phosphorus
        iodine
    (3) Blood proteins:
        albumin
        globulin, gammaglobulin
        fibrinogen
    (4) Digested food products:
        amino acids from proteins
        fats, fatty acids, glycerine from fats
        glucose from sugars and starches
    (5) Products of glands of internal secretion; antibodies, etc.
    (6) Gases in solution:
        oxygen
        carbon dioxide
        nitrogen
    (7) Vitamins
    (8) Waste products from body cells and tissues.

2. Blood cells.
    (1) Red blood cells or corpuscles (R.B.C.)
    (2) White blood cells or corpuscles (W.B.C.)
        (a) lymphocytes, large and small
        (b) monocytes, mononuclear and transitional
        (c) granulocytes:
            i. polmorphonuclear (polys)
            ii. eosinophil (eosinofil) (eos)
            iii. basophil or basofil (bas)
    (3) Blood platelets.

S. 107 THE BLOOD PLASMA.

The fluid part of the blood, the plasma, is colorless if the blood cells are removed. It is composed of water, digested food products, salts and vitamins, which have been absorbed into the blood from the digestive tract. In addition, it contains many substances manufactured by the glands of internal secretion including those from the thyroid, pituitary gland, etc. Blood proteins, albumin, globulin, and fibrinogen are also present. There are also antibodies, and substances that aid in, or prevent, the clotting of blood. All of these are dissolved in the blood plasma. They are carried in the blood to every part of the body that is supplied with blood. Waste products from cell activity are collected by the plasma for transportation to the various organs of excretion.

The exchange of these substances from the blood to body cells or from body tissues into the blood occurs through the walls of the capillary blood vessels. The lining membrane of these vessels is very thin. This exchange may occur in one of three ways:

(a) they may be carried through the capillary walls along with water;
(b) when the concentration of a substance is lower on one side of a cell membrane than on the other that substance will pass through the membrane towards the side with the lesser concentration;
(c) some cells, tissues or organs have a selective action and absorb such substances as they require to manufacture their product, e.g., iodine by the thyroid.

The function of the respiratory system is to supply the body with oxygen and to get rid of carbon dioxide produced in body cells. As a subject breathes in, a quantity of fresh oxygen reaches the air sacs of the lungs; so the concentration of oxygen in these air sacs is high. As the subject breathes out, carbon dioxide is expelled through the nose to keep the concentration of carbon dioxide low in the air sacs. The blood from the entire body must circulate through the lungs. This blood which is returned from the body tissues and organs will have lost its supply of oxygen to these tissues or organs. The concentration of oxygen will, therefore, flow from the air sacs into the capillaries, i.e., from an area of high, to one of lower, oxygen concentration.

The carbon dioxide content of this same blood will be high as it has received this gas from the body tissues. Carbon dioxide will therefore flow in the reverse direction, i.e., from blood capillaries into the air sacs, from a higher to a lower concentration.

The body tissues and organs use up oxygen; so their oxygen concentration is kept low. Blood returned to them from the lungs will have a high concentration of oxygen. Oxygen will therefore flow from the capillaries to these tissues. Body tissues and cells produce carbon dioxide; so the concentration of this gas in them will be high. The blood upon its return from the lungs has a low concentration of carbon dioxide. The flow of carbon dioxide will, therefore, be from body cells and tissues into the blood capillaries.

Other waste products will pass into the blood capillaries from body tissues and cells for the same

formed elements; corpuscles a. erythrocytes b. Leukocytes c. Platelets

Average = 4.5-5 million/cubic millimeter.

reason. These will be carried in the blood stream to the organs of excretion: the lungs, kidneys, skin, or liver, to be excreted from the blood. The concentration of these waste products will be kept low if these excretory organs are functioning properly.

S. 108   THE BLOOD CELLS.

1. RED BLOOD CELLS or CORPUSCLES (ERYTHROCYTES).

These are disc-shaped cells which are formed in the reticulo-endothelial tissue of the bone marrow. After losing their nuclei they are discharged into the blood capillaries. They are very small and number about 4,500,000 in females and 5,000,000 in males per cubic millimeter of blood. They remain in the blood for a period of from three to five weeks and are then destroyed, possibly by the spleen and liver.

Hemoglobin or haemoglobin. This is a compound of iron and protein, which is contained within the red blood cells. Hemoglobin unites readily with oxygen to form oxyhemoglobin, and oxygen is transported in the blood stream as oxyhemoglobin. Oxyhemoglobin gives the blood a bright red color. Blood appears to be darker in color when oxygen is given up.

Function of red blood cells. These cells transport oxygen to body cells and tissues through the circulation of blood. The oxygen is then transferred to the body cells so that they may carry on their functions.

2. WHITE BLOOD CELLS OR CORPUSCLES.

less W.B.C. than red   total

The term "leucocyte" is sometimes applied to any white blood cell. By some authorities its use is restricted to include the granulocytes only.

White blood cells have nuclei. They are not as numerous as red blood cells and average from 6,000 to 10,000 cells per cubic millimeter of blood, or about one for every seven hundred red blood cells. White blood cells are classified according to their size, the shape of the nucleus, and the reaction to dyes used in staining them.

(a) Lymphocytes are one type of white blood cells in which there is a large circular nucleus. This stains a deep blue color, while the cytoplasm is faintly blue with no granules present. There are large and small lymphocytes. Together they make up from 20 to 25% of the total white blood cells. They are formed in the reticular tissue of lymph glands.

(b) Monocytes make up from 2 to 5% of white cells. They have large irregular nuclei which stain blue with faintly stained cytoplasm. They are divided into mononuclear and transitional forms.

(c) Granulocytes are often referred to as leucocytes (G. leukos - white). They are called granulocytes because of the granules in the cytoplasm. They are formed in the reticular tissue of the bone marrow. After a series of cell divisions they are discharged into the blood. They retain their nuclei. In one stage of their development they are called myelocytes, which are sometimes discharged prematurely into the blood. A sternal puncture consists of puncturing the sternum with a large hollow needle to obtain the developing cells, for microscopic examination. There are three recognized types of granulocytes which are classified according to their reaction to staining dyes.

(i) Polymorphonuclear leucocytes or neutrophils (fils) make up from 60 to 70% of white blood cells. Their nuclei are lobulated, and the cytoplasm stains purple. The nucleus looks like several nuclei joined together.

(ii) Eosinophils account for about 2% of white blood cells. Their nuclei stain blue, and granules in the cytoplasm stain red.

(iii) Basophils or basofils form about 0.5% of the white blood cells. The granules in the cytoplasm stain blue.

Functions of white blood cells

1. They help protect the body from infection by "eating" up bacteria or by breaking up and liberating substances which destroy bacteria. The polymorphonuclear cells are most active in this. During an attack of appendicitis, for instance, the number of these cells per cubic centimeter of blood becomes increased. This occurs in other infections as well. This increase may be determined in the laboratory by taking a sample of blood and counting the number of cells to determine whether there is an increase. A sample of blood may also be taken and centrifuged, i.e., rotated rapidly. The white blood cells will settle to the bottom, the red cells will from the next layer, while the plasma will remain on top. The tube is graduated so that the thickness of each layer may be measured and compared with the normal.

2. They aid in the absorption of food from the intestines, particularly the fats.

3. They help to repair damaged tissues.

4. They aid in the clotting of blood.

blood - From lungs to art to tissue - bright red cause of new oxy.

blood - veins - darker red (back to lungs)

3. BLOOD PLATELETS.

These are minute bodies in the blood that help to form blood clots following injury to blood vessels.

S. 109 SOME PATHOLOGICAL TERMS - THE BLOOD.

Leucocytosis is an increase in the number of white blood cells above the normal.

Leucopenia is a term used to denote a decrease in the number of white blood cells below the normal.

Agranulocytosis is an absence or marked decrease in the number of granulocytes in the blood. This may occure to a patient receiving radiation therapy. The bone marrow is depressed and will not produce new white blood cells. For this reason periodic checks are made during the therapy.

Anemia or anaemia is either a decrease in the number of red blood cells in the circulating blood or a decrease in the percentage of hemoglobin present, i.e., the iron content.

Polycythemia is a condition in which there is an increase in the number of red blood cells above the normal.

Hema, haema, ema, aema, are derived from the Greek word haima - the blood. The terms anemia (anaemia), hemorrhage, (haemorrhage) are derivatives. There are many others.

S. 110 LIST OF TERMS USED IN CHAPTER XIII.

agranulocytosis
albumin
anemia (anaemia)
basophil (basofil)
carbon dioxide
eosinophil (eosinofil)
fibrinogen
globulin
granulocyte
haima or aima - he (ae) mo
hemoglobin (haemoglobin)
leucocyte
leucocytosis
leucopenia
leukos (white)
lymphocyte
monocyte
neutrophil (neutrofil)
nitrogen
oxygen
oxyhemoglobin (haemo)
platelets
polycythemia (aemia)
polymorphonuclear
protein
red blood cell (corpuscle)
transitional
white blood cell (corpuscle)

F. 127 BLOOD CELLS

Red blood cells (erythrocytes)	Lymphocytes small large	Polymorphonuclear Leucocytes
Eosinophil red granules	Basophil blue granules	Monocytes

CHAPTER XIV. THE CIRCULATORY SYSTEM.

S. 111 THE CONTENTS OF THE CHEST OR THORAX.

1. Right lung
2. Left lung
3. Mediastinum containing the following:
   (1) trachea or windpipe
   (2) esophagus or gullet
   (3) thymus gland
   (4) aorta - thoracic part, including the ascending part, aortic arch, descending part
   (5) superior vena cava
   (6) inferior vena cava, thoracic part
   (7) phrenic and vagus nerves, a pair of each
   (8) heart
   (9) lung roots - two each consisting of:
      (a) a main bronchus
      (b) a pulmonary artery
      (c) bronchial arteries
      (d) two pulmonary veins
      (e) bronchial veins
      (f) lymph nodes or glands
   (10) other lymph nodes, the thoracic duct, and right lymph duct.

The mediastinum (middle septem) is the partition between the two halves of the chest, the right hemithorax and the left hemithorax. It extends from the base of the neck above, to the diaphragm below. It lies between the sternum in front, and the thoracic vertebrae behind. Its width varies with the contents. It separates the right and left lungs. To help in accuracy in locating structures, it is divided into:

(a) the superior mediastinum, above the heart;
(b) the anterior mediastinum, in front of the heart;
(c) the middle mediastinum, containing the heart;
(d) the posterior mediastinum, behind the heart.

In section 15 the body cavities were defined. The chest or thorax extends from the base of the neck to the diaphragm below. It is enclosed by the chest wall consisting of: the sternum, costal cartilages, ribs, and dorsal vertebrae. Many of the contents of the chest will be studied in subsequent sections. These are listed above so that the student may have a bird's eye view of the subject as a whole, and may refer back for quick reference.

S. 112 THE PARTS OF THE CIRCULATORY SYSTEM.

1. The heart
2. Arteries - carry blood A W A Y from the heart
3. Arterioles - little arteries
4. Capillaries - hairlike vessels
5. Venules - little veins
6. Veins - carry blood T O W A R D S the heart
7. Lymph vascular or lymphatic system:
   (a) lymph capillaries
   (b) lymph vessels
   (c) lymph nodes or glands
   (d) thoracic duct and right lymph duct
8. Reticulo-endothelial structures - spleen, bone marrow.

S. 113 DETAILED STUDY - THE CIRCULATORY SYSTEM.

I. THE HEART (Anglo-Saxon - hoerte. L. cor)
(G. kardia or cardia - the heart; adj. cardiac).

The heart is the pump for the circulatory system, and lies in the lower anterior chest in the middle mediastinum. It rests upon the left diaphragm. The pointed end or apex lies medial to the left nipple, in the fifth left intercostal space. The broad base is directed to the right and extends slightly to the right of the right sternal border. Most of the heart lies to the left of the median line. The heart has three coverings, four chambers, and eight openings.

A. THE COVERINGS OF THE HEART:
   (a) endocardium
   (b) myocardium
   (c) pericardium - visceral and parietal

(a) The endocardium (endo - inside) is the lining membrane of the heart. It also covers the surfaces of the valves within the heart. This membrane is thin. Endocarditis is an inflammation of the endocardium.

(b) The myocardium (myos - muscle) is the special straited muscle of the heart. This muscle is thick at the left ventricle. It contracts to decrease the size of the heart and force blood out of its chambers. Myocarditis is an inflammation of the cardiac muscle.

*Ant prt of the rt ventricle open.
into the pulmonary art.*

108

F. 128 THE HEART AND GREAT BLOOD VESSELS

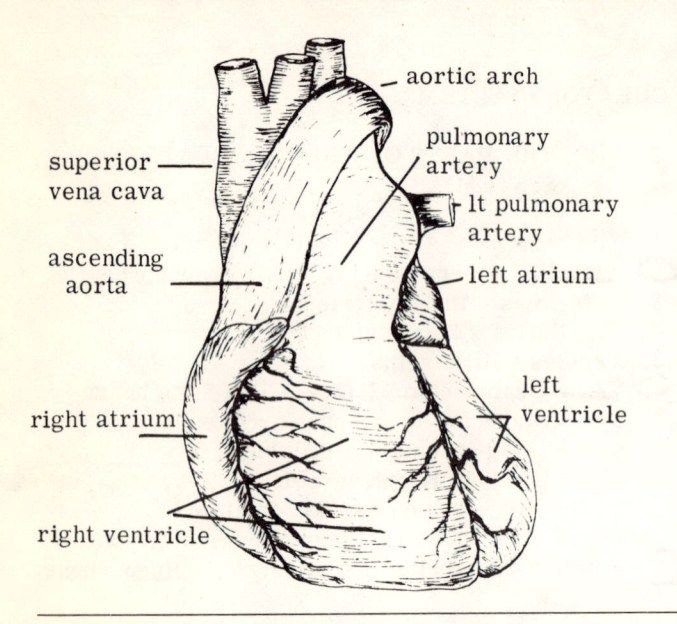

- aortic arch
- pulmonary artery
- lt pulmonary artery
- superior vena cava
- ascending aorta
- left atrium
- left ventricle
- right atrium
- right ventricle

F. 129 RADIOGRAPHIC APPEARANCE OF THE CHEST AND HEART

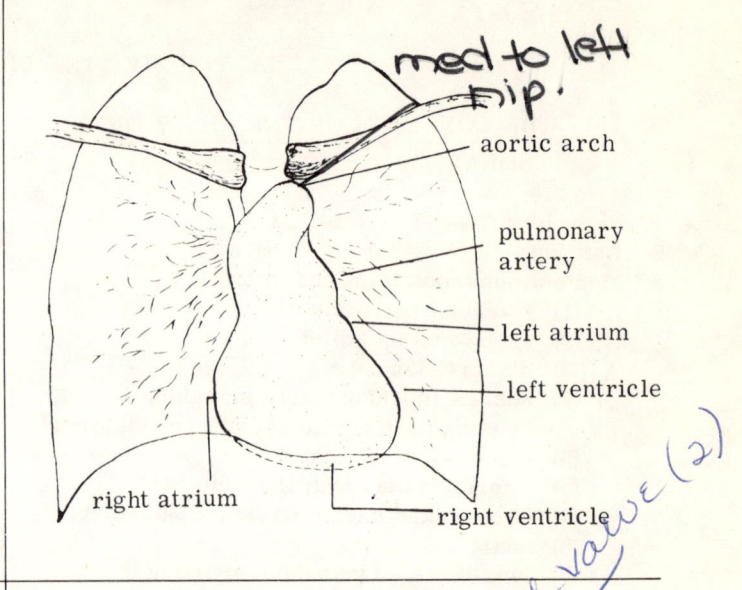

med to left nip.

- aortic arch
- pulmonary artery
- left atrium
- left ventricle
- right atrium
- right ventricle

F. 130 THE CHAMBERS OF THE HEART - diagramatic -

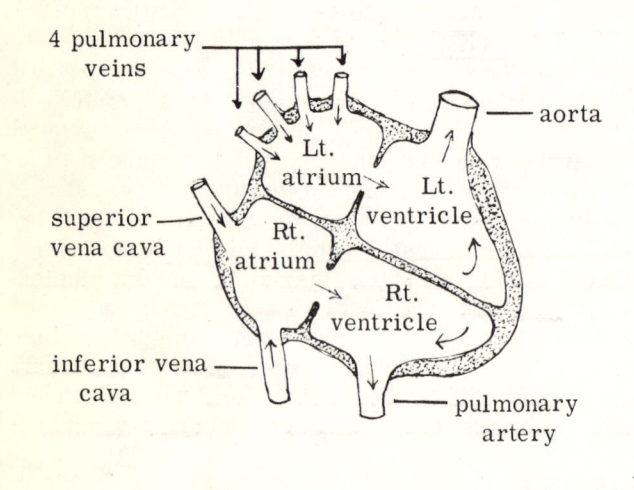

- 4 pulmonary veins
- aorta
- Lt. atrium
- Lt. ventricle
- superior vena cava
- Rt. atrium
- Rt. ventricle
- inferior vena cava
- pulmonary artery

F. 131 THE HEART - frontal view - semidiagramatic -

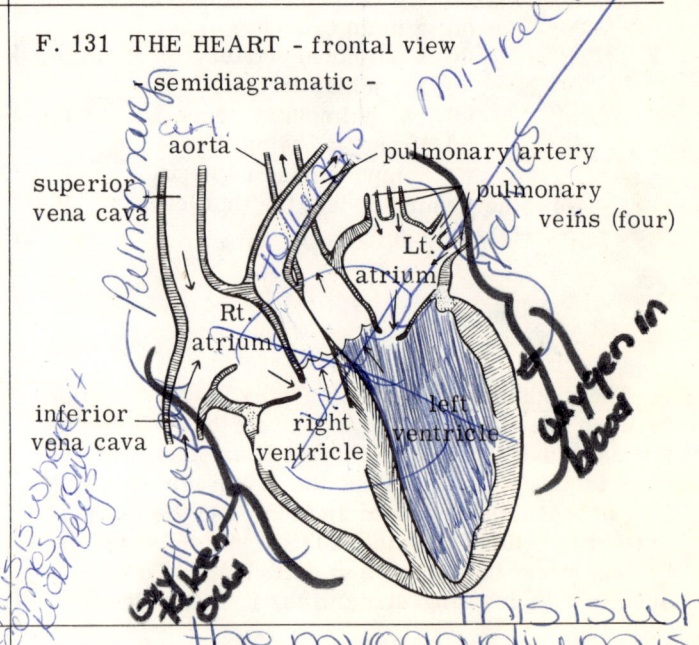

- aorta
- pulmonary artery
- superior vena cava
- pulmonary veins (four)
- Lt. atrium
- Rt. atrium
- inferior vena cava
- right ventricle
- left ventricle

mitral valve (2)
oxygen in blood
This is where the myocardium is thick

F. 132 THE HEART - cross section -

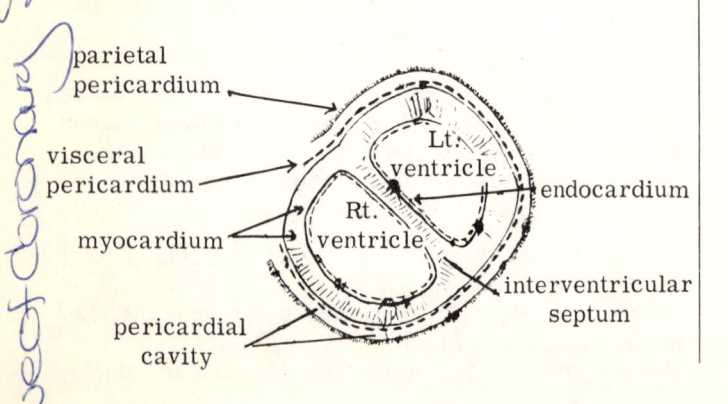

Valves of coronary sinuse

- parietal pericardium
- visceral pericardium
- myocardium
- Lt. ventricle
- Rt. ventricle
- endocardium
- interventricular septum
- pericardial cavity

F. 133 DIAGRAM OF PORTAL VEIN AND BRANCHES

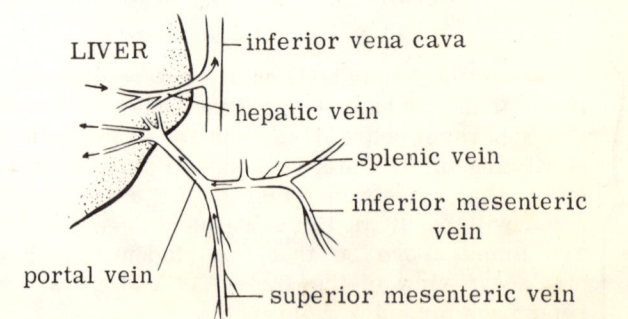

- LIVER
- inferior vena cava
- hepatic vein
- splenic vein
- inferior mesenteric vein
- portal vein
- superior mesenteric vein

The arteries that supply the heart c̄ blood = coronary arteries

70-90/min
18 - respiration

(c) The pericardium (peri - around) is the outer covering of the heart. It consists of two layers.

   (i) The visceral pericardium (viscus - an organ) or the inner layer is closely applied to the heart outside of the muscle layer. Its outer surface is smooth.

   (ii) The parietal pericardium (paries - a wall) is the outer layer. It forms a thin sac within which the heart contracts. Its inner surface is smooth and lies in contact with the smooth outer surface of the visceral layer. The two are not attached except above the heart. The student may visualize the arrangement by using the fist and a partly inflated toy balloon. Push the fist, which represents the heart, into one side of the inflated balloon until the two layers of the balloon are in contact. The inner layer will be closely applied to the fist. The outer layer will be attached to the inner layer at the wrist only. Pericarditis is an inflammation of the pericardium.
   Pericardial effusion - fluid in the pericardial sac.

B. THE FOUR CHAMBERS OF THE HEART:

   (a) left atrium (pl. atria) (auricle)
   (b) right atrium (auricle)
   (c) left ventricle
   (d) right ventricle
       (septa - partitions between the chambers)

The heart is divided into two halves, the right and left, by a main septum which extends from the base to the apex. There is no communication between these halves after birth. Each half is further divided into an atrium, sometimes called an auricle, and a ventricle by a further septum, the atrioventricular septum. These are the right and left atria and ventricles. Openings are present between the right atrium and right ventricle, and between the left atrium and left ventricle. These are called the atrioventricular openings or orifices. Flap valves guard these openings to prevent blood from flowing back to the atria from the ventricles. The valves on the right side are called the tricuspid (3 flaps), those on the left are the bicuspid (2 flaps) or the mitral valves.

The interatrial septum is that part of the main septum between the two atria.

The interventricular septum is that part of the main septum that separates the two ventricles.

The auricles are the two ear-shaped forward extensions of the atria, one continuous with each atrium. Occasionally this term is applied to the whole atrium.

The conus arteriosus or pulmonary conus is the anterior part of the right ventricle that opens into the pulmonary artery.

The coronary arteries (corona - a crown) are the first two branches of the aorta and supply the heart with blood.

C. OPENINGS IN THE HEART.

The atrio-ventricular openings, between the atrium and ventricle on each side have been described.

The right atrium has separate openings for the superior and inferior venae cavae (sing. vena cava).

The left atrium has four openings, one for each of the four pulmonary veins.

The right ventricle has an opening, the pulmonary orifice of the pulmonary artery. Three semilunar (half-moon) valves guard this opening to prevent blood from flowing back into the ventricle from the pulmonary artery.

The left ventricle has an opening, the aortic orifice, opening into the aorta. This has a similar set of three semilunar valves, the aortic valves, to prevent backflow of blood from the aorta to the ventricle.

There are two distinct systems of blood vessels in the body: the pulmonary arteries and veins and the systemic arteries and veins.

   (a) The pulmonary arteries and veins carry blood from the heart to the lungs and return it to the heart.
   (b) The systemic arteries and veins carry blood from the heart to all other parts of the body and return it to the heart, via the aorta and venae cavae.

2. ARTERIES.

All arteries carry blood AWAY from the ventricles of the heart. As stated above, there are two systems, the pulmonary and systemic. These may be compared to a tree with two trunks, the pulmonary artery and the aorta. Each trunk gives off many branches, which in turn branch and rebranch to become smaller and smaller vessels. Sometimes one of these branches divides into two similar vessels which further divide.

Many arteries are named from their location in the body. The same artery receives a different name as it proceeds to a new part of the body. The arteries of the extremities illustrate this. The subclavian artery in the chest becomes the axillary artery as

109

it passes out to the axilla (armpit). It becomes the brachial artery as it reaches the arm (brachium). At the elbow it divides into the radial and ulnar arteries. The external iliac artery in the pelvis becomes the femoral artery as it enters the thigh. Behind the knee in the popliteal space, it is called the popliteal artery. It then divides into the anterior and posterior tibial arteries. There are cerebral, gastric, renal, uterine, ovarian and many other branches.

3. ARTERIOLES.

These are the final branches of the arteries and are present in all tissues supplied with blood.

4. CAPILLARIES.

(L. capillaries - hairlike). These very minute hair-like vessels form networks between the small arterioles and the venules. Each arteriole divides into many of these thin walled vessels. They join together at their other ends to form the smallest veins. The passage of blood constituents into the tissues and the return of waste products into blood vessels occurs through these capillaries.

5. VENULES.

These are the smallest veins, and correspond to the arterioles. They are formed by the union of the capillary vessels.

6. VEINS.

(L. vena - a vein, pl. venae) (G. phleb - a vein).
The veins form the two collecting systems and bring blood back to the heart. They are formed by the union of venules. Larger and larger veins are formed by the union of smaller veins as they approach the heart. The systemic veins end in two large trunks, the superior and inferior venae cavae. In most parts of the body there are two sets of veins. The superficial veins lie close to the skin. The deep veins lie at a deeper level and usually accompany an artery. The vein often has the same name as the artery, e.g., femoral vein. The superficial veins can often be seen under the skin, and usually pass in to join a deep vein. Those in the extremities are frequently used to inject drugs etc. into the blood. Veins unlike arteries have valves to prevent backflow of blood in the wrong direction, especially those in the legs. The veins from the lungs form the pulmonary veins.

ARTERIAL AND VENOUS TRUNKS.

The aorta is the trunk artery of the systemic circulation. It begins at the left ventricle. It receives all the

F. 134 THE HEART - OPENINGS & SEPTA - PARTITIONS

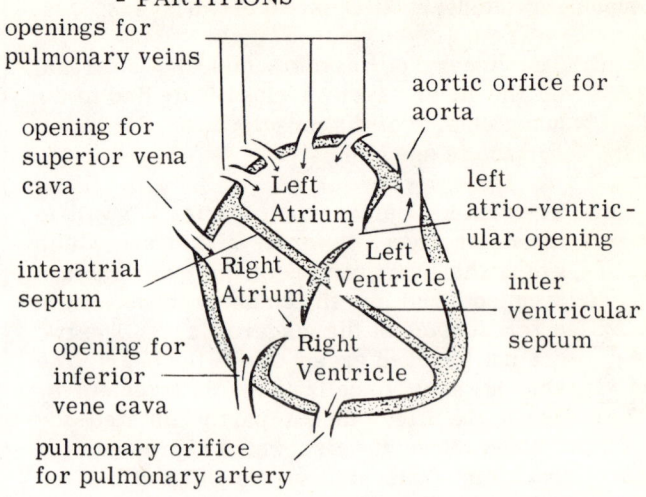

F. 135 PULMONARY ARTERIES AND VEINS

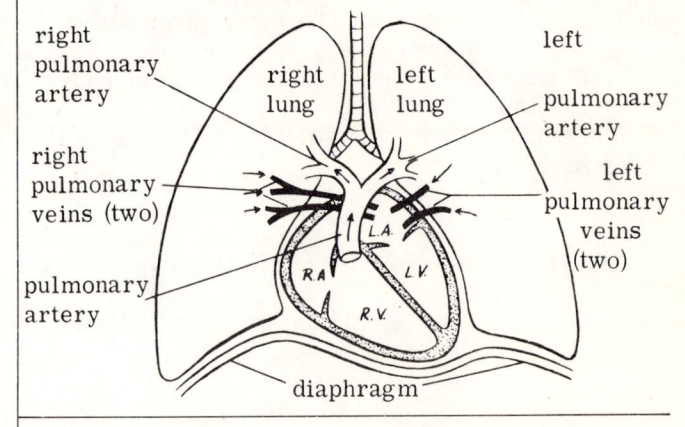

F. 136 SYSTEMIC TRUNKS - AORTA and VENAE CAVAE

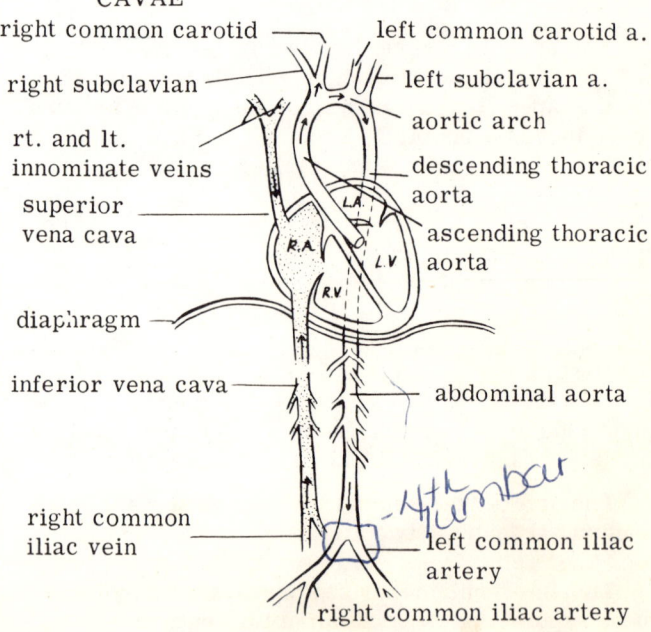

blood from this ventricle and through its many branches distributes blood to all parts of the body except the air sacs of the lungs. That part of the aorta in the chest is called the thoracic aorta. From the left ventricle it passes up behind the sternum. This part is the ascending aorta. At the sternal angle it turns to the left and arches downward - the arch of the aorta. It then descends along the left borders of the thoracic vertebrae - the descending aorta. It passes through the aortic hiatus (opening) in the diaphragm into the abdomen - the abdominal aorta. It divides opposite the body of the fourth lumbar vertebra into the left and right common iliac arteries.

The superior vena cava is one of the large trunk veins of the systemic circulation. It receives branches from all of the body above the diaphragm except the air sacs of the lungs. Veins from the head, neck, both upper extremities, and the thorax drain into it. It lies behind the right upper sternum and empties into the right atrium. It is formed by two innominate veins.

The inferior vena cava is the other trunk vein for the systemic circulation. It is formed in the lower abdomen by the union of the two common iliac veins. It drains blood from the lower extremities; and the veins from the abdominal organs empty into it. It lies in front of the lumbar vertebrae and passes up through the vena caval foramen in the diaphragm to enter the right atrium.

The portal vein is a trunk vein that receives branches from the stomach, small and large intestine, the spleen, pancreas, and gall bladder. It enters the liver and breaks up into capillaries. These reunite to form the hepatic vein which empties into the inferior vena cava. Blood returning from the digestive tract must therefore pass through the liver before re-entering the general blood stream.

The pulmonary artery is the trunk artery of the pulmonary circulation. It begins at the right ventricle at the conus arteriosus. It passes up along the left border of the heart and divides into the right and left pulmonary arteries. These enter the corresponding lung root and divide and redivide into smaller and smaller arteries and arterioles. Finally they form networks of capillaries which surround the air sacs of the lungs. It is through these capillaries that the exchange of oxygen and carbon dioxide takes place. The student should note that bronchial arteries also enter each lung and supply the bronchi with blood.

Four pulmonary veins, two right and two left, collect the blood from the lung capillaries and return it to the left atrium. These veins are formed by the lung capillaries forming venules and veins and finally ending in the trunk veins of the pulmonary circulation.

Each pulmonary vein has a separate opening in the left atrium.

7. THE LYMPH VASCULAR OR LYMPHATIC SYSTEM.

   (a) lymph capillaries
   (b) lymph vessels
   (c) lymph nodes or glands
   (d) lymph ducts - thoracic and right lymph

The lymph vascular system is a second collecting system. It functions like the venous system in draining off tissue fluids and products of cell activity. Considerable water and some waste products get back into the blood stream by this route. Fat is absorbed from the intestines by the lymphatics and not by the blood capillaries. Lymph is the name given to the fluid circulating in the lymphatic vessels. It is colorless except when fat is being absorbed.

Lymph capillaries form a closed network of very thin walled vessels like the blood capillaries. These are present in every part of the body and are numerous in the lining membranes of the body cavities, the pleura, pericardium, peritoneum, and synovial membranes of joints. These capillaries unite to form lymph vessels.

Lymph vessels are tubes formed by the union of lymph capillaries. The smaller vessels unite to form larger and larger trunks. As in the case of the veins, there is a superficial set under the skin, and a deeper set. These trunks from the deep vessels accompany the artery and veins of the same part. The superficial vessels empty into the deep trunks. The large trunks eventually empty into either the thoracic duct, or right lymph duct, which in turn empty into the large veins of the neck.

Lymph nodes or glands are small oval bodies ranging in size from a pin head to a broad bean. These are distributed along the course of the lymph vessels, sometimes singly but usually in groups or chains. The lymph vessels open into these nodes. Larger trunks leave the nodes. The contents of every lymph vessel must pass through one or more of these nodes before entering the blood stream. There are superficial and deep nodes grouped at strategic points throughout the body close to a large artery and vein. They are named from the location in the body or the artery they accompany. Only the larger groups are listed below.

The cervical nodes, superficial and deep, lie in the neck close to the sternomastoid muscle. They drain lymph from the head and neck on both sides.

The axillary nodes, in the armpit or axilla, drain the upper extremity, chest wall, and breast.

The inguinal (L. inguen - groin) nodes in the groin drain lymph from the lower limb and the skin of the lower abdomen and buttock.

The iliac nodes lie beside the iliac artery in the pelvis and receive lymph from the deep vessels of the lower extremity.

The hypogastric or internal iliac nodes drain lymph from the pelvic organs and other structures there.

The aortic nodes lie along the abdominal aorta and drain lymph from abdominal organs.

The hilar and tracheal nodes lie in the hila and about the trachea.

Each node has a covering or capsule with fibrous tissue strands or trabeculae passing into the gland. A network of reticular tissue is present within each node. Groups of lymphoid tissue are placed at intervals throughout this network. Spaces between these cell nests form channels for the passage of lymph.

Lymph nodes form new lymphocytes and discharge them into the lymph stream. They also act as filters to prevent bacteria from passing into the blood stream.

Cancer cells may grow along lymph vessels, or may break off from the parent growth and lodge in regional lymphnodes starting secondary growths. The therapy technician must know what nodes drain each area.

The thoracic duct is a large lymph trunk which begins in the upper abdomen by the union of lymph vessels here. It passes through the aortic opening in the diaphragm into the thorax. It passes in front of the thoracic vertebrae to the neck. It empties into the left subclavian vein above the clavicle where that vein joins with the left common carotid vein. It drains lymph from the lower extremities, pelvis, abdomen, left upper extremity, left side of head and neck, and the left half of the thorax.

The right lymph duct is formed by the union of the lymph vessels of the thorax, the right jugular and subclavian lymph trunks. It empties into the right subclavian vein and drains the right half of the head neck, thorax, and right upper extremity. Each of the trunks may open separately into the vein.

8. RETICULO-ENDOTHELIAL STRUCTURES.

These include the bone marrow, lymph nodes, spleen, and liver. They have a reticular network, and a lining of reticulo-endothelial cells. These cells take up foreign material, dead bacteria, dead cells, dyes, etc., and are called phagocytes. They act as filters of the blood and store lipoids and iron. They form some of the blood cells, monocytes, and red blood cells. Most of these structures are described under other headings.

The spleen is an organ that lies under the left diaphragm and left costal margin in the upper left abdomen. It has a capsule from which partial partitions, the trabeculae, extend into its substance. It has lymph follicles - nests of lymphoid tissue - like lymph glands. The splenic pulp is composed of reticulo-endothelial cells and reticular fibers. Lymph sinuses or spaces lie between. The function of the spleen is debatable. It may filter out worn-out red blood cells; it may manufacture new red blood cells; and may store red cells. It is also said to form antibodies.
(Splenomegaly - enlargement of spleen).

S. 114 THE STRUCTURE OF A BLOOD VESSEL.

Blood vessels have three coats or coverings.

1. The internal coat or tunica intima consists of a layer of flat endothelial cells lining the vessel like a cobblestone pavement. A layer of elastic tissue surrounds the endothelial layer.

2. The middle coat or tunica media consists of a layer of visceral or involuntary muscle fibers which encircle the vessel. Larger vessels have elastic tissue layers between muscle layers.

3. The outer coat or tunica adventitia consists of a layer of connective tissue.

Veins and lymphatic vessels have thinner walls than arteries. The smaller vessels have less muscle tissue. Capillaries have the endothelial layer only.

Because of the muscle and elastic tissue blood vessels can expand and contract to accommodate the amount of fluid in them.

Special nerves, the vaso-constrictors and the vasodilators, can also cause them to contract and dilate.

An anastomosis is a joining together of a branch of one vessel with a branch of another one. If one of these branches becomes blocked, blood from the other branch will supply the part with blood.

S. 115 THE FUNCTIONS OF THE CIRCULATORY SYSTEM.

The heart is a pump to force blood through the blood vessels.

[handwritten top: Which part of the heart does not appear on an IH?]
[handwritten: Pul circ = Rt at to Lt at. Syst " = Lt at to Rt at]

The **arteries** form a distributing system, and carry blood to all parts of the body.

The **veins and lymphatics** are collecting systems which return blood to the heart.

In section 105 the function of the blood plasma was outlined, and the various substances dissolved in it were enumerated. The circulatory system must carry these products to all parts of the body and return the waste products for excretion from the body.

The two atria of the heart contract together forcing blood into the right and left ventricles. The ventricles then contract together forcing blood into the pulmonary artery and aorta. When the ventricles contract, the atrio-ventricular valves, between them and the atria, close. This prevents blood from flowing back into the atria. While the ventricles are contracting, the two atria dilate and fill the blood from the venae cavae and pulmonary veins. The ventricles, having emptied, now relax, and blood is forced into them from the atria, which now contract again. As the ventricles contract, the aortic and pulmonary valves open, and blood flows into the expanded aorta and the pulmonary artery. At the end of the ventricular contraction the aortic and pulmonary valves close to prevent blood from flowing back into the ventricles from these arteries.

Systole is the contracting phase. *[handwritten: 120/80 normal]*

Diastole is the dilatation or dilating phase.

The **pulmonary circulation**. Blood which has been returned to the right atrium through the venae cavae passes into the right ventricle. With contraction of the right ventricle, blood passes into the pulmonary artery to the lungs. It passes through the capillary vessels of the air sacs. It receives a supply of oxygen and gives off carbon dioxide and moisture. It is then collected by the two pulmonary veins of each lung and is returned to the left atrium to be pumped out to the body tissues.

COURSE: right atrium - to right ventricle - to pulmonary artery - to lung capillaries - to pulmonary veins - to left atrium.

The **systemic circulation**. Oxygenated blood from the left atrium enters the left ventricle. It is pumped into the aorta. Through the branches of the aorta it goes to all organs and tissues of the body. It enters the capillaries of these structures. It gives up its supply of oxygen and other products. It takes up carbon dioxide and waste products. The blood then passes through veins to the superior or inferior venae cavae and back to the right atrium.

[handwritten: BP is ↑ in arteries than in veins]

F. 137 THE LYMPHATIC DUCT

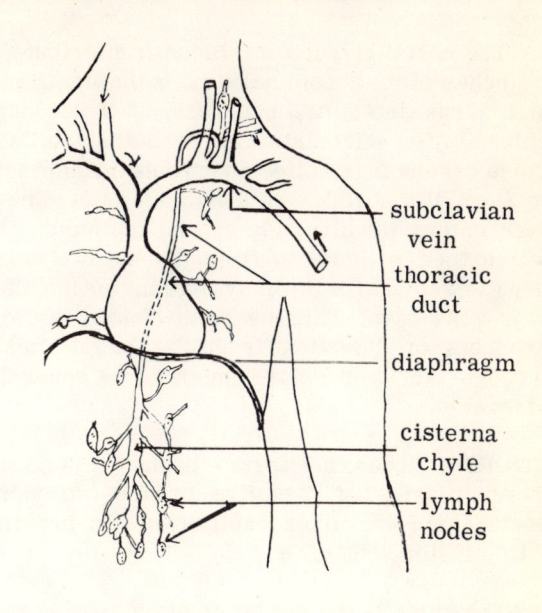

- subclavian vein
- thoracic duct
- diaphragm
- cisterna chyle
- lymph nodes

F. 138 SYSTEMIC, PULMONARY, PORTAL CIRCULATIONS

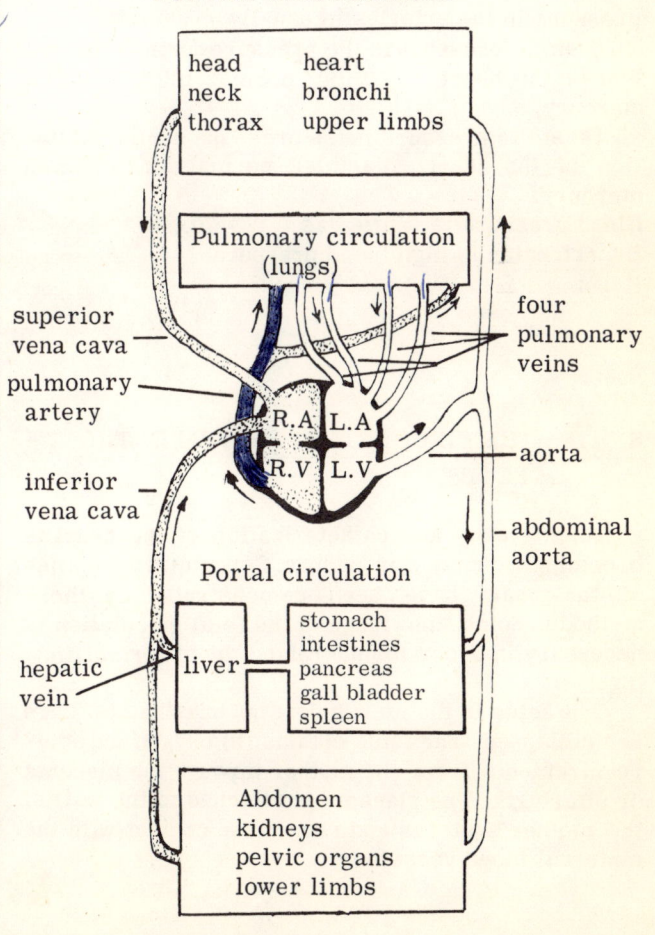

head   heart
neck   bronchi
thorax upper limbs

Pulmonary circulation (lungs)

superior vena cava
pulmonary artery
inferior vena cava

R.A L.A
R.V L.V

four pulmonary veins
aorta
abdominal aorta

Portal circulation

hepatic vein — liver — stomach, intestines, pancreas, gall bladder, spleen

Abdomen
kidneys
pelvic organs
lower limbs

COURSE: left atrium - to left ventricle - to aorta - to its branches - to tissue capillaries - to veins - to superior or inferior venae cavae - to right atrium.

The portal circulation. Blood is distributed by the branches of the abdominal aorta to the stomach, small and large intestine, pancreas, gall bladder, and spleen. After circulating through the capillaries of these organs it is collected in veins that join together to form the portal vein (porta - a gate). The portal vein enters the liver. It breaks up into capillaries which then re-unite to from the hepatic vein. The hepatic vein leaves the liver and empties into the inferior vena cava. This means that blood carrying the products of digestion from the bowel must pass through the liver before entering the general blood stream.

COURSE: abdominal aorta - branches in abdomen - to capillaries of digestive organs - to veins - to portal vein - to liver capillaries - to hepatic vein - to inferior vena cava.

The pulse is the dilatation of an artery caused by contraction of the heart. It may be felt in any larger artery but most conveniently at the wrist.

Blood pressure is the pressure exerted by the blood against the vessel walls, arteries or veins. The pressure in the arteries is usually measured.

Systolic pressure is the pressure during contraction of the heart, (systole); normal 100 to 120 mm mercury.

Diastolic pressure is the pressure during dilatation of the heart, (diastole); normal 65 to 80 mm mercury.

Blood pressure is written as - 120/70. etc.
Hypertension is high blood pressure.
Hypotension is low blood pressure.

S. 116 THE CIRCULATORY SYSTEM IN THE FETUS.

Angiography and catheterization of the heart is becoming a common procedure. Congenital anomalies of the heart have been demonstrated by these methods. Some knowledge of the fetal circulation is necessary in order to understand the abnormal findings.

The fetus in the uterus does not breathe; its lungs are collapsed. The fetus obtains its oxygen and other requirements from the mother through the placenta or afterbirth. The placenta is attached to the wall of the mother's uterus and is in close contact with the maternal blood vessels.

The umbilical cord passes from the naval of the fetus to the placenta. It contains a vein and two arteries.

The two umbilical arteries pass out from the fetus, through the umbilical cord to the placenta. They carry fetal blood to this structure.

The umbilical vein returns fetal blood from the placenta, through the cord to the fetus. This blood will contain oxygen and other necessary products.

The ductus venosus is a vein connecting the umbilical vein with the inferior vena cava of the fetus.

The foramen ovale is an opening in the interatrial septum between the two atria. This is normal for the fetus. Blood entering the right atrium from the inferior vena cava passes directly into the left atrium through this foramen, without entering the right ventricle. This blood therefore does not pass through the lungs. As the lungs in the fetus do not contain air, there is no necessity for blood going through them. The foramen closes soon after birth. Blood must then pass into the right ventricle and out ot the lungs, which have now expanded and contain air.

The ductus arteriosus is a blood vessel connecting the pulmonary artery and aorta. Blood entering the right atrium from the superior vena cava passes into the right ventricle and out through the pulmonary artery. Instead of entering the lungs it passes into the ductus and from there directly to the aorta and systemic circulation, bypassing the lungs. This vessel should close soon after birth.

S. 117 SOME ANOMALIES OF THE HEART AND VESSELS.

Patent foramen ovale. The opening between the two atria does not close after birth but persists.

Interventricular septal defect. This is an abnormal opening between the two ventricles in the interventricular septum.

Patent ductus or ductus arteriosus. The blood vessel connecting the pulmonary artery and aorta does not close as it should but persists.

Stenosis of the pulmonary artery. The pulmonary artery may be narrowed.

Co-arctation of the aorta. This is a narrowing of the aorta usually in the upper descending part.

Right aortic arch. The arch of the aorta is on the right side instead of on the left, its normal site.

Transposition. The heart may be on the right side with the apex close to the right nipple and base directed to the left.

Often the abdominal organs are also reversed. Other anomalies of the larger arterial trunks may occur, particularly in the superior mediastinum. These may cause pressure on the trachea or esophagus.

S. 118 SOME PATHOLOGICAL CONDITIONS.

Phlebitis is an inflammation of a vein (phleb, a vein).
A thrombus is a clot of blood which forms inside of a vessel or the heart. It may partly or completely block the vessel. Any condition in which the flow of blood is slowed down favors its formation. It may follow operations, especially if the patient lies still in bed. This is one of the reasons for having patients, following operations, exercise in bed or get up soon after the operation. A thrombus is more frequently found in the pelvis or lower limbs. Roughening of the lining membrane of a vein from inflammation of its wall also predisposes to thrombosis.
Cerebral thrombosis is the presence of a thrombus in one of the cerebral blood vessels.
Coronary thrombosis is a thrombus in one of the coronary blood vessels of the heart.
An embolus is a foreign body obstructing a blood vessel. This may be part of a thrombus, or a blood clot, fat, a bubble of air, a globule of oil, a clump of bacteria, or a group of cancer cells. This foreign body becomes lodged in a vessel when the vessel is too small to allow it to pass through. This may be at the forking of a vessel. It may have come from some distant part of the body. It may lodge in the lungs, brain, heart, kidneys, or any other body organ.
A coronary embolus is an embolus lodged in one of the coronary blood vessels of the heart, or a branch.
A cerebral embolus is an embolus in one of the cerebral vessels.
An infarct is the condition produced in an organ or tissue beyond the block of an artery due to embolus. If other blood vessels supply this area with blood, it does not suffer. If the blood supply is cut off by the embolus, these tissues will die and will be replaced by fibrous tissue.
Cardiac infarction is this condition affecting the wall of the heart following a coronary embolus.
Coronary occlusion is the blocking of a coronary artery or one of its branches. This may be due to a thrombus, an embolus or to filling in of the vessel.
An aneurysm is a sac-like bulging of the wall of a blood vessel due to weakness of the wall. It resembles a bulge in a tire when the fabric is broken. It follows degeneration of a vessel from disease, often syphillis. It frequently occurs in the thoracic aorta. Often there is calcification of the vessel.
Arteriosclerosis is a thickening of blood vessel walls due to degeneration of the normal coats, and replacement with fibrous tissue, fat, and calcium. The vessel becomes rigid, and the lumen smaller.
Phlebothrombosis or thrombophlebitis are terms used to designate inflammation in a vein with thrombus formation.
Varicose veins are dilated veins due to weakening of the vessel walls. The veins dilate, the valves cannot close properly and blood may flow in the opposite direction to the normal.
The lower extremities are frequently involved.
Hemorrhoids (piles) are varicose veins in the rectum and may bleed, resulting in blood in the bowel movements.
Varicosities (varicose veins) may occur in the lower esophagus. These may also bleed. The patient may vomit blood or pass black bowel movements.

S. 119 APPLICATION TO RADIOGRAPHY.

As the heart lies immediately behind the anterior chest wall, views in the postero-anterior projection will bring the heart close to the film and will show minimal magnification.

The heart also lies obliquely and is rotated so that the right half lies in front of the left half. On the right side in front is the right atrium. The right ventricle forms all of the remainder of the anterior surface except at the extreme left. Here the left ventricle forms a very small part, and above this the left atrium forms a smaller part. The left atrium is posterior, and if enlarged, will displace the esophagus back. Oblique and lateral views must be taken to outline all the chambers. Barium in the esophagus will help to demonstrate displacement of it.

In cardiography opaque dye may be very rapidly injected into a larger vein to flow to the heart. Films of the heart are taken in rapid succession to outline the chambers. Instead, a catheter may be threaded through a vein in the upper limb to the right heart. Opaque dye may then be injected, and films taken.

Arteriography is a procedure whereby opaque dye is injected into an artery to outline the artery and its branches. Films are then taken. Such a film is called an arteriogram. The dye may be injected into the abdominal aorta through a long needle inserted through the back to outline the abdominal aorta and its branches.

Venography is the procedure whereby dye is injected into the main artery of the part. This dye will return through the veins, and films are taken to outline the veins. A venogram is such a film.

Angiography is a term used with reference to these procedures for an artery or vein (G. angeion - vessel)

S. 120 TERMS USED IN CHAPTER XIV.

anastomosis	endocardium (endo - inside)	reticulo-endothelial	thrombosis
aneurysm		septum	thrombophlebitis
aorta	foramen ovale	right lymphatic duct	tricuspid valves
aortic (adj.)	hemorrhoid, haemorrhoid	spleen	varicose veins
aortic valves	heart	splenic (adj.)	vein
apex	hypertension	superior vena cava	venous (adj.)
artery	hypotension	systemic circulation	venule - little vein
arterial (adj.)	inferior vena cava	systole	vena cava
arteriole	infarct	systolic (adj.)	venae cavae (pl.)
arteriogram	interventricular defect	thoracic duct	venogram, venography
arteriography	interventricular septum	thrombus	
atrium	intertrial septum		
atrail (adj.)	lymph		
atrio-ventricular orifice	lymph vessel		
atrio-ventricular septum	lymph duct		
atrio-ventricular valves	lymph node		
auricle	lymphatic (adj.)		
auricular (adj.)	mediastinum		
bicuspid valves	mediastinal (adj.)		
capillary	mitral valves		
capillaries (pl.)	myocardium		
cardia (kardia)	myocardial (adj.)		
cardiac (adj.)	parietal pericardium		
conus arteriosus	patent ductus		
cor - heart	pericardium (peri - around)		
coronary			
coronary arteries	pericardial (adj.)		
coronary embolus, embolism	pericarditis		
	phleb - vein		
coronary occlusion	phlebitis		
coronary thrombosis	phlebothrombosis		
diastole	portal vein		
diastolic (adj.)	portal circulation		
ductus arteriosus	pulmonary valves		
ductus venosus	pulmonary circulation		
embolus	pulmonary artery		
emboli (pl.)	pulmonary veins		
embolic (adj.)	semilunar valves		

S. 121 LARGER SYSTEMIC ARTERIES - for reference only.

The ascending thoracic aorta [ascending aorta] gives off two branches:
1. right coronary artery to the heart,
2. left coronary artery to the heart.

The arch of the aorta gives off three large branches:
1. innominate artery which divides into the right common carotid and right subclavian arteries;
2. left common carotid, dividing into:
    (i) the left internal carotid to cranial cavity;
    (ii) the left external carotid to neck, face, scalp;
3. left subclavian, which gives off the left vertebral artery, arteries to the neck, shoulder, and chest, and then continues as the axillary artery.

The descending thoracic artery gives off:
   pericardial, esophageal, intercostal, and bronchial arteries.

The abdominal aorta extends from the diaphragm to the fourth lumbar vertebra and divides into two common iliac arteries.

F. 139
PATENT FORAMEN OVALE

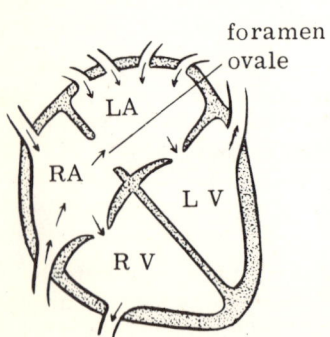

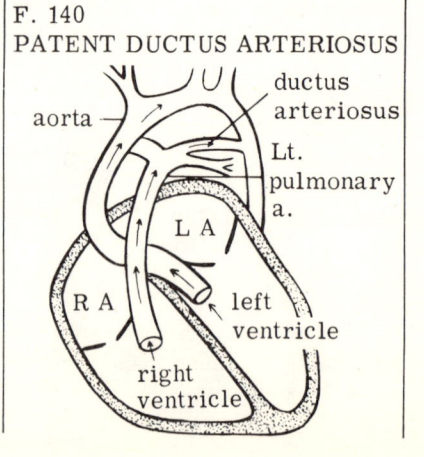

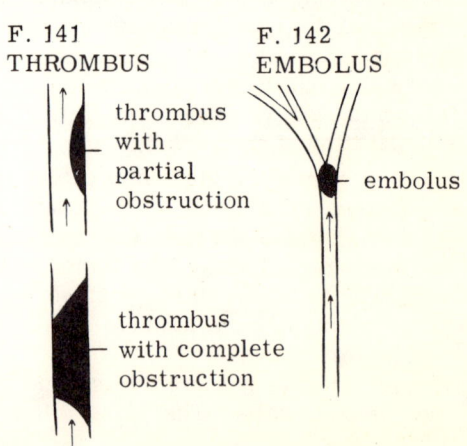

F. 140
PATENT DUCTUS ARTERIOSUS

F. 141
THROMBUS

thrombus with partial obstruction

thrombus with complete obstruction

F. 142
EMBOLUS

Unpaired branches of the abdominal aorta:
1. celiac: left gastric, splenic, hepatic;
2. superior mesenteric - to small bowel, 1/2 of colon;
3. inferior mesenteric - to distal 1/2 of colon.

Paired branches of the abdominal aorta:
1. phrenic - to diaphragm;
2. suprarenal - to suprarenal glands;
3. renal - to kidneys;
4. testicular or ovarian - to testes or ovaries;
5. terminal division - two common iliac arteries.

Blood supply to the brain:
1. left and right internal carotid arteries, each passing through the carotid canal and foramen lacerum in the base of the skull to the cranial cavity;
2. left and right vertebral arteries, branches of the sub-clavian to the cranium.
Note: a middle meningeal artery enters the cranium through the foramen spinosum on each side and forms grooves on the inner surface of cranial bones.

Blood supply to the upper extremity:
1. each subclavian artery becomes the axillary artery in the armpit (axilla);
2. each axillary artery becomes the brachial artery in the arm;
3. each brachial artery divides at the elbow into the radial and ulnar arteries;
4. radial and ulnar arteries form arches of the hand.

Blood supply to the lower extremity:
the common iliac artery on each side divides into the internal and external iliac arteries; the internal iliac arteries, left and right, supply branches to the uterus (uterine) and pelvic organs;
1. the external iliac artery on each side becomes the femoral artery in the thigh, and gives off the deep femoral branch;
2. the femoral artery becomes the popliteal artery behind the knee;
3. the popliteal artery divides into the anterior and posterior tibial arteries below the knee. The posterior tibial gives off the peroneal branch;
4. the anterior and posterior tibial arteries and the peroneal supply the leg and foot.

S. 122   PULSE - LOCATIONS USED TO PALPATE.

In taking the pulse two or three fingers should be used. The flat surfaces in front of the distal phalanges should be used, not the finger tips, and care should be taken not to dig the finger nails in. The pulse may be counted at the points below.

1. Radial artery at lateral border and the anterior surface of the wrist.
2. Ulnar artery at medial border of anterior surface of wrist.
3. Brachial artery at inner surface and middle of arm.
4. Superficial temporal in front of ear.
5. Facial artery in front of the angle of mandible.
6. Femoral artery in the groin.
7. Popliteal artery behind the knee.
8. Dorsalis pedis.

S. 123   PRESSURE POINTS - TO ARREST HEMORRHAGE.

1. Radial artery at wrist.
2. Ulnar artery at wrist.
3. Brachial artery in front of elbow.
4. Brachial artery on medial border of arm.
5. Subclavian artery over first rib above clavicle.
6. Abdominal artery in midabdomen.
7. Femoral artery in groin.
8. Popliteal artery behind knee.

S. 124   LARGER SYSTEMIC VEINS - for reference only.

UPPER EXTREMITY - superficial veins:
1. cephalic - lateral border of hand, forearm, arm, ends in axillary vein;
2. basilic vein - medial border hand, forearm, arm, becomes axillary vein at axilla;
3. median vein - anterior surface of forearm, divides at elbow, branches to cephalic and basilic.

UPPER EXTREMITY - deep veins:
1. two ulnar veins with ulnar artery to elbow;
2. two radial veins with radial artery to elbow;
3. two brachial veins formed at elbow from two ulnar and two radial veins, accompany brachial arteries;
4. axillary vein, a continuation of basilic veins and is joined by cephalic;
5. subclavian is continuation of axillary, and united with internal jugular to form innominate vein in thorax, receives lymph ducts.

VEINS OF THORAX:
1. innominate vein on each side formed by union of subclavian and internal jugular, receive internal mammary vein;
2. superior vena cava formed by union of right and left innominate veins, empties into right atrium;
3. azygos veins formed by union of lumbar and intercostal veins pass up beside the vertebrae, and empty into superior vena cava.

VEINS OF HEAD AND NECK:
1. venous sinuses within cranium: (superior sagittal, inferior sagittal, straight, transverse, sigmoid and cavernous) form internal jugular vein on each side which leaves cranium by the jugular foramen;
2. internal jugular a continuation of sigmoid sinus at jugular foramen, joins subclavian to from innominate right, and left;
3. external jugular vein on each side drains veins of the scalp and face, joins subclavian above the clavicle.

LOWER EXTREMITY - superficial veins:
1. long saphenous on inner border of foot, leg, and thigh joins femoral vein;
2. short saphenous on lateral border of foot and leg ends in popliteal vein behind the knee.

LOWER EXTREMITY - deep veins:
1. two posterior tibial on each side from foot along with posterior tibial artery to knee;
2. two anterior tibial veins from anterior leg with anterior tibial artery to knee;
3. popliteal vein behind the knee formed by two posterior and anterior tibial veins, beside popliteal artery;

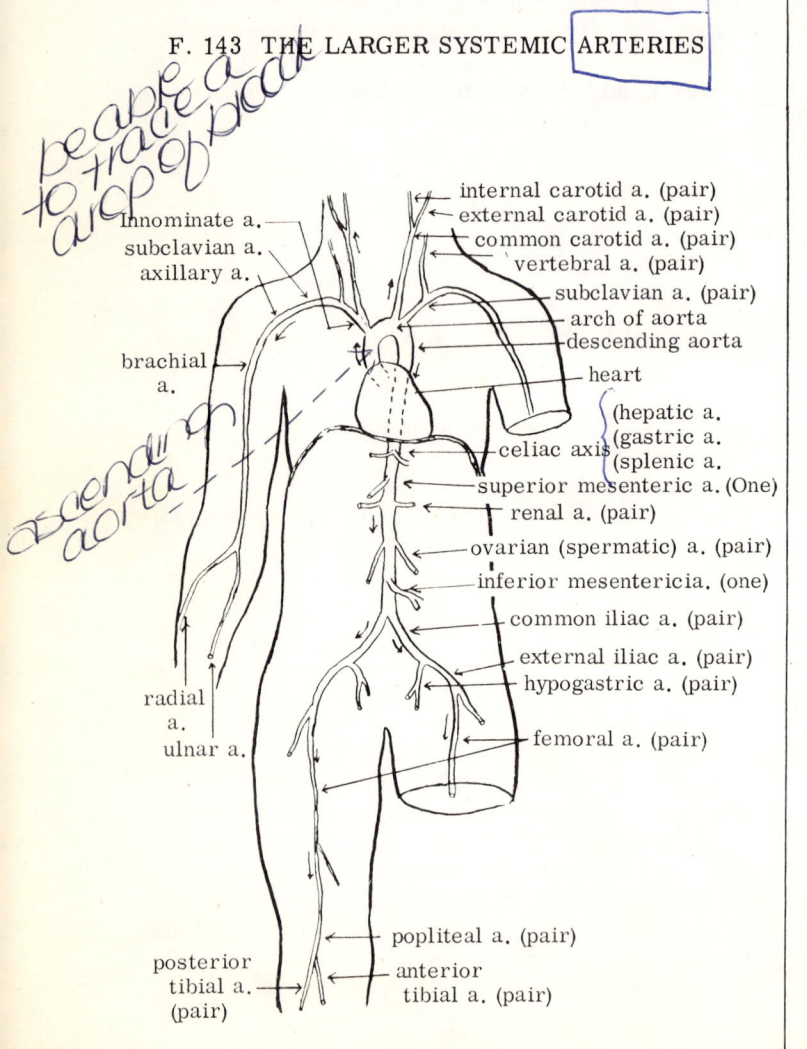

F. 143 THE LARGER SYSTEMIC ARTERIES

F. 144 THE LARGER SYSTEMIC VEINS

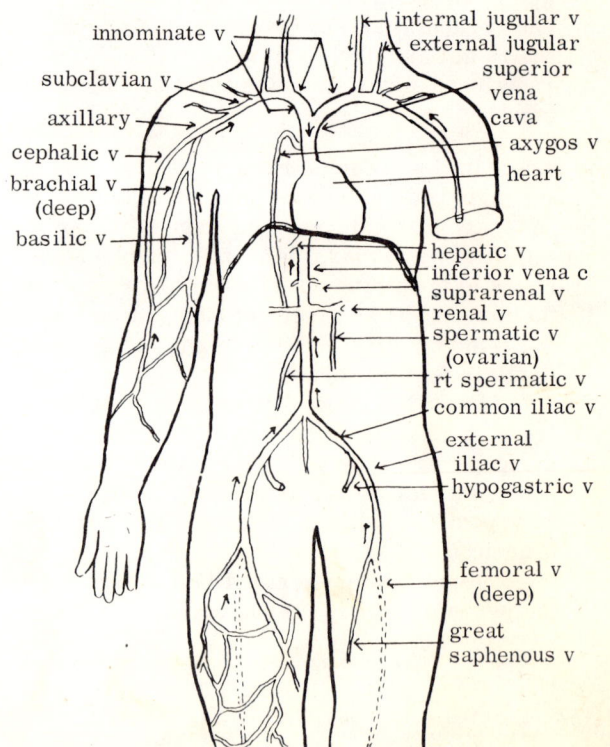

4. femoral vein, a continuation of popliteal vein accompanies femoral artery in thigh;
5. external iliac vein, a continuation of the femoral into the pelvis, to common iliac vein.

ABDOMEN AND PELVIS:
1. internal iliac vein, on each side drains veins from pelvic organs;
2. common iliac vein, on each side formed by the union of the external and internal iliac veins;
3. inferior vena cava formed by union of the two common iliac veins, at fifth lumbar vertebra, enters thorax and empties into right atrium. It has tributaries: testicular or ovarian (pair)
   renal (pair)
   suprarenal (pair)
   phrenic veins
   hepatic veins

S. 125 THE PORTAL SYSTEM OF VEINS:

1. portal vein by union of superior mesenteric and splenic veins, and enters liver to divide into capillaries;
2. superior mesenteric vein drains small bowel and colon to transverse part;
3. splenic vein drains spleen and receives the inferior mesenteric, gastric, and pancreatic veins; joins superior mesenteric to form portal;
4. inferior mesenteric drains distal half of colon and drains into splenic vein;
5. hepatic vein collects blood in liver to drain into inferior vena cava.

pulmonary circulation
Rt Atrium
Rt Ventricul
pulmonary artery
pulmonary arterioles
"   capillaries
"   venules
"   veins
Lt atrium
Lt ventricul
ascending aorta

F. 145 THE UPPER RESPIRATORY PASSAGES
- lateral view -

Labels: sphenoid sinuses, nasal cavity, nares, palate, mouth, tongue, mandible, nasopharynx, opening of auditory tube, tonsil, oropharynx, epiglottis, R. (lower) inferior lobe, opening into larynx, larynx, esophagus, thyroid cartilage

Handwritten annotations: nasal septum = in nose; nasal lacrimal = tear duct; (nostrils); laryngeal part.

F. 146 THE TRACHEA AND LUNGS
- frontal view -

Labels: cricoid cartilage, thyroid cartilage (Adam's apple), trachea, apex, Rt superior (upper) lobe, Lt superior (upper) lobe, main fissure, Rt. middle lobe, Lt. inferior (lower) lobe, base, heart and other mediastinal structures

F. 147 RESPIRATORY BRONCHIOLE AND ALVEOLI

Labels: alveolar duct, alveoli surrounded by capillary networks, atrium, respiratory bronchiole

F. 148 TRACHEA AND MAIN BRONCHI
- frontal section -

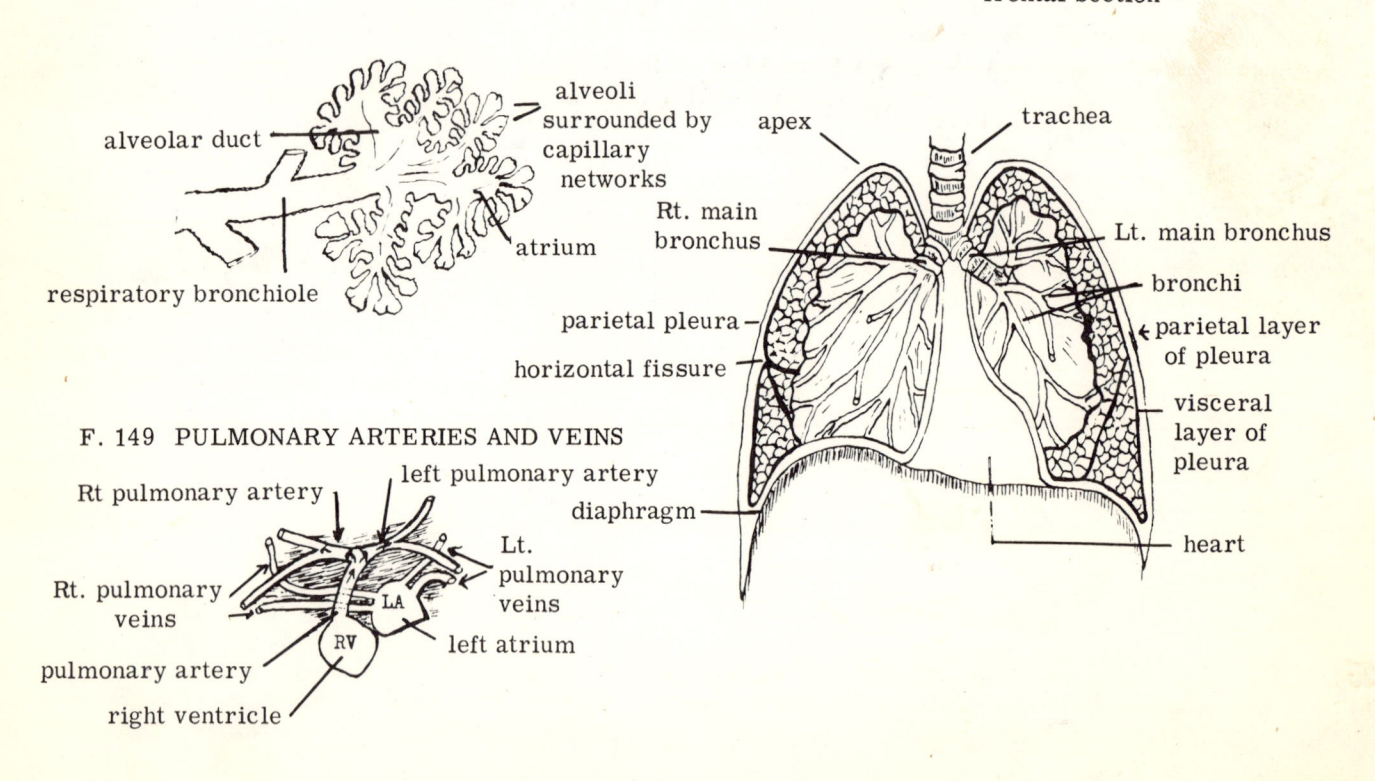

Labels: apex, trachea, Rt. main bronchus, Lt. main bronchus, bronchi, parietal pleura, parietal layer of pleura, horizontal fissure, visceral layer of pleura, diaphragm, heart

F. 149 PULMONARY ARTERIES AND VEINS

Labels: Rt pulmonary artery, left pulmonary artery, Lt. pulmonary veins, Rt. pulmonary veins, left atrium, pulmonary artery, right ventricle, LA, RV

CHAPTER XV. THE RESPIRATORY SYSTEM.

4/30/73

S. 126 PARTS OF THE RESPIRATORY SYSTEM.

1. RESPIRATORY PASSAGES:
   (1) nasal cavities or nasal fossae
   (2) pharynx or throat
       (a) nasopharynx
       (b) oropharynx
       (c) laryngeal part
   (3) larynx or voice box
   (4) trachea or windpipe
   (5) bronchi or bronchial tubes (s. bronchus)
   (6) bronchioles - little bronchi

2. LUNGS:
   (1) right lung - three lobes
   (2) left lung - two lobes

S. 127 DETAILED STUDY OF THE RESPIRATORY SYSTEM.

1. The nostrils or nares are the two openings of the nose.
The nasal cavities or nasal fossae are the two chambers of the nose. They are separated by a vertical partition, the nasal septum. They open behind into the nasopharynx. They are lined with mucous membrane with hairs in the anterior part. Openings are present in each nasal cavity from the corresponding frontal, ethmoidal, maxillary, and sphenoidal sinuses, and the naso-lacrimal or tear duct. Three curved bony shelves project into each nasal cavity from its lateral wall, the conchae. These partly divide each cavity into four parts. The lower shelf is the inferior concha or inferior turbinate bone. "flipper" (epiglottis)

2. The pharynx or throat lies behind the nasal cavities and mouth and extends down to the opening into the esophagus or gullet.

The soft palate projects back into the pharynx (throat) from the posterior end of the hard palate.

The epiglottis is a flat leaf-shaped plate of cartilage, with free upper border, that projects back from the front wall of the pharynx, below the base of the tongue.

The nasopharynx is that part of the pharynx (throat) behind the nasal cavities and above the soft palate.

The oropharynx (os, oris - mouth) lies behind the mouth, between the soft palate above, and the upper border of the epiglottis below.

The laryngeal part of the pharynx extends from the epiglottis down to the esophagus.

The auditory (Eustachian) tube is a passage from the nasopharynx to the cavity of the middle ear, and its opening is in the lateral wall of the nasopharynx.

The adenoids are masses of lymphoid tissue in the roof and posterior wall of the nasopharynx.

The tonsils are oval masses of lymphoid tissue, one on each side of the opening between the mouth and oropharynx. Infections of the adenoids, tonsils, or throat may tract up through the auditory tubes into the middle ear, causing otitis media with earache.

The laryngeal opening is in the front part of the laryngeal part of the pharynx below the epiglottis.

3. The larynx or organ of voice is a triangular box-like structure that lies in the front of the neck. Its upper end opens into the laryngeal part of the pharynx. Its lower end is continuous with the trachea. This box is composed of nine cartilages. Only one, the thyroid cartilage, is important to the technician. It is visible in lateral views of the cervical spine.

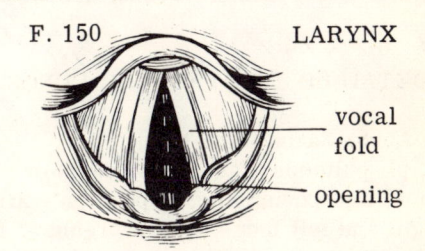

F. 150   LARYNX

- vocal fold
- opening

The thyroid cartilage is composed of two flat plates of cartilage placed vertically and meeting in front at the midline. The posterior ends are separated, and the larynx lies between them. This cartilage forms the prominence in the front of the neck, the Adam's apple.

Vocal Folds: a fold of the lining membrane extends in from each side wall of the larynx, and a vocal cord lies within the fold on each side. It extends from the front to the back of the larynx.
The glottis is the slit-like opening between the two folds. Air must pass in and out through this slit.

4. The trachea or windpipe is a hollow tube about 4.5 inches in length extending from the larynx above to the bronchi below. It commences opposite the

sixth cervical vertebra and extends down to the fourth dorsal body. The upper part lies in the neck below the Adam's apple. The rest lies in the superior mediastinum and in front of the esophagus. It, like the larynx, is lined by epithelium. Its walls are also strengthened by the incomplete rings of cartilage. These rings are open behind like the letter "C", and these prevent collapse of the trachea. Muscle fibers fill in the gap behind. A coin in the trachea will lie in the "on edge" position when viewed from the front as the muscle can be pushed back by the coin.

5. The bronchi (s. bronchus). The trachea divides into two tubes or bronchi, the right and left main bronchi, one for each lung. The right main bronchus divides into three divisions, one for each lobe of the right lung, the lobar bronchi. The left main bronchus divides into two lobar bronchi, one for each lobe of the left lung. Each lobar bronchus divides into segmental bronchi. A segmental bronchus enters a segment of a lobe. The number of segmental bronchi is constant for each lobe. Each segmental bronchus divides and re-divides into smaller and smaller bronchi as they extend into lung tissue. The larger bronchi have rings of cartilage in their walls. All have muscular coats and epithelial linings.

6. The bronchioles (little bronchi) are the final minute tubes and are continuous with the air sacs of the lungs. The respiratory bronchioles are the final branches.

S. 128 DETAILED STUDY OF THE LUNGS.

(Lungen - Anglo-Saxon - the lung)
(L. pulmo, pl. pulmones, adj. pulmonary)
(G. pneumon, adj. pneumonic; G. pneuma - air)

The right and left lungs are the organs of respiration, and occupy the right and left chest cavities. They are separated by the mediastinum. See S. 111. Each lung is cone-shaped with pointed end or apex at the top, reaching about one inch above the clavicle, the lower end or base rests upon the upper convex surface of the diaphragm.

The lungs are spongy, crepitant, float on water, and have elastic tissue in their walls. This tissue tends to decrease the size of the lung. A lung removed from the body appears small. At birth the lungs are pink, but with increasing age become a mottled grey color due to inhaled dust.

The right lung is partly divided into three lobes or divisions:
 (a) the upper or superior lobe,
 (b) the middle lobe,
 (c) the lower or inferior lobe.

Fissures or grooves separate these lobes. The main oblique fissure can be traced along the chest wall from the level of the fifth dorsal body around and obliquely downwards and forward to the anterior end of the sixth right rib. The lower lobe lies behind and below this fissure. The upper and middle lobes lie above and in front of this fissure. A further horizontal or transverse fissure passes back horizontally from the fourth right costal cartilage to the lateral chest wall. The middle lobe lies below this fissure and occupies the same position in the right chest as the heart in the left chest.

The left lung has two lobes or divisions:
 (a) the upper or superior lobe,
 (b) the lower or inferior lobe.
These lobes are separated by an oblique fissure similar to that on the right side. The heart occupies the lower left central part.

Bronchopulmonary segments. These are structural units or divisions of the lobes. There is one for each segmental bronchus. See No. 5 page 95 - bronchi. The bronchpulmonary segments are named as follows:

	RIGHT LUNG	LEFT LUNG
Upper lobe	apical posterior (axillary) anterior	apical posterior anterior superior lingual inferior lingual
Middle lobe	lateral medial	
Lower lobe	superior suprabasal posterior basal anterior basal medial basal	superior suprabasal posterior basal anterior medial basal

Lobules. Each bronchopulmonary segment is made up of many small units called lobules (little lobes). Each lobule has many minute air sacs. The walls of these are cup-shaped and called alveoli. Alveoli have very thin walls and are surrounded by capillary networks from the pulmonary arteries. If all the alveoli were flattened out, their surface in contact with the air would be ninety times the area of the skin on the whole body surface. Terminal bronchioles open into these air sacs, and through these bronchioles air is admitted to the sacs.
The parenchyma is the active tissue of the lungs.
The hilum or hilus is a depression on the medial surface of each lung like the depression on one side of a garden bean. Vessels and bronchi enter the lung at this depression.

Lining of ad: pelvis = Peritoneum

18/min is normal respiration.

The lung root is its attachment to the mediastinum and is composed of all the structures entering or leaving the lung. These are the pulmonary artery and veins, the bronchial arteries and veins, the main bronchus, lymph vessels and nodes, and nerves.

The pleura is the lining membrane of the chest cavity and the covering membrane of each lung. It includes:
(a) the visceral pleura, which like the visceral pericardium of the heart covers each lung, except at the root; its outer surface is smooth;
(b) the parietal pleura lines the chest cavity; its inner surface is smooth. It is in contact with, but not attached to, the visceral pleura, except at the lung root.

The pleural cavity is the space between the lung and chest wall between the visceral and parietal pleura. With the lung expanded there is no actual space.

The costophrenic sinus or sulcus is the triangular space in the lower chest between the chest wall and the adjacent rounded margin of the diaphragm. It is readily seen in P.A. views of the chest at the lateral border of the diaphragm. A pleural effusion will fill this space.

Blood supply to the lungs.
(a) The bronchial arteries, branches of the aorta supply blood to the lungs.
(b) The pulmonary arteries distribute blood to the capillaries about the air sacs for exchange of gases.

S. 129 THE PHYSIOLOGY OF RESPIRATION.

Respiration is the act of breathing.
Inspiration is the taking in of air, breathing in.
Expiration is breathing out, expelling air from the lungs.

At inspiration the intercostal muscles contract to elevate the ribs, and the diaphragm contracts and is displaced downwards. This increases the size of the chest cavity. Air pressure within the lungs is decreased by this increase in the size of the chest cavity as compared to air pressure outside. Therefore air rushes in through the respiratory passages to equalize the pressure - inspiration.

Following this, the intercostal muscles and the diaphragm relax, decreasing the size of the chest cavity. Air pressure within the lungs becomes greater than that of the outside air. Air then passes out of the lungs to equalize the pressure - expiration.

Respiration occurs about eighteen times per minute. The contraction of the muscles is due to impulses transmitted to them by nerves from the respiratory center in the brain.

In section 107, under "blood plasma", the method of exchange of gases was described. It is only necessary to add that the function of the lungs is to provide the blood with oxygen, and to get rid of carbon dioxide and moisture.

S. 130 SOME PATHOLOGICAL TERMS DEFINED.

Atelectasis is the collapse of the whole or a part of a lung. This is due to obstruction of a bronchus so that air cannot enter. The degree of collapse depends upon the size of the bronchus obstructed. The obstruction may be due to:
   a tooth in a bronchus following dental extraction;
   a blood clot in a bronchus following tonsillectomy;
   a mucous plug following an anesthetic;
   a peanut or other foreign body aspirated;
   a growth in a bronchus, or outside of a bronchus, pressing upon it from without; i.e. extrinsic.

Bronchiectasis is dilatation of bronchi.

Bronchitis is an inflammation of the bronchi.

Tracheo-bronchitis is an inflammation of the trachea as well as bronchi.

Pneumonitis is an inflammation of the lungs.

Lobar pneumonia is an inflammation of one or more lobes by a specific organism, the pneumococcus.

Bronchopneumonia is an inflammtion of a part of a lobe or segment. Several areas may be involved.

Virus pneumonia is an inflammation caused by a virus.

Pleurisy is an inflammation of the pleura.

A pleural effusion is fluid in the pleural cavity.

An empyema is pus in the pleural cavity.

Hemothorax is blood in a pleural cavity. Distinguish from hemithorax - half the thorax.

Pneumothorax is air in the pleural cavity.

Encapsulated empyema or effusion refers to pus or fluid not free but walled off in a part of the pleural cavity or in an interlobar sulcus.

we use 1/30 of our normal capacity of lungs

S. 131 APPLICATION TO RADIOGRAPHY.

The scapulae normally overlie the upper lateral chest on each side. The upper extremities must be placed so that these bones are off the lung fields.
The apices of the lungs extend one inch above the clavicles. They must be included in the film.
The costophrenic sinuses (sulci) extend down almost to the costal margins, and should be included.
The heart obscures some lung tissue behind it on both sides, more so on the left side; hence lateral views.

Following expiration, the chest becomes smaller, and the vessel markings become compressed together. Films after expiration may be misinterpreted as infiltrations at the bases.

Two types of movement may occur during the x-ray exposure of the chest. The patient may breathe, or may move the body as a whole. In either event lung detail will be blurred.

The trachea, bronchi, and lungs contain air and are radiolucent, so do not absorb many x-rays. There is a tendency to over expose chest radiographs.

Routine films are taken in the postero-anterior position, after a deep inspiration, with the scapulae off the chest, and with no breathing nor body movement during the exposure. The apices and bases must be included as well as the lateral chest walls.

Lateral views are taken to outline the lungs behind the heart.

Oblique views are often indicated to obtain further information of shadows seen on the above views.

Lordotic views should throw the clavicles above the upper lung fields and should show the apices.
Patients, particularly elderly people and those who do not understand, should be practised several times by having them take a deep breath and hold it, and remain still, several times before the chest exposure is actually made.

THIS IS IMPORTANT, AND WOULD SAVE MANY LARGE FILMS.

The markings seen in the lung fields on a film are due to the blood and lymph vessels, not the bronchi. Bronchi with thin walls and filled with air are not opaque. Opaque media must be used to fill them for radiography. See below.

Bronchography is a procedure that consists of instilling an opaque medium into the throat or directly into the trachea to outline the bronchi. Films are then taken. A scout film should always be taken before the opaque medium is instilled.

Bronchogram - films of the filled bronchi.

S. 132 TERMS USED IN CHAPTER XV.

hyperventilation breathes air in but none is given out

Adam's apple	cardiophrenic angle	interlobar fissure	pharyngeal (adj.)
adenoids	costophrenic sinus, sulcus	larynx	pleura
alveolus	diaphragm	laryngeal (adj.)	pleural (adj.)
alveoli (pl.)	diaphragmatic (adj.)	lobe	pleural effusion
alveolar (adj.)	dyspnoea	lobar (adj.)	pleurisy
apex	effusion	lobar pneumonia	pneuma - air
apices (pl.)	encapsulated effusion	lobectomy	pneumon - lung
atelectasis	empyema	lobule	pneumonic (adj.)
atrium	epiglottis	lung	pneumonia
atria (pl.)	Eustachian tube	mediastinum	pneumonitis
air sac	expiration	mediastinal (adj.)	pneumothorax
auditory tube	fissure	mediastinitis	pulmo - lung
azygos lobe	glottis	nares	pulmonary (adj.)
base of lung	haemothorax	nasal cavities	pulmonary artery
bronchus	hemothorax	nasal fossae	pulmonary vein
bronchi (pl.)	haemoptosis	nasal septum	root of lung
bronchial (adj.)	hemoptosis	nose	soft palate
bronchiole	hemithorax	nostril	tonsil
bronchiectasis	hilum	oropharynx	tonsillitis
bronchitis	hila (pl.)	orthopnoea	trachea
bronchogram	hilar (adj.)	parenchyma	tracheal (adj.)
bronchography	hilus	parenchymal (adj.)	transverse fissure
bronchoscopy	inspiration	parietal pleura	thyroid cartilage
capillary	intrathoracic	pharynx	visceral pleura

CHAPTER XVI. THE DIGESTIVE SYSTEM.

S. 133 DIVISIONS OF THE ABDOMEN.

I. DIVISION OF THE ABDOMEN INTO FOUR QUADRANTS.

A line is drawn transversely around the abdomen at the level of the umbilicus (navel).

A further line is drawn perpendicularly through the umbilicus - the median line.

These lines divide the abdomen into four quadrants:
(1) right upper quadrant   (R U Q) or (U R Q)
(2) right lower quadrant   (R L Q) or (L R Q)
(3) left upper quadrant   (L U Q) or (U L Q)
(4) left lower quadrant   (L L Q)

II. DIVISION OF THE ABDOMEN INTO NINE REGIONS.

One line is drawn transversely around the body at the level of the ninth costal cartilage.

A second line is drawn transversely around the body at the level of the iliac crests.

Two perpendicular lines are drawn, one on each side of the abdomen, at points midway between the anterior superior spines of the ilia and the symphysis pubis, upwards towards the chest.

These four lines divide the abdomen into nine parts or regions. From right to left they are named:

upper
   (1) right hypochondriac region (hypo - below)
   (2) epigastric region (epi - upon)
   (3) left hypochondriac region

middle
   (4) right lumbar region
   (5) umbilical region (umbilicus - navel)
   (6) left lumbar region

lower
   (7) right iliac region
   (8) hypogastric region (hypo - below)
   (9) left iliac region.

In section 15 the body cavities were defined. The abdomen extends from the under surface of the diaphragm to the pelvic brim. The pelvic cavity reaches from the pelvic inlet to the floor of the pelvis. There is no separation between these two cavities. A part of the organ may lie in the abdomen and the remainder may be in the pelvis. The same organ may lie in the abdomen under certain conditions and in the pelvis at other times.

The position of an organ may vary with respiration with position (upright or horizontal) and with condition (full or empty). Technicians may find the gall bladder in one patient well up under the costal margin, and in another overlying the iliac crest. Colons following evacuation contract and lie at a lower level then when filled with barium.

The technician must realize:
(a) that the diaphragm extends well up under the costal margins because it is dome shaped;
(b) that broad stocky individuals will have their organs at higher levels than long lanky individuals;
(c) that the abdominal organs descend with inspiration, with the assumption of the upright position, and if filled.

As a guide to the technician for localizing the position of different structures in the abdomen, the division into four quadrants is most rational. These organs vary so much in position that the division into small regions is not practical.

In actual radiography the crests of the iliac bones are very practical landmarks. They can be palpated in either the prone or supine positions. The locating of an organ above or below the crests is sensible.

F. 151 FOUR QUADRANTS   NINE REGIONS

126

S. 134 STRUCTURE OF WALLS OF THE DIGESTIVE TRACT.

The walls of all parts of the digestive tract are very similar. A general description is therefore included below. The walls or coverings consist of four layers:

(1) the serous coat, or visceral peritoneum covers all parts except the posterior wall of some organs. These lie against the posterior abdominal wall. The esophagus lies in the chest and has no peritoneal coat;
(2) the muscular coat usually consists of two layers of smooth or involuntary muscle. The inner, circular layer has its fibers passing around the gut; The outer layer has fibers running lengthwise along the gut.
(3) the submucous coat is a layer of connective tissue under the muscle layer and contains blood vessels, lymphatics, and nerves to these organs;
(4) the mucous coat or mucosa is the lining membrane, a layer of epithelium containing glands. These glands differ in the different parts.

S. 135 DEFINITIONS OF SOME TERMS USED.

The lumen is the cavity in any hollow organ.

The peritoneum is a thin layer of epithelium which lines the abdominal and pelvic cavities, and is reflected over the surface of most abdominal organs. Compare this with the pericardium and pleura.

The mesentery is a double layer of peritoneum that extends from the posterior abdominal wall to some of the abdominal organs. It gives support to these organs. Blood vessels, lymphatics, and nerves pass to the organs between the two layers of mesentery.

Omentum is a term used to describe a fold of peritoneum between various abdominal organs.

A sphincter is a thickened ring of involuntary muscle encircling an opening in a hollow organ, to keep the opening closed. Sphincters are present at both openings of the stomach, at the anus, etc.

Peristalsis: waves of alternating contraction and dilatation occurring in the walls of hollow organs such as the esophagus, stomach, small and large intestines, bile ducts, ureters, etc. Peristalsis helps to push the contents along the lumen towards the exit, e.g., watch the throat of a horse drinking from a trough.

Stenosis is a constriction or narrowing of a lumen, e.g., the esophagus after swallowing lye.

S. 136 DEVELOPMENT OF DIGESTIVE SYSTEM.

The digestive tract extends from the mouth to the anus, and is about thirty feet in length. It develops as a solid cord of cells closed at each end. The central cells disappear to form a hollow tube. Openings are formed at each end for the mouth and anus. Buds are given off to form the lungs, liver, pancreas, and gall bladder. By changes in the size and shape of the tube, the different parts of the digestive system are differentiated. As the intestine increases in length, it folds upon itself. The small intestine lies in the right abdomen and the colon in the left half. length, it folds upon itself. The small intestine resembles a coil. The colon becomes an inverted "U" shaped structure. Early in fetal life the small intestine lies in the right abdomen and the colon in the left half. Later the cecum changes its position to the right upper abdomen and the colon in the left half. Later the cecum changes its position to the right upper abdomen. It then descends to lie in its normal position in the right lower abdomen. Sometimes this sequence is not completed; so the cecum and appendix may lie in the left abdomen or up under the right liver border. This accounts for the abnormal position of the appendix at operation in unusual cases.

S. 137 PARTS OF THE DIGESTIVE SYSTEM.

1. Mouth:
   (1) teeth
   (2) tongue
   (3) salivary glands:
       (a) parotid glands (two)
       (b) submandibular or submaxillary (two)
       (c) sublingual (two)

2. Pharynx:
   (1) nasopharynx
   (2) oropharynx
   (3) laryngeal part

3. Esophagus or gullet

4. Stomach:
   (1) fundus
   (2) body
   (3) pylorus

5. Small intestine:
   (1) duodenum
   (2) jejunum
   (3) ileum

Pancrease lies in the Loop of the duodenum

127

6. Colon:
    (1) cecum (caecum) and appendix
    (2) ascending colon
    (3) right colic or hepatic flexure
    (4) transverse colon
    (5) left colic or splenic flexure *(found near spleen)*
    (6) descending colon
    (7) pelvic or sigmoid colon
    (8) rectum - anal canal and anus

7. Accessory organs of digestion:
    (1) pancreas and pancreatic duct
    (2) liver
    (3) gall bladder and bile ducts

S. 138 DETAILED STUDY - THE DIGESTIVE SYSTEM.

1. THE MOUTH.

The mouth contains the teeth, tongue, and the openings of the salivary glands.

(1) The teeth have been studied in sections 82, 83, page 65.

(2) The tongue is a muscular organ attached to the floor of the mouth. It, as well as the cheeks, forces the food between the upper and lower premolar and molar teeth so that food may be masticated (chewed). The tongue then rolls the food into a bolus (ball) and directs this ball back into the pharynx.

(3) Salivary glands: there are three pairs. These are the parotid, submandibular, and sublingual glands. Each gland opens into the mouth. These glands secrete saliva which contains a digestive juice to act upon starches and sugar. This juice enters the mouth and mixes with food during mastication. It passes with food into the stomach to continue its action.

    (a) The parotid glands lie in front of, and below the cartilage of the ear on each side.
    The parotid (Stenson's) duct passes from the gland across the cheek to open into the mouth at the second upper molar tooth.
    (b) The submandibular or submaxillary glands lie on the medial (inner) side of the angle of the mandible on each side. There are two submandibular

Stensons

F. 152 PARTS OF THE DIGESTIVE SYSTEM

mouth — 10"
pharynx
Rt — esophagus
liver — stomach
gall bladder — pancreas (Lt side)
duodenum — ampulla of Vater (c sphincter of Oddi)
common duct — colon
small intestine — small intestine
colon
appendix — rectum

F. 153 DIAGRAM OF PERITONEUM - lateral view -

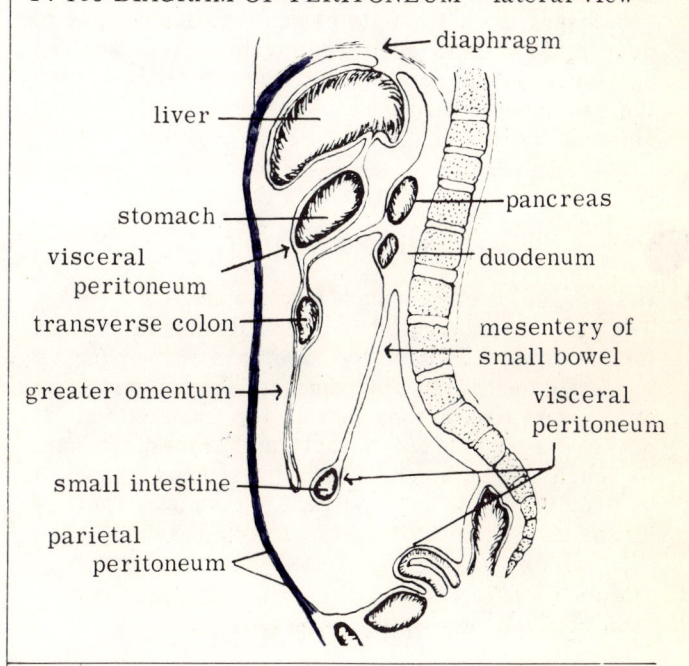

diaphragm
liver
stomach — pancreas
visceral peritoneum — duodenum
transverse colon — mesentery of small bowel
greater omentum — visceral peritoneum
small intestine
parietal peritoneum

F. 154 CROSS SECTION OF ABDOMEN
- to show peritoneum -

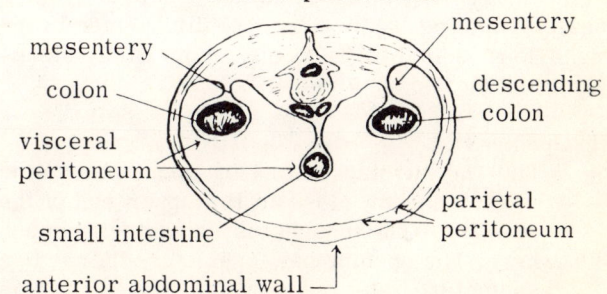

mesentery — mesentery
colon — descending colon
visceral peritoneum
small intestine — parietal peritoneum
anterior abdominal wall

(Wharton's) ducts. One passes forward in the floor of the mouth on each side of the midline to open beside the frenulum of the tongue. The frenulum is a fold under the tongue at the midline of the floor.

(c) The sublingual glands lie in the floor of the mouth, one on each side of the midline.

Several sublingual ducts open on a curved ridge on the floor of the mouth.

Calculi sometimes form in these glands or ducts and may obstruct the flow of saliva. The accumulation of secretion in the gland causes it to swell up.

2. THE PHARYNX.

This was studied in section 127, page 95. It was stated that the mouth opens into the oropharynx, which lies behind the mouth. The pharynx conveys food to the esophagus as well as air to the larynx. During swallowing the soft palate closes the nasopharynx to prevent food from regurgitating into the nose. The epiglottis, larynx, and trachea become elevated, and the epiglottis covers the glottis to prevent food from entering the trachea.

3. THE ESOPHAGUS.

(Esophagus or oesophagus; adj. esophageal).

The esophagus or gullet is a tube about ten inches in length. It extends from the lower end of the pharynx to the stomach. It lies in front of the dorsal vertebrae and behind the trachea, within the mediastinum. It passes through the esophageal hiatus of the diaphragm to reach the stomach. Fluids pass down through it by gravity, solids by gravity and peristalsis. There is no serous (peritoneal) coat on the esophagus.

4. THE STOMACH.

(G. gaster; adj. gastric; L. ventriculus).

The stomach lies in the upper left abdomen. When empty, it is collapsed except for the upper part, which usually contains some air. The lining membrane forms longitudinal folds (rugae) which partly disappear when the stomach is full.

(1) Openings.
(a) The cardiac orifice or opening is on the medial border close to the upper end of the stomach. The esophagus joins the stomach here. The opening has a sphincter - the cardiac sphincter. Note: the term cardiac is used as this part of the stomach lies close to the heart.

(b) The pyloric orifice or opening is at the lower end of the stomach. The small bowel continues from this opening. This opening has a sphincter - the pyloric sphincter.

2. Curvatures. The stomach, when viewed from the front, is curved to the right. The right and left borders are called curvatures.
(a) The lesser curvature is the shorter, concave, right border.
(b) The greater curvature is the longer, convex, left border.
The incisura angularis is the sharp bend on the lesser curvature side below its midpoint.

(3) Parts of the stomach.
(a) the fundus is that part above the cardiac opening. (often filled air)
(b) the body is that part between the cardiac opening and the incisura angularis.
(c) The pylorus is that part between the incisura angularis and the pyloric opening or outlet. The last part of the pylorus is sometimes called the pyloric antrum or canal.

(4) Coats. The stomach has the usual four coats, but the muscular layer has an oblique layer added.

5. THE SMALL INTESTINE.

The small intestine is smaller in caliber, and with thinner walls than the colon. It is about twenty-three feet in length, and is coiled up within the abdomen. It extends from the pyloric opening of the stomach to the opening in the colon, the the right lower abdomen. It is described as consisting of three parts, but there is no actual division. These parts are: duodenum, jejunum, and ileum.

(1) The duodenum or first ten inches of the small bowel forms a double loop, first up and to the right, then a "U" shaped curve down and to the left. The duodenum has four parts described below.
(a) The superior duodenum or its first part extends up and to the right. It includes the cap or bulb.
(b) The descending duodenum passes downward to the right of the midline. The common bile duct opens into it.
(c) the horizontal or transverse duodenum passes to the left across the midline.
(d) The ascending duodenum passes up behind the stomach to join the jejunum, usually at the lesser curvature side of the body of the stomach.

The head of the pancreas lies in the curve of the duodenum, and if enlarged may press upon it.

Stomach has four layers.

F. 155 THE NOSE, MOUTH, AND PHARYNX
- left lateral view -

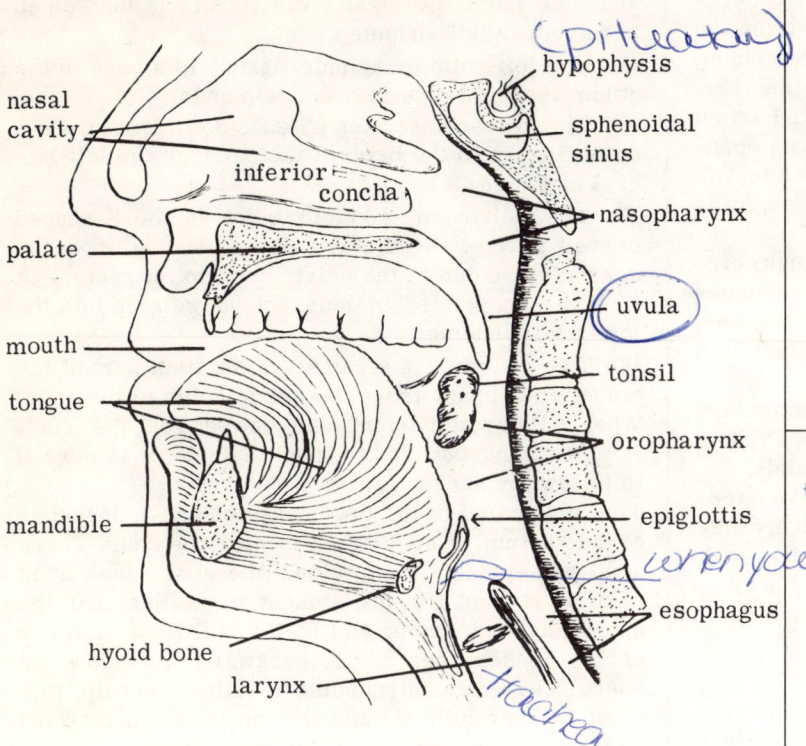

- nasal cavity
- inferior concha
- palate
- mouth
- tongue
- mandible
- hyoid bone
- hypophysis *(pituitary)*
- sphenoidal sinus
- nasopharynx
- uvula
- tonsil
- oropharynx
- epiglottis
- esophagus *when you swallow*
- larynx *trachea*

F. 156 CONTENTS OF THE ABDOMEN
- anterior wall removed -

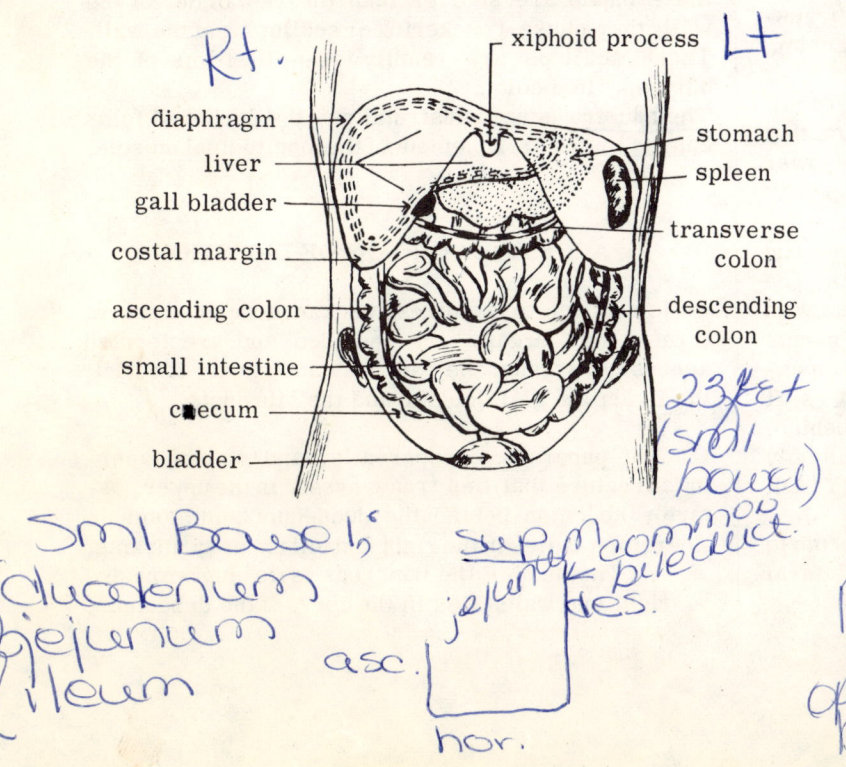

Rt. Lt.

- diaphragm
- liver
- gall bladder
- costal margin
- ascending colon
- small intestine
- caecum
- bladder
- xiphoid process
- stomach
- spleen
- transverse colon
- descending colon

Sml Bowel:
duodenum
jejunum
ileum

23 feet (sml bowel)
super common bile duct
jejunum ties
asc.
hor.

F. 157 THE SALIVARY GLANDS
- left lateral view -

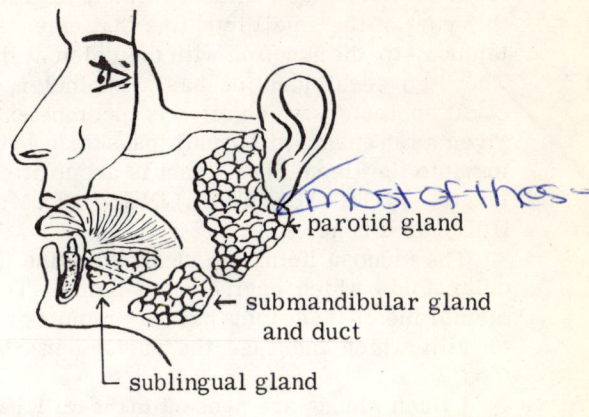

- parotid gland *most of these*
- submandibular gland and duct
- sublingual gland

F. 158 THE ESOPHAGUS - frontal view -

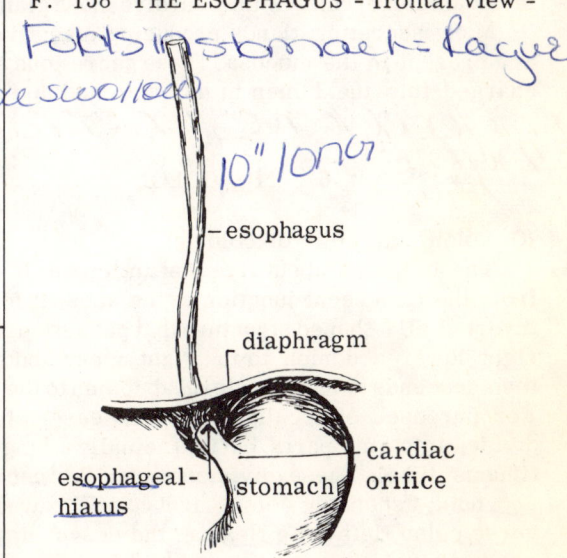

Folds in stomach = rugae
10" long

- esophagus
- diaphragm
- esophageal hiatus
- stomach
- cardiac orifice

F. 159 THE STOMACH - frontal view -

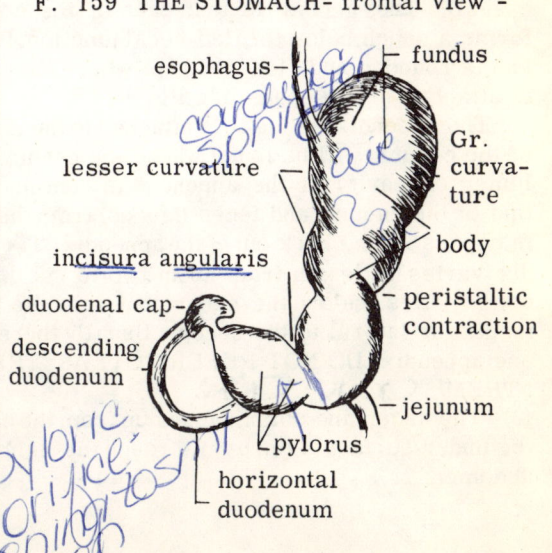

- esophagus
- fundus
- lesser curvature *cardiac sphincter* *air*
- Gr. curvature
- body
- incisura angularis
- peristaltic contraction
- duodenal cap
- descending duodenum
- jejunum
- pylorus *pyloric orifice - opening to sml bowel*
- horizontal duodenum

(2) The jejunum (adj. jejunal - empty bowel) is about eight feet in length, and extends from the duodenum to the ileum. It lies in the upper and middle abdomen.

(3) The ileum (adj. iliac - twisted or rolled up) is that part of the small intestine that extends from the jejunum to the junction with the colon at the cecum. The ileo-cecal junction has a sphincter, the ileo-cecal sphincter, which often is incompetent. Barium given as an enema will usually pass through this opening into the ileum. The ileum is about fifteen feet in length. NOTE THE SPELLING - ILEUM; whereas ILIUM is a bone.

The mucosa lining the small intestine forms circular folds which encircle the lumen. The mucous membrane on these folds has very minute projections, or villi which increase the surface in contact with food.

Lymph glands are present in the wall, particulary of the ileum, and are called Peyer's patches. Typhoid fever and tuberculosis may involve these glands.

Many secreting glands producing digestive juices are present in the mucosa. These secretions are discharged into the lumen to mix with and digest food.

6. THE COLON.

(G. kolon; adj. colic or colonic).

The colon is about five feet in length. It extends from the ileo-secal junction to the anus. It forms an inverted "U" shaped structure that passes up from the right lower abdomen to the right upper abdomen. It then descends to the left lateral abdomen to the pelvis. For purposes of localization of disease, etc., it is divided into nine parts, but it is actually a single continuous tube. These divisions are: the cecum and appendix, ascending colon, right colic flexure, transverse colon, left colic flexure, the descending colon, pelvic colon, rectum, and anal canal.

(1) The cecum, caecum (blind pouch; adj. cecal, caecal). The cecum is that part of the colon that forms a pouch below the ileo-cecal junction. Its lower end is rounded and closed except where the appendix is attached to and opens into it.

The appendix, since it is attached to the lower end of the cecum, will be found where the cecum is. The lumen or cavity of the appendix is continuous with that of the cecum, and feces (faeces) from the cecum may pass in and back out of the appendix. The appendix varies in length from about two to six inches. It usually lies below the cecum but may lie behind, medial or lateral to the cecum. Usually there is only one appendix. DO NOT REFER TO IT AS "THEY" OR "THEM".

(2) The ascending colon passes up from the cecum to the under surface of the liver through the right lateral abdomen.

(3) The right colic or hepatic flexure is a bend to the left under the right liver surface.

(4) The transverse colon passes across the upper abdomen from the right colic flexure to the spleen in the upper left abdomen.

(5) The left colic or splenic flexure is a bend in the colon where the transverse colon ends.

(6) The descending colon extends down from the left colic flexure to the brim of the pelvis in the left lateral abdomen.

(7) The pelvic or sigmoid colon is the S-shaped curved part of the distal colon extending from the descending colon at the pelvic brim to the rectum. It lies in the pelvis but may extend well up into the lower left abdomen.

(8) The rectum (L. straight) is the final part of the colon. It extends from the pelvic colon to the anus. When filled with barium, and viewed from the front, it is straight, but viewed from the side, it is curved to follow the sacral curve.

The anal canal is the lower one and one-half inches of the rectum. It ends at an opening, the anus. There are two sphincters to close the anal canal. It is very important for the student to realize that the anal canal extends up and FORWARD for a distance of 1.5 inches then turns backward to follow the sacral curve. In introducing a stiff enema tip, this must be appreciated, and the tip directed forward first.

The wall of the colon is composed of the usual four layers, but the arrangement of the longitudinal muscle is different. Instead of covering the entire surface, this layer is arranged in three bands of muscle which pass lengthwise along the colon. As these bands are shorter than the remainder of the wall, they cause a puckering or scalloping of the wall. These scallops are readily seen in films of the barium-filled colon.

The haustra (sing. haustrum) are the puckered folds caused by the arrangement of the longitudinal muscle.

7. ACCESSORY ORGANS OF DIGESTION.

In addition to the digestive tract described above, three other organs are included and are termed accessory organs: the pancreas and pancreatic duct; the liver; the gall bladder and the bile ducts.

(1) The pancreas or pancreatic gland is a long tapering structure that lies transversely in the upper posterior abdomen behind the duodenum and stomach. Therefore it lies in the right and left upper quadrants.

(a) The head of the pancreas is its blunt, rounded right end which lies in the curve of the duodenum.

30' long

F. 160 THE FOUR LAYERS OF THE SMALL INTESTINE

Four Layers of The Small Intestine.
- peritoneum (serous)
- muscular
- submucosa
- mucosa (lining)
- mesentery (peritoneal fold)

Inner wall of digestive tract

F. 161 THE FOUR LAYERS OF THE SMALL INTESTINE

Longitudinal Section of small intestine.

circular folds of mucosa (lining membrane)

F. 162 THE COLON

9 parts

- transverse colon
- Lt colic (splenic) flexure — *spleen*
- Rt colic (hepatic) flexure
- longitudinal muscle band
- ascending colon — *Rt liver*
- *ileo-cecal junction sm/bowel*
- descending colon — *Lt*
- *haustra (puckered yolds)*
- cecum
- terminal ileum
- haustra
- appendix — 2"-6
- rectum
- pelvic (sigmoid) colon — 5'

anal/caudal

F. 163 THE CECUM AND APPENDIX

- ileo-cecal valve
- sm/bowel
- terminal ileum
- cecum
- appendix

The cavities of the cecum and appendix are continuous.

F. 164 THE LIVER

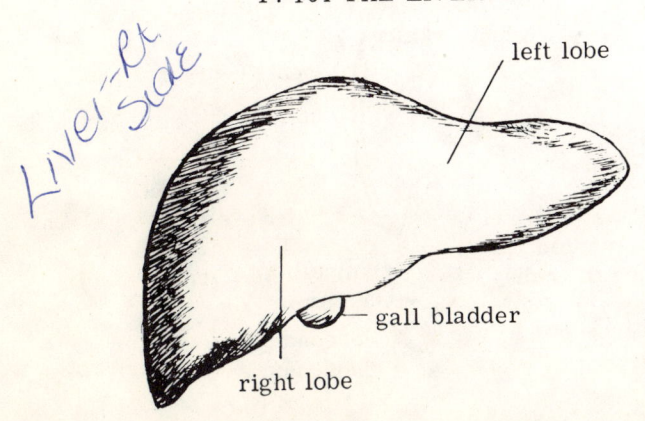

ver is out
Liver - Rt side

- left lobe
- gall bladder
- right lobe

F. 165 THE PANCREAS AND PANCREATIC DUCT

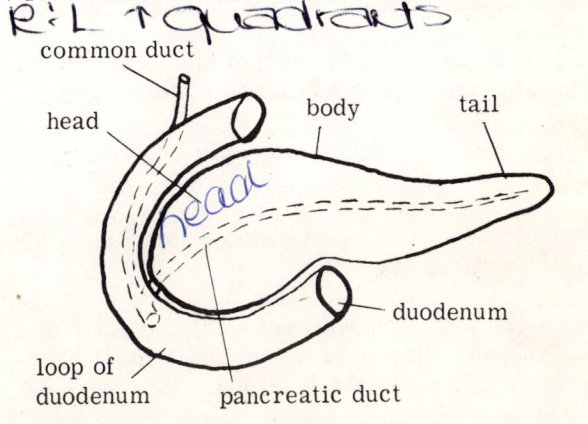

R & Lt quadrants

- common duct
- head
- body
- tail
- *head*
- duodenum
- loop of duodenum
- pancreatic duct

Insulin shock.
Fat in duodenum cause G.B. contract

(b) The **body** of the pancreas is the long tapering part extending to the left behind the stomach.
(c) The **tail** of the pancreas is its pointed left end.

The pancreas is made up of many minute glands that manufacture and secrete digestive enzymes (pancreatic fluid or juice). Tiny ducts collect the secreted fluid.

important
The pancreatic duct is a hollow tube that extends from the tail, through the body and head to join the common bile duct. Small ducts empty into this one which carries the pancreatic fluid to the duodenum. Sometimes there is an accessory pancreatic duct.

The Islets of Langerhans are small clumps of cells scattered throughout the pancreas. These have no ducts, but their secretion, insulin, is absorbed by capillary blood vessels. Insulin is necessary for the utilization of glucose by body cells. Its absence causes diabetes. (See endocrine glands P. 117).

Enlargement of the pancreas from inflammation, or cysts or tumors may cause pressure upon the stomach, duodenum or bile duct.

(2) The **liver** (G. hepar; adj. hepatic) is the largest solid organ in the body and may weigh three pounds. It occupies the upper right abdomen but extends to the left of the midline. It, therefore, lies in the upper right and left quadrants. When viewed from the front, it is roughly triangular in shape. Its upper surface is convex, corresponding to the dome of the diaphragm, below which it lies.

It is attached to the diaphragm by ligaments. The under surface of the liver is concave and passes from the right costal margin obliquely up and to the left. This surface has impressions for the right kidney, right colic flexure, and the gall bladder.

GB takes excreted by liver
Like the lung the liver is incompletely divided into lobes. Each lobe is composed of many lobules. Each lobule has columns or cords of liver cells. These columns as well as the capillaries of the hepatic artery and venous sinuses of the portal vein converge towards the center of each lobule. An interlobular vein lies here. These veins unite to form the hepatic vein. Bile ducts have their origin between the columns of hepatic cells, and unite to form larger trunks, eventaually emptying into the hepatic ducts. The hepatic cells secrete bile into the bile ducts.

The right and the left hepatic ducts or tributaries pass out of the liver.

The hepatic duct is formed by the union of the right and left hepatic ducts.

(3) The **gall bladder** (cholecyst - adj. cholecystic) is a pear shaped hollow organ which lies in an impression on the under surface of the liver. It is therefore in the right upper quadrant, about opposite the ninth costal cartilage, but may be much lower. It has a fundus, body and neck.

The **cystic duct** (ductus cysticus) is a hollow tube that passes from the gall bladder to join the hepatic duct.

The **common bile duct** (ductus choledochus) or bile duct is formed by the union of the hepatic and cystic ducts. It passes down behind the descending duodenum. It opens into the duodenum at the ampulla of Vater. There is a sphincter, the sphincter of Oddi, at this opening. The pancreatic duct usually joins the common duct close to its lower end.

The gall bladder and bile ducts have involuntary muscle in their walls and are therefore capable of contracting to force bile into the duodenum. The presence of fat in the duodenum stimulates their contraction; hence the fat meal for gall bladder examination. *GB takes in water*

dialate = lrg contraction open grow sl

S. 139 FUNCTIONS OF THE DIGESTIVE SYSTEM.

1. To take in water, salts, vitamins, and food, and to digest the food so that it may be absorbed.
2. To absorb these food constituents.
3. To get rid of waste products as feces.

Digestion (L. digerere - to divide or dissolve) is the breaking up of the large complex molecules of food into simple small molecules that can pass in solution through cell membranes.

Absorption is the taking up of substances into or through body cells. In the digestive system it means

---

F. 166 THE GALL BLADDER and BILE DUCTS

Liver — Rt. — Lt.
cystic duct — hepatic duct
gall bladder — common duct (bile)
sphincter of Oddi — pancreatic duct — ampulla of Vater — descending duodenum

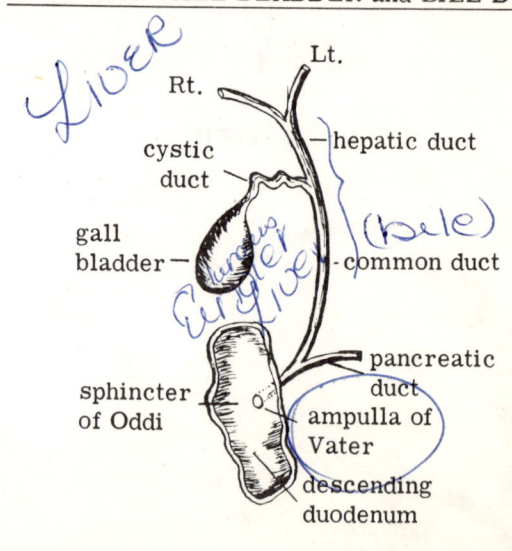

the passage of digested products through the lining membrane of the bowel into the blood or lymph capillaries. Then body cells absorb these products that are brought to them by the blood.

An enzyme is an organic substance manufactured and secreted by body cells (glands), which causes chemical changes in other substances. In the digestive tract, enzymes formed in the salivary glands, in the stomach, the small intestine, the pancreas and the liver, digest food.

Food contains three essential types of compounds: proteins, carbohydrates and fats, as well as salts, etc.

(a) Proteins are complex organic compounds containing nitrogen. They are found in lean meat (muscle) milk, eggs, grains, and such legumes as beans. They must be digested to amino acids before they can be absorbed. There are many proteins and several amino acids. All are necessary for the building up and repair of body cells. Excess amino acids are converted into urea and sugar. The urea is excreted by the kidneys.

(b) Carbohydrates include starches and sugars. They must be digested into simple sugars such as glucose and fructose before absorption can occur.

(c) Fats are also complex molecules of fatty acids and glycerine. The fat must first be emulsified or broken up into minute globules. These globules are then split into fatty acid and glycerine before absorption.
Amino acids, glucose and fructose are absorbed by the blood capillaries. Fats are absorbed by the lymph capillaries (lacteals) with the help of white blood cells.

Mouth: food masticated (chewed) mixed with saliva.

Stomach: a reservoir for food, and mixing bowl; food becomes semiliquid (chyme). Proteins are partly digested by pepsin. Hydrochloric acid is necessary for this process. Milk is curdled by rennin in the stomach.

Small intestine, three separate juices:

(1) bile from the liver emulsifies fats;

(2) pancreatic fluid is secreted into the duodenum by the pancreatic duct, and digests proteins, fats, carbohydrates;

(3) intestinal fluid (succus entericus) is formed by glands in the mucosa of the small bowel, is secreted into its lumen and digests proteins and carbohydrates. Most of the absorption of digested food takes place in the small intestine. There is no absorption from the stomach.

Colon: there are no digestive enzymes secreted by the colon, but the process started in the small intestine is continued in the colon. Water as well as digested food products are absorbed from the colon.

Pancreas: secretes digestive enzymes, pancreatic fluid, and the internal secretion, insulin.

Liver:
   (a) secretes bile into the duodenum through the bile ducts;
   (b) manufactures glycogen from glucose and stores it in the liver for further use;
   (c) releases glycogen as glucose as required;
   (d) converts excess amino acids into urea and glucose;
   (e) breaks down worn-out red blood cells, producing the bile pigments;
   (f) manufactures heparin, an anticoagulant of blood;
   (g) a reticulo-endothelial organ.

S. 140 SOME CONGENITAL ANOMALIES.

Cleft palate: an opening in the roof of the mouth, so that food and liquids may pass up into the nose.

Atresia of esophagus: the esophagus is closed at some point, and may communicate with the trachea.

Hypertrophic pyloric stenosis: a narrowing of the pyloric canal causing obstruction at the distal end of the stomach, usually detected in early infancy.

Hernia: a rupture - protrusion of an organ either through a weak part in the wall, or a part where the wall has not formed. Some are congenital, some due to injury or straining as in lifting.
Defects or weak areas in the diaphragm may result in herniation of the stomach or bowel into the chest. One type occurring through the esophageal opening in the diaphragm is called paraesophageal or hiatal hernia. Hernias frequently form in the groin or at the umbilicus.

Imperforate anus: there is no opening at the anus; the infant cannot move the bowels.

Interposition: the right colic flexure of the colon lies between the liver and diaphragm.

Meckel's diverticulum: a diverticulum of the ileum about three feet above the ileo-cecal junction. It may sometimes be demonstrated radiographically by taking films at frequent intervals following a barium meal.

Situs inversus or transposition: a reversal of the position of abdominal organs. Those normally found in the right abdomen may lie in the left abdomen. The unusual positions of the appendix have been studied. Many other anomalies may occur.

S. 141   SOME PATHOLOGICAL CONDITIONS.

"Itis" denotes an inflammation. Some inflammatory conditions of the gastro-intestinal tract are:
appendicitis - an inflammation of the appendix
cholecystitis - an inflammation of the gall bladder (cholecyst)
colitis - an inflammation of the colon
duodenitis - an inflammation of the duodenum
diverticulitis - an inflammation of diverticula
enteritis - an inflammation of the bowel
esophagitis - an inflammation of the esophagus
hepatitis - an inflammation of the liver
mediastinitis - an inflammation of the mediastinum
pancreatitis - an inflammation of the pancreas
peridiverticulitis - inflammation around diverticula
peritonitis - an inflammation of the peritoneum
regional enteritis - chronic inflammation of bowel.

Appendiceal abscess: an abscess of the appendix.

Calculi (sing. calculus) stones may form in any of the bile ducts but occur most frequently in the gall bladder. They may be calcified stones and show as dense grey shadows. They may have an outer layer of calcium and cast ring-like images. They may have no calcium. These noncalcified or nonopaque calculi are not visible in films unless the gall bladder is outlined by opaque dye. Then they are visible as lucent or dark shadows within the opaque gall bladder shadow. Scout films will not demonstrate this type.

Cholelithiasis: calculi in the gall bladder.

Diverticula (sing. diverticulum) are pouch-like protrusions of the wall of an organ. These occur anywhere in the gastro-intestinal tract, and frequently in the colon of older patients. A pulsion diverticulum, an outpouching of the pharynx at its junction with the esophagus.
A traction diverticulum - in the esophagus due to the pull on the wall from outside by scarred glands, etc.

Fissure: a slit or crack, common at the anus.

Fistula: an opening between two organs that is not normally present, e.g., gastro-colic between the colon and the stomach.

Intussusception: a telescoping of one part of the bowel into the part beyond it, as if the bowel were swallowed up, e.g., terminal ileum into the cecum.

Mesenteric thrombosis: a thrombus in a mesenteric artery. This results in death of the part of the intestine supplied by this artery.

Volvulus: a twisting of a loop of bowel upon itself.

Jaundice: the skin, eyeballs and nails are yellow. This may be due to obstruction of the hepatic or common bile ducts by calculus, tumor or to pressure from without, caused by enlargement of the head of the pancreas. It may also result from very rapid destruction of red blood cells (hemolytic jaundice), or from inability of the liver to secrete bile as in infectious hepatitis, etc.

S. 142   TERMS USED TO DESCRIBE OPERATIONS.

Cholecystectomy: removal of the gall bladder.

Cholecystotomy: a cutting into the gall bladder.

Cholecystenterostomy: making an opening between the gall bladder and small bowel, and sewing the edges together. This allows bile to enter the small bowel and may be used when the common duct is obstructed.

Cholecystduodenostomy: as above into duodenum.

Colostomy: an opening into a part of the colon. A loop of colon is brought out through an incision in the abdominal wall. This loop is then opened to allow feces to get out. It is used when the colon is obstructed by cancer, etc.

Enterocolostomy: an opening between the small bowel and colon to bypass an obstruction in the small bowel.

Gastrectomy: removal of the stomach, partial or complete.

Gastro-enterostomy: an opening is made between the stomach and small bowel, usually the upper jejunum.

Colectomy: removal of the colon; a hemicolectomy would be the removal of one-half of the colon.

S. 143   APPLICATION TO RADIOGRAPHY.

The following facts can be demonstrated.

(1) Hollow organs such as the parts of the digestive tract and bile system will not be outlined as separate images on an x-ray film, if they are empty.
(2) In normal adults there is usually some air in the stomach, duodenum and colon, but none in the jejunum, ileum nor esophagus.

(3) In infants, small children, and old subjects there is usually air in the jejunum and ileum as well.

(4) In bowel obstruction, air will accumulate in the small bowel or colon or both, and will outline the bowel. This fact is utilized and films are taken.

(5) Most parts of the digestive system lie closer to the anterior than the posterior abdominal wall. The films are usually taken in the postero-anterior position. This may be awkward in colon examinations. The fundus of the stomach fills with barium when the patient lies supine, as it lies close to the posterior abdominal wall. Films are taken in this position. The body and pylorus, lying closer to the anterior abdominal wall, fill best with the patient prone; so this position is utilized.

The duodenal cap or bulb often lies directly behind the pylorus and can be seen with the patient oblique.

The colon examination is usually done with the patient in the supine position. It is thus easier to handle the patient, enema tube, and tip. It is simple to rotate the patient to oblique positions to view those parts of the colon that overlap, especially the flexures and sigmoid.

Opaque media. Since the empty organs do not show on films, it is necessary to use some opaque medium to outline them. Barium sulphate is the medium in common use to visualize the parts of the digestive tract. It is mixed with water and given by mouth or as an enema. In esophageal examinations thin barium passes down too rapidly; so a thick barium paste is employed.

Gall bladder. This organ usually lies in the upper right abdomen opposite the ninth costal cartilage and close to the anterior abdominal wall. Films are therefore taken in the prone position. If empty, the gall bladder is not visible. A special examination is done to outline it.

In examinations of the gall bladder or bile ducts a medium containing iodine is used. The various media are usually referred to as dyes - not strictly correct.

Cholecystography is the procedure used to visualize the gall bladder. It consists of giving the opaque medium (dye) by mouth and of taking films at proper intervals.

A cholecystogram is a film or series of films outlining the gall bladder.

Some knowledge of the function of the gall bladder is necessary to understand what instructions have been given the patient regarding diet, the time to take the dye, and when to report to the department for films.

The gall bladder dye containing iodine is given the patient after a fat-free supper. This medium (dye) is absorbed from the small intestine and passes through the portal vein to the liver. It is excreted by the liver along with bile, into the bile ducts. Some of the bile and dye enter the gall bladder. Water is

---

F. 167 A CHOLANGIOGRAM

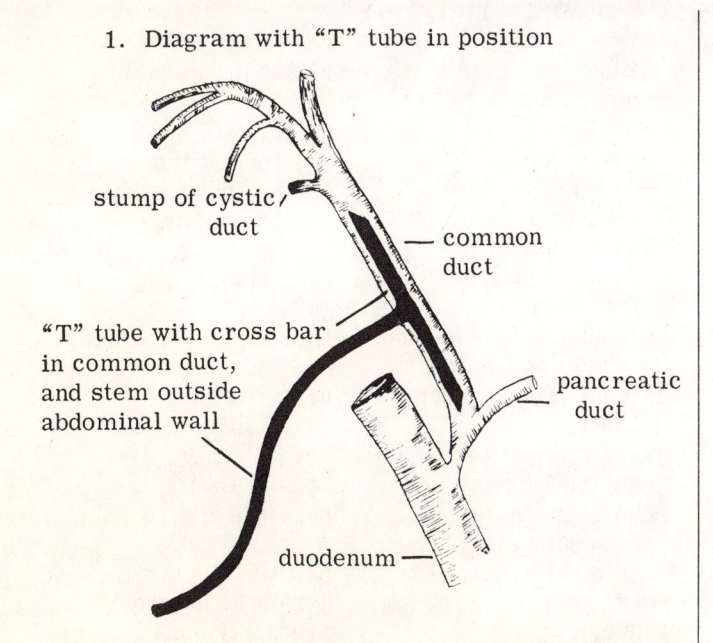

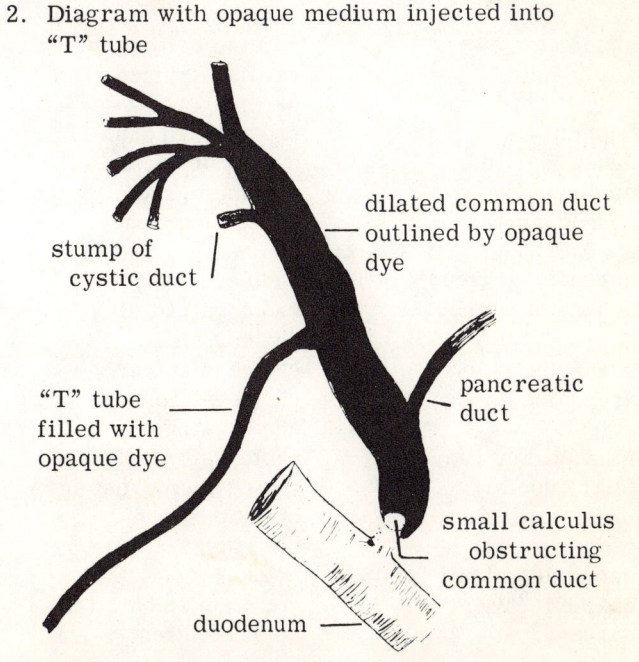

1. Diagram with "T" tube in position

stump of cystic duct
common duct
"T" tube with cross bar in common duct, and stem outside abdominal wall
pancreatic duct
duodenum

2. Diagram with opaque medium injected into "T" tube

stump of cystic duct
dilated common duct outlined by opaque dye
"T" tube filled with opaque dye
pancreatic duct
small calculus obstructing common duct
duodenum

absorbed from the bile in the gall bladder so that the bile and dye become more concentrated - thick. More bile enters the gall bladder, more water is absorbed, and by morning there is a sufficient concentration of dye in the bile in the gall bladder to render the gall bladder opaque to x-rays. Films are taken before the patient eats breakfast. Sometimes a fat meal is then given. Fat in the duodenum stimulates the gall bladder and bile ducts to contract and empty. Further films taken after the fat meal should show a smaller gall bladder or no shadow if the gall bladder has emptied. These films may also outline the bile ducts.

In cholecystitis the gall bladder will not concentrate bile, and films will show a faint image or no image. Other factors may be responsible. The patient may have vomited the dye. If there is obstruction at the pylorus or duodenum, dye will not pass into the small bowel and will not be absorbed. In diseases of the liver such as hepatitis the liver will not excrete bile nor dye. If a fat meal is taken in the morning before the films, the gall bladder will be empty. Under any of these conditions the gall bladder may not outline. In section 138 gallstones were discussed. The student must remember that nonopaque calculi will not be visualized if the gall bladder is not outlined.

Cholangiography (chole, bile; angeion, a vessel). This is the procedure used to outline the bile ducts, particularly the common bile duct.

(1) Pre-operative. If, weeks or months after a gall bladder operation, symptoms suggest obstruction of the common duct from calculi, etc.; or if the patient vomits gall bladder dye when given by mouth for a gall bladder examination, an intravenous cholangiogram is done. Opaque dye, containing iodine, may be injected intravenously. The dye will pass through the heart to the liver and should be excreted into the bile ducts and gall bladder if present. Films are taken at intervals following the injection.

(2) During operation. After the abdomen is opened for removal of the gall bladder, opaque dye may be injected directly into the common duct, by means of a syringe and needle. This may outline calculi or obstruction in the common duct.

(3) Post-operative. If calculi are found in the common duct at operation, these are removed. The crossbar of a rubber T tube is then passed into the common duct. One limb is directed upwards towards the liver; the other end is passed down towards the duodenum. The stem of the T tube is brought out through the skin. Bile may pass through the cross bar to the duodenum. If the common duct is still obstructed, bile can drain off through the stem of the tube. Opaque dye may be injected through the stem and films taken to determine if obstruction is present and if calculi are still blocking the duct.

S. 144 TERMS USED IN CHAPTER XVI DIGESTIVE SYSTEM

absorption	cardiac orifice, stomach	colitis	fundus of stomach
amino acids	cardiac sphincter	common duct	gallstone
ampulla of Vater	cardiospasm	cystic duct	gaster (adj. gastric)
anomaly	caecum or cecum	descending colon	gastrocolic fistula
anus, anal (adj.)	caecal or cecal (adj.)	descending duodenum	gastro-intestinal tract
anal canal	cholangiogram	digestion	gastro-enterostomy
anal sphincter	cholangiography	diverticulum	glucose
appendix	chole-bile	diverticula (pl.)	glycerine
appendiceal (adj.)	cholecyst	diverticulitis	gullet
appendiceal abscess	cholecystic (adj.)	duodenum (adj. duodenal)	haustra (adj. haustral)
appendectomy	cholecystitis	duodenal cap (bulb)	head of pancreas
ascending colon	cholecystectomy	duodeno-jejunal junction	hematemesis, haematemesis
ascending duodenum	cholecystotomy	epigastrium	hepar - liver
atresia	cholecystogram	epigastric (adj.)	hepatic (adj.)
bile, biliary (adj.)	cholecystography	epigastric region	hepatic duct
bilary ducts	cholecystenterostomy	esophagus	hepatic flexure
biliary calculus	choledochus	esophageal (adj.)	hepatitis
body of stomach	cleft palate	esophageal hiatus	hernia (adj. hernial)
calculus, calculi (pl.)	colon	esophagitis	hypogastrium
canine teeth	colic, or colonic (adj.)	fatty acid	ileum (adj. ileac)
carbohydrate	colic flexures	fundus of gall bladder	

ileocecal junction
incisura angularis
insulin
imperforate anus
interposition
intussusception
jaundice
jetjunum (adj. jejunal)
large intestine
left colic flexure
left hypochondrium
left iliac region
left lumbar region
left lower quadrant,
   L. L. Q.
liver
lumen
Meckel's diverticulum
melena
mesentery
   (adj. mesenteric)
mesenteric thrombosis
mouth

mucous membrane
mucosa (adj. mucosal)
mucus (adj. mucous)
omentum
pancreas (adj.
   pancreatic)
pancreatitis
parotid duct - gland
pharynx (adj.
   pharyngeal)
pharyngitis
pelvic colon
peristalsis
peritoneum (adj.
   peritoneal)
peritonitis
polyp (pl. polypi)
ptosis
protein
pulsion diverticulum
pylorus (adj. pyloric)
pyloric orifice
pyloric sphincter

rectum (adj. rectal)
retrocecal
right colic flexure
right hypochondrium
right iliac region
right lumbar region
right lower quadrant, R. L. Q.
right upper quadrant, R. U. Q.
rugar (sing. ruga)
saliva (adj. salivary)
salivary glands
sigmoid colon
situs inversus, transversus
small intestine
sphincter
sphincter of Oddi
spleen (adj. splenic)
splenic flexure
stenosis
stomach
sublingual duct
sublingual glands
Stensen's duct

submaxillary duct
submaxillary gland
submandibular duct
submandibular gland
superior duodenum
tail of pancreas
teeth
tongue
traction diverticulum
transverse colon
umbilicus
umbilical (adj.)
umbilical region
ventriculus
volvulus
Wharton's duct

Lt kidney usually ↑ than the right.

138

F. 168 DIAGRAM OF THE URINARY TRACT

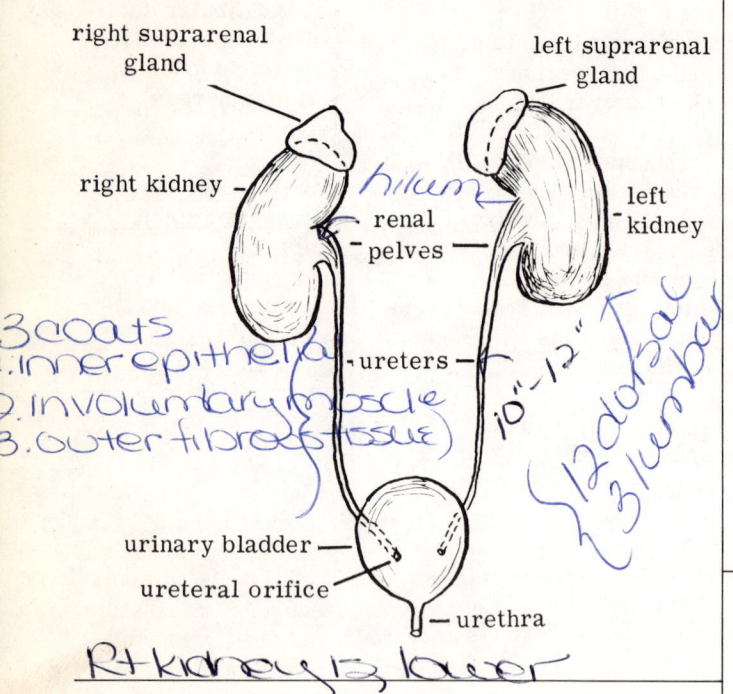

- right suprarenal gland
- right kidney
- left suprarenal gland
- left kidney
- renal pelves — *hilum*
- ureters — *10"-12"* *1 dorsal sac / 3 lumbar*
- urinary bladder
- ureteral orifice
- urethra

3 coats
1. inner epithelia
2. involuntary muscle
3. outer fibrous tissue

Rt kidney is lower

F 169 RADIOGRAPHIC APPEARANCE OF A KIDNEY "pyelogram"

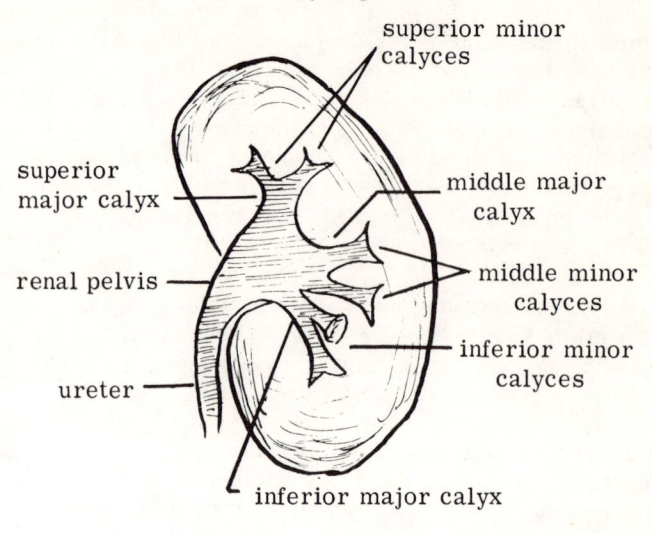

- superior minor calyces
- superior major calyx
- renal pelvis
- ureter
- middle major calyx
- middle minor calyces
- inferior minor calyces
- inferior major calyx

F 170 FEMALE BLADDER AND URETHRA - lateral view

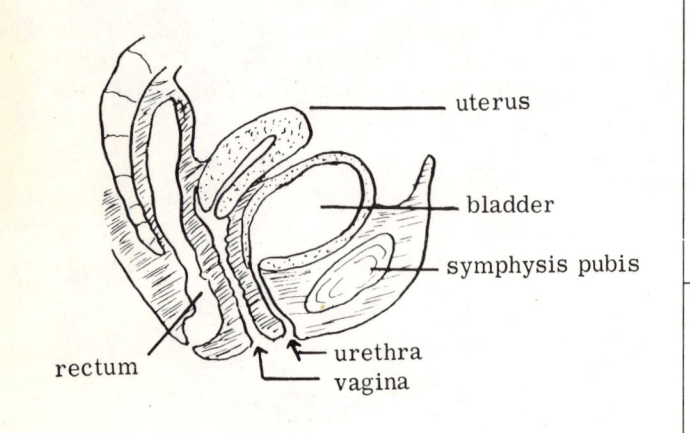

- uterus
- bladder
- symphysis pubis
- rectum
- urethra
- vagina

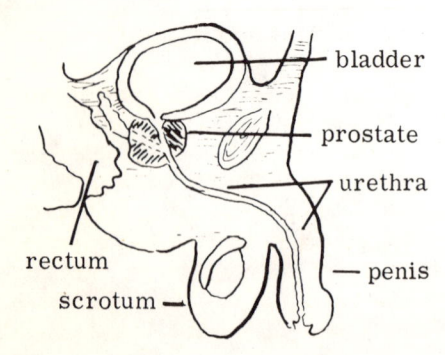

F. 172 KIDNEY - longitudinal, frontal section -

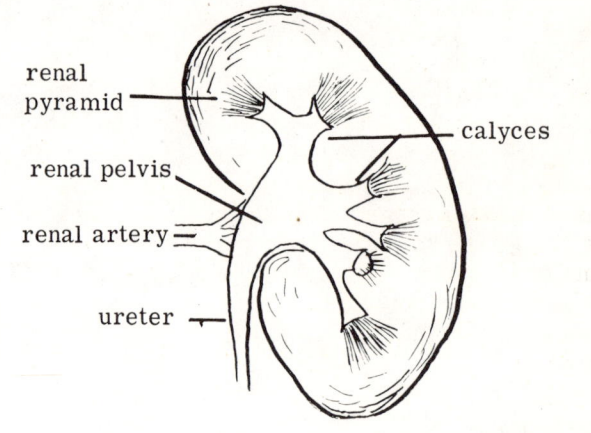

- renal pyramid
- renal pelvis
- renal artery
- ureter
- calyces

F. 171 MALE BLADDER, PROSTATE and URETHRA

- bladder
- prostate
- urethra
- rectum
- penis
- scrotum

F. 173 DIAGRAM OF A RENAL CORPUSCLE

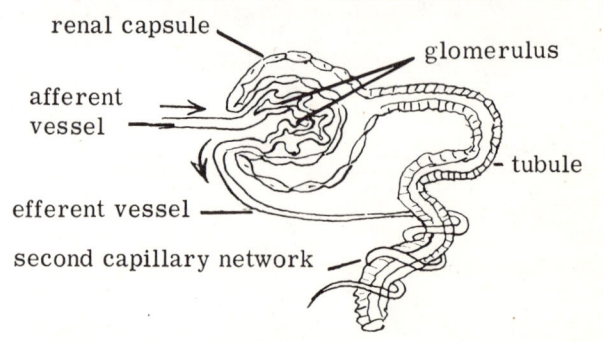

- renal capsule
- afferent vessel
- efferent vessel
- second capillary network
- glomerulus
- tubule

ANATOMICAL TERMS

pelvis (s), pelves (pl); calyx (s), calyces (pl);
kidney - ren, renal (adj); nephros, nephritic (adj);
urethra and ureter - note similarity.

kidney occupies D-12-L3
outside of kidney - cortex

139

CHAPTER XVII. THE URINARY SYSTEM.   5/7/73

The excretory organs include:
1. the skin: excretes moisture and salts;
2. the lungs: excrete carbon dioxide and moisture;
3. the digestive tract: excretes solids, water;
4. the kidneys: excrete water, dissolved salts, organic and inorganic.

S. 145 PARTS OF THE URINARY SYSTEM.

1. Kidneys (two) are excretory organs:
   (1) cortex
   (2) medulla
2. Ureters (two) are pipelines.
3. Urinary bladder (one) is a reservoir.
4. Urethra (one) is a waste pipe.

S. 146 DETAILED STUDY - PARTS - URINARY SYSTEM.

1. THE KIDNEYS.

(L. ren, adj. renal; G. nephros, adj. nephritic).

The kidneys are two bean-shaped organs which lie in the upper posterior abdomen, one on each side. They occupy the space between the twelfth dorsal to the third lumbar vertebra. The right lies at a slightly lower level than the left. They are behind the peritoneum, which covers their anterior surfaces except where some other organ lies against them. Each has a capsule, is surrounded by fat and moves with respiration.

The hilum (hilus) is a depression on the medial or inner border where the renal artery, renal vein, the lymphatics, and pelvis enter the kidney.

The renal pedicle includes the renal artery, vein, lymphatics, and renal pelvis (pedicle - stalk, little foot).

2. THE URETERS.

The ureters are two tubes about ten to twelve inches in length which extend from the kidney to the urinary bladder on each side. Each ureter passes down along the posterior abdominal wall, behind the peritoneum. It crosses the pelvic brim and runs down along the lateral wall of the pelvis to the pelvic floor. It enters the bladder obliquely at the ureteral orifice. The ureter has three coats, an inner epithelial lining, a layer of involuntary muscle and an outer fibrous layer. The ureter conducts urine from the kidney to the urinary bladder.

The renal pelvis (pl. pelves) is the upper expanded funnel-shaped end of the ureter, in contact with the kidney.

The major calyces (sing. calyx) are the two or three divisions of the renal pelvis: superior, middle and inferior major calyces.

The minor calyces are the cup-shaped divisions of the major calyces, and each minor calyx overlies a renal pyramid.

3. THE URINARY BLADDER.

The urinary bladder is a reservoir for urine and lies in the pelvis behind the symphysis pubis. It is in front of the rectum, and in the female is anterior to the uterus. Like the ureters it has three coats; the circular layer of involuntary muscle is thickened at the outlet or bladder neck to form a sphincter.

bladder in front of uterus

4. THE URETHRA.

The urethra is the passage from the urinary bladder to the outside. In the female it is about 1.5 inches in length. In the male it is much longer and passes through the prostate gland, perineum and the entire length of the penis.

The right and left renal arteries, branches of the abdominal aorta, supply blood to the kidneys. The renal veins collect blood from the kidneys and empty into the inferior vena cava.

THE MINUTE STRUCTURE OF THE KIDNEYS.

Each kidney consists of a cortex or outer part containing the renal tubules, and a medulla or inner part made up of renal pyramids.

The renal tubule is the unit structure and is a minute tube with cup-shaped upper end (renal capsule) and a long hollow tube bent upon itself at intervals

The renal capsule is the upper, expanded, cup-shaped end of each tubule. It has a small arteriole (afferent vessel) entering its open end. This breaks up into a capillary network. These capillaries are in close contact with the lining membrane of the renal capsule. It is through the walls of the capillaries and this membrane that urine is excreted. The capillaries unite to form a small vein (efferent vessel) which

leaves the capsule. It forms a second network around the bent part of the corresponding tubule.
The glomerulus (pl. glomeruli) is the name given to the tuft of capillaries in each renal capsule.
A renal corpuscle is a renal capsule and glomerulus. The other end of each tubule joins with others to form collecting tubules.

Each renal pyramid in the medulla is made up of many collecting tubules. The pyramids are cone-shaped with base towards the cortex. The collecting tubules enter at this broad end. The other small, rounded end fits into a minor calyx. Each collecting tubule has an opening into this minor calyx.

S. 147 PHYSIOLOGY OF THE KIDNEY.

According to one theory of the method of excretion of urine, blood enters the renal capsule through the glomerulus. Water and dissolved salts are filtered through the inner layer of this capsule to the renal tubule. It has been suggested that more than 1000 quarts of water pass out in twenty four hours. The second set of capillaries around the tubule re-absorb most of the water and some of the salts. Enough is re-absorbed to keep the fluid content and salt concentration of the blood at a normal level. The rest is excreted as urine. The amount of urine excreted in a day varies with the intake of liquids, the external temperature, etc. It may amount to one quart.

The proteins, albumin and globulin, of the blood have molecules too large to pass through the membranes and will remain in the blood. If the kidneys are damaged, proteins may pass out in the urine, The urine will give a reaction for albumin. In diabetes the blood sugar is high, as it cannot be utilized by body cells. It is then excreted in the urine.

S. 148 THE FUNCTIONS OF THE KIDNEYS.

1. The kidneys excrete urine which contains water and waste products in solution.
2. The kidneys regulate the fluid content of the blood.
3. They regulate the concentration of the various salts circulating in the blood.

Urine is excreted into the renal tubules, and passes through the collecting tubules to the renal pelves. It passes down the ureters to the urinary bladder and out through the urethra. When the pressure of the urine in the bladder reaches a certain level, sensory nerves in the bladder wall convey impulses to the brain. These are interpreted as an urge to void or urinate.

S. 149 SOME CONGENITAL ANOMALIES.

Absence of a kidney.
Microkidney: a small kidney.
Horseshoe kidney: the two kidneys are joined together across the midline of the body, usually at the lower ends.
Polycystic kidneys: large cysts in the kidneys.
Double kidney, double pelvis, double ureter: sometimes the superior major calyx has a separate pelvis and a partial or completely separate ureter.
Ectopic kidney (G. ektopos - out of place): the kidney is not in its normal position.
Exstrophy of bladder: the bladder may lie outside of the pelvis, and may have no anterior wall.
Hypospadias: the urethra opens on the under surface of the penis.
Epispadias: the urethra opens on the upper surface of the penis.

S. 150 SOME PATHOLOGICAL CONDITIONS.

Anuria (an - without): the kidneys do not EXCRETE urine.
Uremia (uraemia): an accumulation of poisonous waste products in the blood and body tissues due to the kidneys not excreting (anuria).
Calculus: stones may form in the kidney or bladder. Most urinary calculi are radiopaque, as they contain calcium. A calculus may obstruct a pelvis or ureter.
Staghorn calculus: one conforming to the shape of the renal pelvis - like the horn of a deer.
Cystitis: an inflammation of the urinary bladder.
Extravasation of urine: an escape of urine into the surrounding tissues. This follows a tear or rupture of the kidney, pelvis, ureter or bladder or urethra.
Hydronephrosis or pyelonephrosis: dilatation of a renal pelvis and its calyces due to obstruction in the renal pelvis or ureter, e.g., calculus in ureter.
Polyuria: an excess of urine is excreted, e.g., in diabetes.
Perinephritic abscess: an abscess about a kidney.
Ptosis: a kidney lying at a lower level than usual.
Pyelitis: an imflammation of a renal pelvis.
Retention: the urine is excreted by the kidneys but is retained in the bladder and not voided. This is due to some obstruction at the bladder neck such as an enlarged prostate, bladder calculus, or tumor, etc. It may be due to a disturbance of the nerve control.

S. 151 APPLICATION TO RADIOGRAPHY.

The student should bear in mind the following facts.

(1) Since the kidneys lie in the posterior abdomen, there will be less distortion of their images if the antero-posterior position is used in radiography.

(2) Calculi within a kidney or pelvis will also lie in the posterior abdomen. Calculi in the gall bladder will be in the anterior abdomen. Lateral views may help to determine the location in a puzzling case.

(3) The kidneys are solid organs except for the calyces and pelves and will show a separate image.

(4) The calyces, pelves, ureters, and the bladder if empty will not be outlined in films.

It is necessary to use some opaque medium to outline their cavities.

Urography or pyelography (IVP) is a procedure used to outline the calyces, pelves, ureters, and bladder, by filling them with opaque dye (iodine) and taking films. Two methods are utilized: see below 1 & 2.

A urogram or pyelogram is the film or films taken to demonstrate these structures.

1. Intravenous urography or pyelography consists of injecting opaque dye into a vein and taking films at intervals. The dye passes through the heart to the kidneys where it it excreted with urine.

2. Retrograde urography or pyelography is a special procedure done by a urologist using a cystoscope. This consists of a hollow metal tube with mirrors and a small electric bulb at one end, and an eye piece at the other end through which the urologist may look. The instrument is passed through the urethra until its mirrored end reaches the bladder. The openings of the ureters into the bladder are located, and long plastic catheters are inserted into the ureters and pushed up on them. Grooves are present in the sides of the cystoscope for passage of these. Specimens of urine are collected from each ureteral catheter for examination later. Opaque dye is then injected through each catheter to outline the calyces and pelves. Sodium iodide is often used. Films are then taken. Retrograde urogram - the resulting films.

SCOUT FILM: in intravenous urography a film of the abdomen should always be taken before injecting dye. In retrograde - with catheters in and before injection of dye.

Cystography: a procedure consisting of the injection of opaque dye into the urinary bladder to outline it. Films are then taken. Occasionally air is used instead of an opaque medium.

Abdominal arteriography: the injection of opaque dye into the abdominal aorta to outline its branches. This procedure outlines the renal arteries and their branches. It is used to demonstrate deformities of the vessel pattern in the kidneys from tumors, etc.

Psoas muscle shadows: see section 104, page 81, for loss of psoas muscle shadows in kidney films.

S. 152 TERMS USED IN CHAPTER XVII.

calculus	pelvic (adj.)
calculi (pl.)	perinephritic
calyx	polycystic
calyces (pl.)	polyuria
cortex	prostate
cystogram	ptosis
cystography	pyelitis
ectopic kidney	pyelogram
epispadias	pyelography
exstrophy	pyramid
extravasation	ren (adj. renal)
glomerulus	renal capsule
hilum (pl. hila)	renal corpuscle
horseshoe kidney	retrograde urogram
hydronephrosis	pyelogram
hypospadias	retrograde urography
inferior major or	pyelography
minor calyx	superior major or
intravenous urogram	minor calyx
pyelogram	trabeculae
kidney	ureter
medulla	ureteral (adj.)
microkidney	ureteral calculus
middle major or	urinary bladder
minor calyx	urogram
nephros	urography
nephritic (adj.)	uremia
pedicle	uraemia
pelvis	urethra
pelves (pl.)	urethral (adj.)

CHAPTER XVIII. THE FEMALE REPRODUCTIVE SYSTEM.

S. 153 PARTS OF THE FEMALE REPRODUCTIVE SYSTEM.

1. Ovaries (two): (a) Graafian or ovarian follicles
 (b) corpora lutea (sing. corpus luteum)

2. Uterine or Fallopian tubes (two) - salpinx

3. Uterus (one): (a) fundus
 (b) body
 (c) cervix uteri

4. Vagina

5. External genital: (a) labia
 (b) mons pubis
 (c) clitoris
 (d) vestibule and glands

6. Breasts.

DEFINITIONS.

The broad ligament is a fold of peritoneum that covers the floor of the pelvis in the female. It crosses the pelvis from one side to the other. It divides the pelvis into an anterior part containing the bladder and a posterior part containing the rectum. The uterus, uterine tubes, and the ovaries, as well as their blood vessels, lie between the folds of the broad ligament. The bladder is in front of, the rectum behind, the uterus.

An ovum (pl. ova) is the female reproductive cell or egg, and is formed in the ovary.

Ovulation is the maturing and expulsion of an ovum from an ovary. It occurs about every 28 days.

Fertilization is the union of a female ovum with a spermatozoon, the male reproductive cell.

Puberty is the age at which ovulation and menstruation begins, usually at fourteen to sixteen years.

Menstruation is the discharge of blood, and the lining membrane of the uterus. It occurs once every 28 days, more or less, and lasts about four days.

S. 154 STUDY OF FEMALE REPRODUCTIVE ORGANS.

1. THE OVARIES.

The ovaries are two flat oval organs which lie one in each side of the pelvis. Each measures about 1.5 to 2 inches in length. Each lies inside of, and is attached to, the posterior layer of the broad ligament. Many nests of cells lie under the epithelial covering of each ovary. Each nest contains an ovum and a ring of other cells. (G. oophoron - ovary).

A Graafian or ovarian follicle is a cell nest that has undergone further development. A layer of fluid forms a vesicle around the ovum, leaving the ovum attached to the ring at one point. As each follicle develops, it comes to lie close to the surface of the ovary. After puberty an ovum is expelled from one of the ovaries every 28 days. The wall of the follicle and covering of the ovary rupture, and an ovum is freed. During development each follicle secretes an internal secretion, theelin, oestrin or folliculin. This secretion is absorbed by blood capillaries and causes changes in the breasts and uterine lining.

A corpus luteum is the follicle AFTER the ovum has been expelled. A small hemorrhage occurs, a new type of cell develops which produces another internal secretion, progestin or progesterone. This is absorbed by the blood and causes changes in the lining of the uterus in preparation for receiving a fertilized ovum. If the ovum is not fertilized, the corpus luteum dries up.

2. THE UTERINE OR FALLOPIAN TUBES.

The uterine tubes are two hollow tubes which pass from the outer upper angles of the uterus to end one close to each ovary. Each passes in the broad ligament. The lateral end is open and has several finger-like processes (fimbriae), one of which is attached to the ovary. The uterine tube is also called a salpinx from its resemblance to a trumpet. An ovum, after it is expelled from an ovary, enters a uterine tube. The spermatozoon may meet it in this tube and fertilization may take place. The fertilized ovum then passes down to the uterus to become imbedded in its wall. If fertilization does not occur, the ovum passes out from the uterus and vagina. Each tube has three coats, an epithelial lining, layers of involuntary muscle, and a peritoneal covering.

3. THE UTERUS.

(Uterus, L. the womb; G. hystera or metra)

This is a flattened pear-shaped organ measuring about 3 by 2 by 1 inches in size. It lies in the fold of the broad ligament in the female pelvis. Its central cavity is triangular, when viewed from the front. It

F. 174 THE FEMALE REPRODUCTIVE ORGANS
- frontal view -

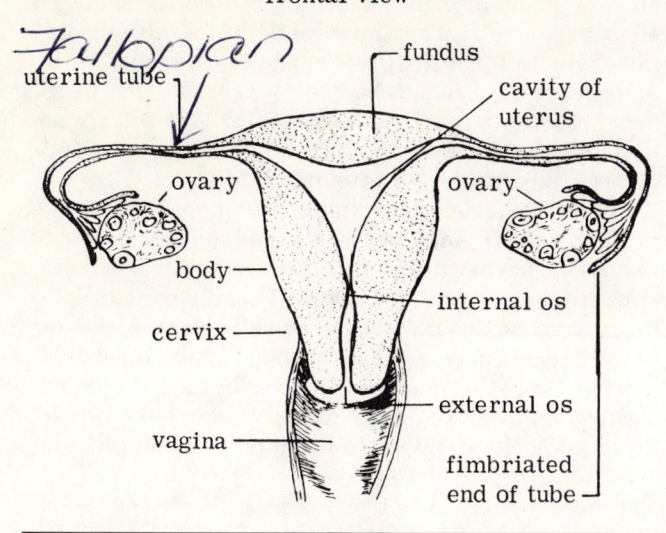

uterine tube (Fallopian) — fundus — cavity of uterus — ovary — body — internal os — cervix — external os — vagina — fimbriated end of tube

F. 175 THE FEMALE REPRODUCTIVE ORGANS
- lateral view -

re, Female reproductive organs

sacrum — sacral promontory — rectum — uterus — bladder — symphysis pubis — urethra — vagina — anus

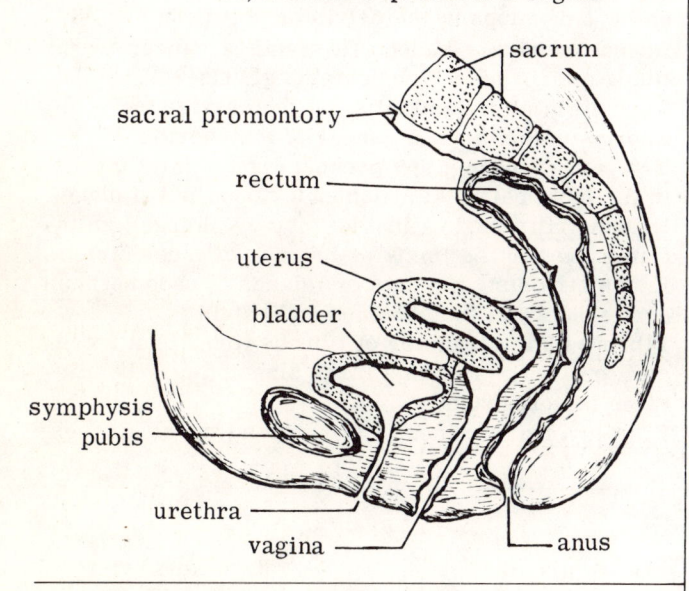

F. 176 CROSS SECTION OF AN OVARY
- (diagramatic)

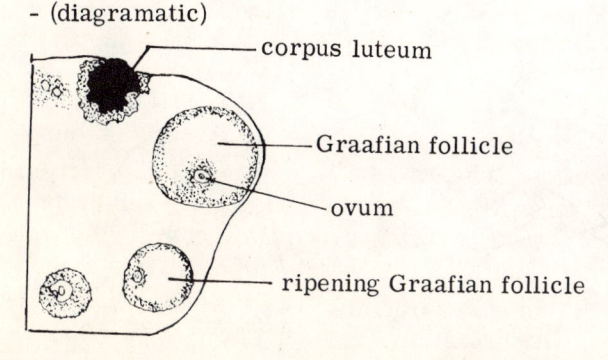

corpus luteum — Graafian follicle — ovum — ripening Graafian follicle

has three coverings:
(a) a lining membrane, the endometrium (endo - inside);
(b) a muscle layer, the myometrium (myos - muscle);
(c) a serous covering, the peritoneum (peri - around).

A uterine tube opens into the cavity of the uterus at each upper lateral angle.

Parts of the uterus:
(a) fundus: that part above the openings of the uterine tubes;
(b) body: that part between the fundus and the lower constricted part;
(c) cervix (pl. cervices): the long narrow constricted lower part. The internal os (opening) is the opening between the cervix and body. The external os is the opening between the lower end of the cervix and the vagina. The lower end of the cervix protrudes into the vagina.

The uterus is the organ in which the fertilized ovum develops. It increases in size along with the fetus. In preparation for the reception of a fertilized ovum the endometrium (lining membrane) becomes thick, swollen and congested. If fertilization does not occur, this membrane is sloughed off and menstruation occurs. Then the lining membrane regenerates. This cycle may be summarized as: premenstrual stage 2 to 3 days, menstruation 4 to 5 days, post-menstrual 2 to 3 days, resting interval about 14 days.

4. THE VAGINA.

(Vagina, L. sheath; G. kolpos or colpos)
This is the passage from the uterus to the outside. The cervix opens into it. The hymen is a membrane which partly or completely covers the outer opening of the vagina. In imperforate hymen there is no opening; menstrual blood remains in the vagina.

5. THE EXTERNAL GENITALS.

These are the structures which are visible from the outside. The labia are four folds of skin, two on each side of the vaginal opening. The mons pubis is the prominence over the pubic bones. The vestibule is the space between the inner folds of labia upon which the urethra and vagina open. The vestibular glands lie in the vertibule.

Blood vessels.
The ovarian arteries (two) are branches of the abdominal aorta, and pass down into the pelvis.
The uterine arteries (two) are branches of the internal iliac or hypogastric arteries.

The student must realize that there is a continuous passage through the vagina, uterus and uterine tubes to the pelvic cavity. Air injected into the uterus under pressure should pass through the tubes to the pelvic cavity. It will come to lie under the diaphragm with the patient upright. A foreign body such as spermatozoon or clump of bacteria may pass to the pelvic cavity in the same manner. If the uterine tubes are both blocked, ova cannot pass down into the uterus. Pregnancy cannot occur. This may be due to inflammation of the tubes, etc.

6. THE BREASTS OR MAMMARY GLANDS.

1. Nipple
2. Areola
3. Lactiferous ducts
4. Lobes
5. Lobules, compound glands.

(Mamma, L. breast; pl. mammae; adj. mammary; G. mastos)

The breast is not actually a reproductive gland, but an organ designed to nourish the young. Animals that feed their young by this method are classified as mammalia. In the human there are two breasts. They lie under the skin on the anterior chest wall over the pectoralis major muscles.

1. The nipple is a small prominence extending out from the breast at about its center.
2. The areola is a circular area of skin about the base of the nipple, colored pink in the young but brown after pregnancy has begun.
3. The lactiferous ducts are 15 to 20 small tubes which pass from the substance of each breast to open at the nipple.
4. The lobes: each breast is divided into from fifteen to twenty subdivisions, each of which drains into one lactiferous duct.

5. The lobules are small divisions of the lobes and contain many branched tubes or ducts with enlarged ends or alveoli. The inner cells of the alveoli disintegrate to form the protein and fat of human milk. At puberty the breasts become larger. During pregnancy and lactation the alveoli enlarge. They decrease in size when the infant is weaned. There is considerable fat in breasts, varying individually.

For the therapy technician the lymphatic drainage is important. Lymph vessels pass from the breast to the axilla, across the midline to the other breast area, down to the diaphragm. Other vessels pass deep to drain into the sheath of the pectoralis muscle. Cancer of a breast may spread through these channels.

The breast is mapped out like the face of a clock. Twelve o'clock would be directly above the nipple, three o'clock would be to the left of the nipple, etc.

S. 155 SOME PATHOLOGICAL TERMS - CHAPTER XVIII.

Abdominal pregnancy: fertilization takes place before the ovum has entered the uterine tube. The embryo develops in the pelvis or abdomen.
Adenocarcinoma: (adeno, a gland) a cancer in the lining membrane which contains glands.
Cervicitis: an inflammation of the cervix uteri.
Chorio-epithelioma: a cancer of the chorion.
Ectopic pregnancy: any pregnancy outside the uterus, in the tube, pelvis or abdomen (ektopos, out of place).
Endometritis (endo - inside; metra - uterus): an inflammation of the lining membrane or endometrium.
Endometriosis: implants or islands of endometrium scattered about the abdomen and pelvis.
Fibroid tumor: a tumor of fibrous tissue, not a cancer, but may grow to a large size and may be mistaken for pregnancy.
Fibromyoma: a tumor of fibrous and muscle tissues.

F. 177 THE FEMALE BREAST: MAMMARY GLAND

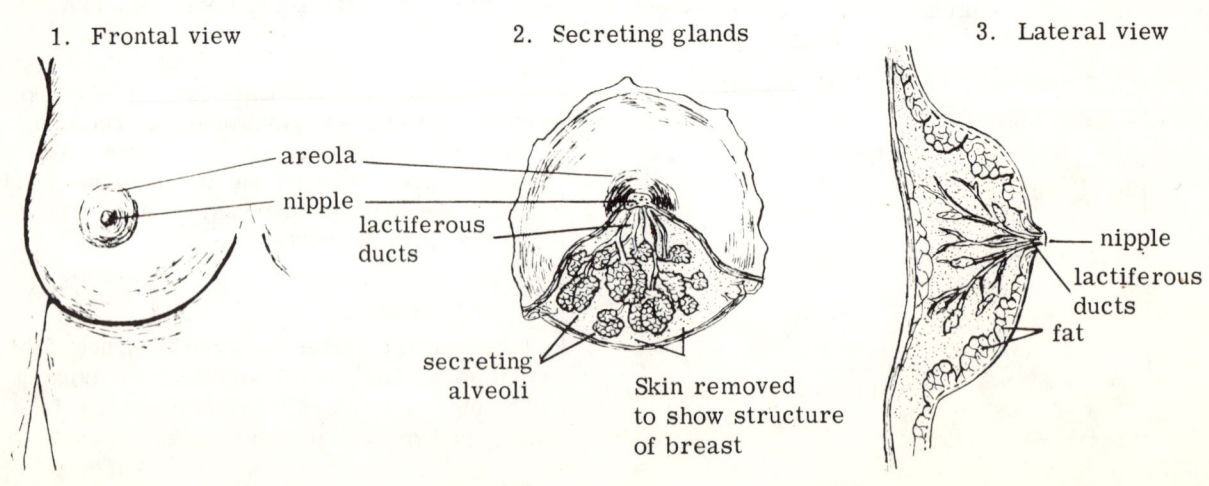

1. Frontal view
2. Secreting glands
3. Lateral view

Hematocolpos (kolpos - G. vagina): a collection of menstrual blood in the vagina due to obstruction at the vaginal opening, usually from imperforate hymen.
Mastitis: an inflammation of the breast.
Menorrhagia: heavy or prolonged menstrual bleeding.
Metrorrhagia: bleeding between menstrual periods.
Ovarian cysts: a cyst of an ovary.
Squamous cell carcinoma: a cancer originating in the squamous epithelium of the skin, lining of the vagina, the external os of the cervix, etc.
Tubal pregnancy: an ectopic pregnancy occurring in a uterine tube. The fertilized ovum does not pass down to the uterus but develops in the tube. The tube is apt to rupture, with fetal death and hemorrhage.

S. 156 SOME OPERATIVE PROCEDURES.

A biopsy of the cervix: a piece of tissue is cut off from a diseased cervix for microscopic examination.
Curettage of the uterus: the lining membrane of the uterus is scraped with a spoon-shaped curette to obtain tissue for microscopic examination.
D & C: a dilation of cervix and curettage of uterus.
Hysterectomy (hystera - womb): removal of the uterus.
Oophorectomy or ovariectomy: removal of an ovary.
Salpingectomy: removal of a uterine tube.
Sterilization: cutting the uterine tubes so that ova cannot pass through them. The ovaries are not removed.
Mammectomy: removal of a breast. (or mastectomy)
Simple mammectomy or mastectomy: the breast only is removed; no other structures are taken out.
Radical mammectomy or mastectomy: breast, pectoral muscle and lymphatics are removed.

S. 157 APPLICATION TO RADIOGRAPHY.

The female reproductive organs are not visible in films of the pelvis. A special procedure is employed.
Uterosalpingography (salpinx - a trumpet, uterine tube):
A procedure consisting of the injection of opaque dye into the uterus to outline the uterus and uterine tubes. This is usually done under fluoroscopic control, and films are taken up to twenty-four hours. This is done in cases of sterility to determine if the uterine tubes are open. If they are open, dye will escape from them into the pelvic cavity; if closed, no dye will escape.
Uterosalpingogram: the resulting films.

S. 158 LIST OF TERMS - CHAPTER XVIII.

abdominal pregnancy
areola
biopsy
body of uterus
breast - mamma
broad ligament
cervix uteri
clitoris
corpus luteum
corpora lutea (pl.)
curettage
ectopic
endometrium
external genitals
Fallopian tubes
fertilization
fibroid tumor
fibromyoma
fundus of uterus
genitalia
Graafian follicle
hematocolpos
hystera - womb
hysterectomy
internal os
labia
lactiferous duct
mamma - breast
mammary (adj.)
mammectomy
mastos - breast
mastitis
mastectomy
mastotomy

menses
menorrhagia
menstruation
menstrual cycle
metra - womb
metrorrhagia
metritis
mons pubis
myometrium
oophoron
oophorectomy
ovary
ovarian (adj.)
ovum (pl. ova)
ovulation
postmenstrual
premenstrual
puberty
salpinx - tube
salpinges (pl.)
salpingography
squamous cell
  carcinoma
tubal pregnancy
uterus - womb
uterine (adj.)
uterine tubes
uterosalpingogram
uterosalpingography
vagina
vaginal (adj.)
vaginitis
vestibule
womb

CHAPTER XIX. THE MALE REPRODUCTIVE SYSTEM;

S. 159 PARTS OF THE MALE REPRODUCTIVE SYSTEM.

1. Glands:
   (1) testes (two) - spermatozoa
   (2) prostate (one)
   (3) seminal vesicles (two)
   (4) bulbourethral glands (two)

2. DUCTS:
   (1) epididymides (two) (sing. epididymis)
   (2) ductus deferens (two)
   (3) ejaculatory ducts

3. PENIS:
   (1) urethra
   (2) glans
   (3) prepuce or foreskin

Some of these structures form a part of both the urinary and reproductive system. Grouped together they are sometimes called the urogenital system.

A study of the male reproductive system is not of much practical value to the radiographic technician, as radiography is of little help in the diagnosis of conditions affecting the male organs. A brief study is included because secondary cancer in the chest or bones from cancer of the prostate or other glands is frequently discovered in radiographs. Then, too, prostatic enlargement often causes urinary disturbances. Further, the therapy technician may be required to treat cancer of the prostate.

DEFINITIONS:

A spermatozoon or sperm (pl. spermatozoa) is the male reproductive cell. It is formed in minute tubules of the testes. A sperm has a body and a pointed tail. It resembles a tadpole, and is capable of movement.

Semen is a sticky, white, thick fluid, the product of the male reproductive glands, and contains sperms. Each cubic centimeter of semen contains about sixty million spermatozoa. During intercourse four or five cubic centimeters of semen may be expelled.

Fertility is the ability to cause pregnancy. In the male it would appear to be dependent upon the number of sperms per cubic centimeter of semen. Semen with ten to twenty million per cubic centimeter is not likely to cause pregnancy. The motility and resistance of sperms seem to parallel the number.

Puberty in the male is the age at which sperms are produced and expelled. This is characterized by changes in the voice, growth of hair upon the face, and by a change in attitude towards the female.

1. GLANDS - (1) TESTES - TESTICLES.

(Testis, pl. testes; testicle, pl. testicles; G. orchis).

The testes are the two glands in which spermatozoa are developed. They lie in a sac, the scrotum, below the pubic bones and are separated by a partition. Each testis is about 1.0 by 1.5 inches in diameter. Each contains many minute tubules in which the sperms are formed. These tubules converge towards the upper end of the testis and join to form larger ducts, the efferent ducts. These in turn unite the duct of the epididymis. Other nests of cells lie in each testis and produce two internal secretions: androsterone, and testosterone. These are absorbed directly into the blood stream.

F. 178 TESTIS - left lateral view -

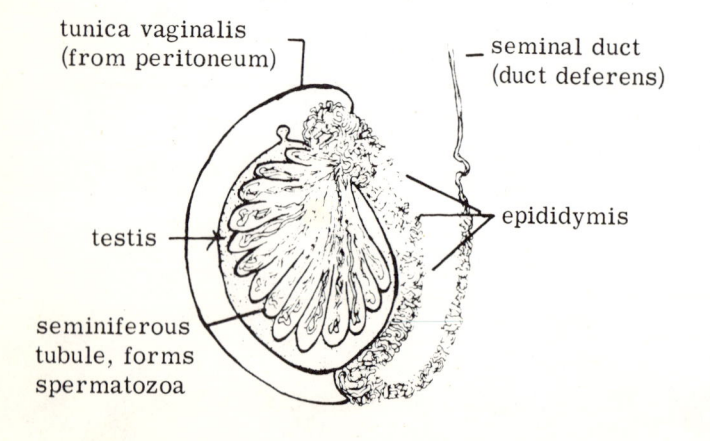

F. 179 MALE REPRODUCTIVE ORGANS
- right lateral view -

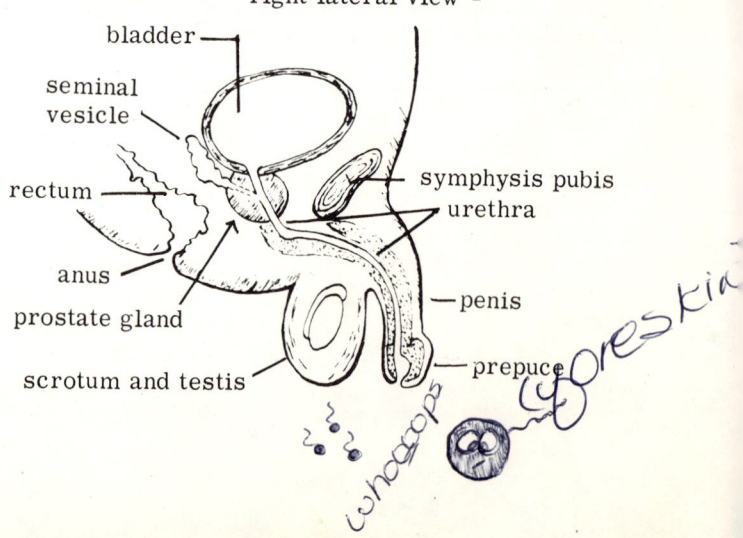

(2) THE PROSTATE GLAND.

The prostate is a single globular gland about 1.5 inches in diameter, and lies below the outlet of the urinary bladder. The urethra passes through it - the prostatic urethra. The prostate is composed of many tubules which form small ducts which empty into the prostatic urethra. It secretes a part of the semen.

(3) THE SEMINAL VESICLES.

These are two tube-like glands which lie obliquely behind the bladder, one on each side of the midline. Each has a main duct that joins the ductus deferens to form an ejaculatory duct. The secretion forms a part of the semen. The seminal vesicles and prostate gland lie in front of the rectum and can be felt by a finger in the rectum.

(4) THE BULBOURETHRAL GLANDS.

These are two small glands that lie one on each side of the urethra below the prostate and drain into it.

2. DUCTS - (1) THE EPIDIDYMIS - EPIDIDYMIDES.

This forms a prominence on the back of each testis. It is composed of a single tube which is coiled upon itself. It begins at the upper end by the union of the efferent ducts of the testis. It extends down to the lower end of the testis and ends in a ductus deferens.

(2) THE DEFERENT DUCTS.

(Deferent duct, ductus or vas deferens, seminal duct).
Each ductus deferens is a continuation of a duct of the epididymis. It passes from the lower end of a testis up through the scrotum and in front of a pubic bone to the lower abdominal wall. It passes through openings (inguinal rings) in the anterior abdominal muscles. It then descends into the pelvis to lie behind the bladder. Here it joins a duct from a seminal vesicle to form the ejaculatory duct.

(3) THE EJACULATORY DUCTS.

The two ejaculatory ducts are formed by the union of the ductus deferens and duct from the seminal vesicle on each side. Each passes through the prostate gland to open into the prostatic urethra.
NOTE: the epididymis, ductus deferens, and ejaculatory duct form one continuous tube passing from the testis to the urethra to carry sperms and semen. The contents are expelled during intercourse.

3. THE PENIS.

This is the male organ of copulation. It is cylindrical in shape and is attached below the pubes in front of the scrotum. The urethra passes through its entire length to open at the distal end, the meatus. The glans is the distal enlarged end of the penis. The skin is attached around the base of the glans, and a fold of skin covers it. Erection of the penis is caused by blood filling three columns of erectile tissue, which extend along the entire length of the penis.

The spermatic cord is a cordlike structure extending from the scrotum on each side up over the lower abdomen to the inguinal rings. It contains the deferent duct, internal spermatic artery and vein, and is palpable between the examining fingers.

S. 160 PATHOLOGICAL CONDITIONS AND OPERATIONS.

Epididymitis: an inflammation of an epididymis.

F. 180 DESCENT OF TESTIS - lateral view -

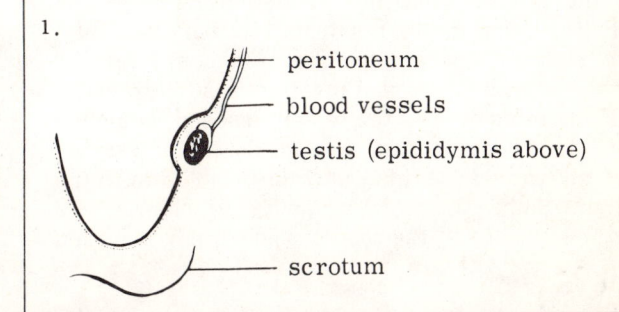

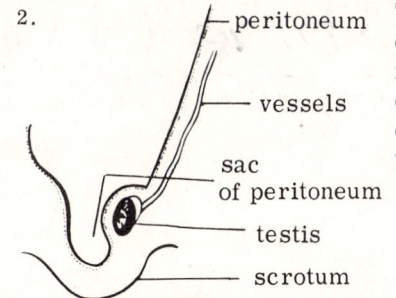

1.
- peritoneum
- blood vessels
- testis (epididymis above)
- scrotum

2.
- peritoneum
- vessels
- sac of peritoneum
- testis
- scrotum

Testis has descended to scrotum, peritoneal sac still open. Blood vessels carried down with testis.

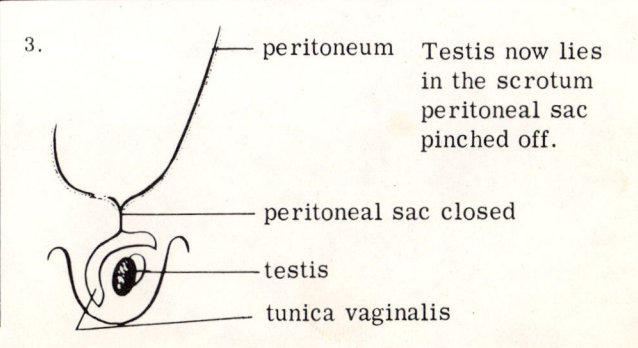

3.
- peritoneum
- peritoneal sac closed
- testis
- tunica vaginalis

Testis now lies in the scrotum peritoneal sac pinched off.

Epididymectomy: removal of an epididymis.
Orchitis: an inflammation of a testis (G. orchis).
Orchidectomy: removal of a testis.
Prostatism: an enlargement of the prostatic gland, occurs in older men, not a cancer. It may cause some obstruction to the flow of urine from the bladder.
Prostatectomy: removal of the prostate gland.
Transurethral prostatectomy: pieces of prostatic tissue are removed through the urethra, using a cystoscope and a special cutting instrument that fits into it.
Seminoma: a cancer of the tubules of a testis.
Sterilization: the deferent ducts are cut to prevent passage of sperms. The testes are not removed.

S. 161 DESCENT OF THE TESTES.

The testes are formed in the posterior abdomen, below the kidneys and behind the peritoneum which covers their anterior surfaces. The internal spermatic arteries, branches of the abdominal aorta below the renal arteries, supply the testes. The right internal spermatic vein empties into the inferior vena cava; the left empties into the left renal vein. The lymphatics from the testes drain into the abdominal lymph nodes. Cancer from the testes may spread along these lymphatics and involve the aortic glands.

As the fetus grows, the testes descend, and pass around the abdomen, out through the inguinal rings in the anterior abdominal muscles, and down to the scrotum. Since the peritoneum is attached to the anterior surfaces of the testes, a pouch of it is pulled down into the scrotum with each testis. That part of the peritoneal pouch in the abdominal wall usually disappears, but a small passage may persist from the abdomen into the scrotum. A hernia of the bowel may pass down through this into the scrotum (inguinal hernia). The peritoneum in contact with the testes forms a closed sac over the front of the testis (tunica vaginalis). Fluid may accumulate in this sac (hydrocele). The ovaries also form in the abdomen and descend into the pelvis, with a similar blood supply.
Cryptorchidsm: a non-descent of testes, resulting in small incompletely developed testes and no sperms.

S. 162 LIST OF TERMS - MALE REPRODUCTIVE SYSTEM.

bulbourethral glands	prostate
cryptorchidism	prostatism
ductus deferens	prostatic (adj.)
efferent ducts	prostatectomy
ejaculatory ducts	semen
fertility	seminal duct
inguinal ring	seminal vesicle
inguinal hernia	sperm
internal spermatic artery	spermatozoon
	spermatoza (pl.)
hydrocele	spermatic vein
meatus	sterilization
orchis - testis	testis
orchitis	testes (pl.)
orchidectomy	testicle
penis	tunica vaginalis

Carcinoma; The ↑ the metabolism (as in a child the faster it will spread)

CHAPTER XX. THE ENDOCRINE OR DUCTLESS GLANDS. 5/8/73

S. 163   A LIST OF THE DUCTLESS GLANDS.

1. <u>Pituitary gland</u> (one) - hypophysis cerebri
    (1) anterior lobe
    (2) posterior lobe
2. <u>Pineal gland or body</u> (one) - epiphysis cerebri
3. <u>Thyroid gland</u> (one)
4. <u>Parathyroid glands</u> (four)
5. <u>Thymus gland</u> (one)
6. <u>Pancreas</u> (one) - islets of Langerhans
7. Suprarenal or <u>adrenal glands</u> (two)
    (1) cortex
    (2) medulla
8. <u>Ovaries</u> (two)
9. <u>Testes</u> (two)
10. Gastro-intestinal - <u>liver</u>, <u>duodenum</u>, <u>stomach</u>.

Glands with ducts: many glands have already been mentioned in connection with the systems studied. Such glands as the sebaceous and sweat glands of the skin, salivary glands, intestinal glands, pancreatic, etc., consist of a tubule. One end of this tubule is the secretory part, the remainder a duct or tube to carry the secretion to the skin or some hollow organ.

<u>Ductless glands are nests or clumps of cells which have no duct; hence ductless. They take up raw material from the blood capillaries. They manufacture new substances and discharge these directly into the blood capillaries.</u> Every structure supplied with the blood therefore receives these secretions. These glands are also called endocrine glands, or glands of internal secretion.

<u>A hormone is a secretion manufactured in a ductless gland. It may stimulate or excite some other gland to secrete. It may inhibit another gland from secreting. It may regulate the function of some tissue or organ.</u>

Mixed glands. <u>Some of these glands secrete one substance into a duct, and one or more hormones as internal secretions, e.g., pancreas, ovaries, testes.</u>

Double glands. <u>Some of the ductless glands have two distinct parts, each manufacturing its own hormone, e.g., cortex and medulla of suprarenal glands, anterior and posterior lobes of pituitary gland.</u>

Multiple functions. <u>Some of these ductless glands have one function in young growing individuals, that are responsible for normal growth and development; and in the adult a different function, e.g., thyroid gland.</u>

Inter-relationship. <u>The secretion of one gland may stimulate or inhibit the secretion of another. The secretion of the second gland may in turn inhibit the secretion of the first gland which was responsible for its activity, e.g., pituitary and thyroid, etc.</u>

Proof of existance of endocrine secretions. This has been secured by a study of:
(1) <u>patients with an absence or under-development of some ductless gland</u>, particularly in the young;
(2) <u>patients in whom disease has destroyed a ductless gland</u>;
(3) <u>patients with a tumor of a ductless gland and an above normal secretion of its hormone;</u>
(4) <u>animals or humans from whom a ductless gland has been removed</u> for disease, or animals from which the gland has been removed experimentally and hormones injected from a similar gland.

Some of these hormones have been isolated and have been used in experiments or in actual treatment of disease. Many of these are not effective when given by mouth but must be injected. (insulin in diabetes).

<u>Metabolism is the chemical changes which occur in body cells as a result of cell activity.</u> It includes the wearing down and the building up activites of each cell, e.g., muscular activity, glandular secretion, etc. These changes require oxygen. <u>The rate of metabolism may be measured by measuring the amount of oxygen breathed in.</u> This is the basis of the basal metabolism test. The subject breathes oxygen from a container so that the amount of oxygen used up may be measured. The basal metabolism is an estimation of the oxygen used with the patient resting. By reference to tables compiled for subjects of the age and weight of the patient the metabolism may be compared to the normal for that age and weight.

cell activity

S. 164   DETAILED STUDY OF THE DUCTLESS GLANDS.

1. THE <u>PITUITARY GLAND</u>.

The pituitary gland or hypophysis cerebri lies in the <u>sella turcica</u> or pituitary fossa of the sphenoid

Thyroid produces Thyroxine & Triiodothyronine

150

F. 181 THE PITUITARY GLAND - lateral view - or hypophysis cerebri.

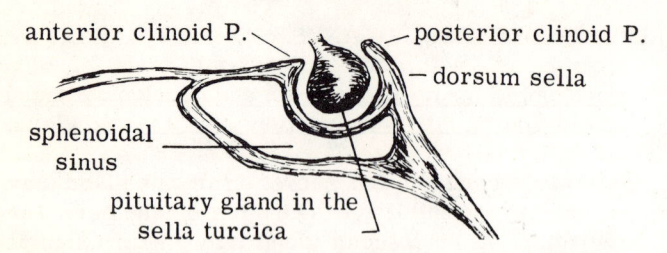

- anterior clinoid P.
- posterior clinoid P.
- dorsum sella
- sphenoidal sinus
- pituitary gland in the sella turcica

F. 182 THE THYROID GLAND - frontal view -

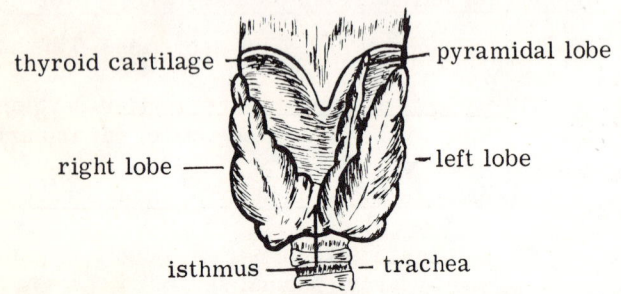

- thyroid cartilage
- pyramidal lobe
- right lobe
- left lobe
- isthmus
- trachea

F. 183 THE PARATHYROID GLANDS - dorsal view -

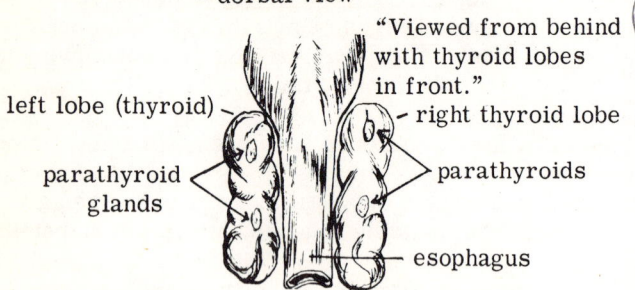

"Viewed from behind with thyroid lobes in front."

- left lobe (thyroid)
- right thyroid lobe
- parathyroid glands
- parathyroids
- esophagus

F. 184 THE THYMUS GLAND - frontal view -

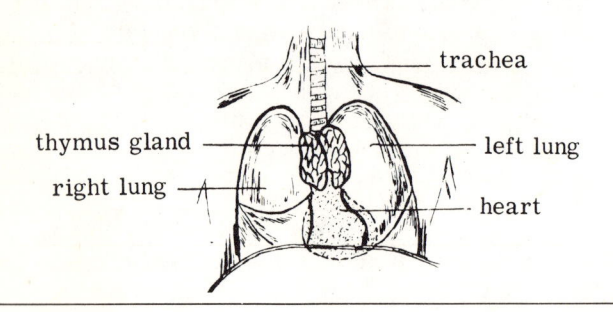

- trachea
- thymus gland
- left lung
- right lung
- heart

See also: Pancreas, p. 131, F. 165

Liver, p. 131, F. 164

Suprarenal glands, p. 138, F. 168

Ovary, p. 143, F. 176

Testis, p. 146, F. 178

bone. It consists of two parts, a posterior and an anterior lobe. Each has its own secretions.

The posterior lobe is derived from a pouch of the third ventricle of the brain extending downwards; hence hypophysis (hypo - below, and physis - growth; i.e., to grow down.)

Secretions of posterior lobe:
(1) pitocin (oxytocin) stimulates uterine contraction;
(2) pitressin, stimulates contraction of some blood vessels, and the bowel, i.e., involuntary muscle;
(3) antidiuretic, stimulates reabsorption of water in the renal tubules.

The anterior lobe is derived from a pouch of the fetal mouth, which has become pinched off. It has two types of cells, acidophil and basophil. It is called the master or dominating gland because its secretions effect the secretions of other glands. Such hormones are termed tropic or trophic hormones (tropic to nourish). It is debatable whether these are separate hormones or not. They are listed below:

thyrotropic - stimulates the thyroid gland;
gonatropic - stimulates the ovaries or testes;
adrenocorticotropic - ATCH - stimulates adrenal cortex;
parathyroidotropic - stimulates the parathyroid;
pancreatotropic - stimulates the pancreatic gland;
lactogenic - stimulates the breasts to secrete milk;
insulin antagonistic - inhibits production of insulin;
growth stimulating - muscles, bones, etc., e.g., the thyrotropic hormone of the pituitary gland stimulates the thyroid to secrete its hormone; the gonadotropic hormone stimulates the testes to produce sperms and the male sex hormones.

2. THE PINEAL GLAND.

calcification is v. bad

The pineal gland or body or epiphysis cerebri is a small gland which lies in the midline of the brain, behind the third ventricle. It is therefore behind and above the pituitary gland. Its function is not known. Its importance to the technician is due to the fact that it becomes calcified in older patients. It is then visible in radiographs. It should be in the midline, but may be displaced to one side by inflammatory lesions or brain tumors. *calcification often occurs*

3. THE THYROID GLAND.

This gland consists of two lobes or parts which lie one on each side of the thyroid cartilage, in the front of the neck above the suprasternal notch. The two lobes are joined across the midline by a narrow isthmus. They move up with the trachea during the act of swallowing and may be felt during this procedure. Occasionally a part of the thyroid lies at a lower level, behind the upper sternum (retrosternal).

Secretion: thyroxine, which contains iodine. This iodine is obtained from water and food intake. Lack of iodine will result in an enlargement of the gland to produce enough thyroxine for body requirements.
Function: to promote normal mental and physical growth in the young; and to regulate metabolism in the adult. Basal metabolism tests therefore give an indication of how the thyroid is functioning.

Goiter

4. THE PARATHYROID GLANDS.

overactive = decrease in bone density, nephrocalcinosis, renal rickets

The parathyroid glands are four small bean-shaped bodies which lie behind the thyroid gland, in the neck. They usually measure less than one-half inch in vertical diameter.
Secretion: parathyroid hormone or parathormone.
Function: regulation of the calcium content of the blood;
regulation of the irritability of nerves.
Note: occasionally when the thyroid gland is removed at operation, one or more parathyroid glands are also taken out; this results in hypoparathyroidism.

test = usually X-rays

5. THE THYMUS GLAND.

What is called the thymus gland (actually two glands which lie close together in the upper anterior chest) is placed behind the sternum and above the heart. In the very young it is quite large but after puberty it become much smaller.
Function: possibly stimulates growth in the young.

6. THE PANCREAS. *(Double gland)*

The pancreas was described under the heading "Accessory Organs of Digestion", number 7, page 103. It is a mixed gland. It secretes pancreatic fluid, a digestive juice, into a duct, which along with the common duct empties into the duodenum. In addition it has cell nests, the islets of Langerhans, that have no ducts but secrete the hormone insulin directly into blood capillaries. Insulin is necessary for the utilization of glucose so that it may be burned or used by body cells. Lack of insulin causes diabetes in which sugar accumulates in the blood and is excreted in the urine.

7. THE SUPRARENAL GLANDS. *(adrenal gland)*

(supra, above; renal, kidney).
The suprarenal or adrenal glands are paired organs which lie one above each kidney, in contact with the upper pole. These are four-sided bodies and measure about two inches in length. The suprarenal gland is a double gland and consists of two distinct parts, a medulla or central part, and a cortex or outer part.

① *medulla*
② *cortex*

cardioconstrictor

① The medulla or central part secretes adrenalin or epinephrin. Injections of adrenalin stimulate those structures supplied by nerves of the sympathetic nervous system. It causes an increase in the rate of the heart beat, and causes contraction of blood vessels, thus raising the blood pressure. It causes dilatation of the bronchi and is used in asthma and in heart failure. Whether adrenalin is secreted into the blood continuously or not is debatable. In case of stress or emergency it does not appear to be secreted. The medulla may be removed without causing death.

② The cortex of the suprarenal gland is essential to life, and its removal in animals causes their death.

Secretions: several somewhat similar chemical substances have been extracted from the suprarenals. Their effects are being studied, but there is still uncertainty. Cortisone and other extracts are among these.

It is known that the cortex is necessary for the normal growth and development of the young. It regulates sodium and water excretion by the kidneys. It has some effect upon the testes and ovaries; and tumors of the suprarenals cause early development of puberty. It has some effect upon the secretion of sex hormones in the adult. Addison's Disease - deficient secretion.

ACTH

8. THE OVARIES.

The ovaries have been described in section 154, page 111. The hormones of the ovaries are termed estrogens. The developing Graafian follicle secretes theelin, or oestrin, or folliculin. In the young female enlargement of the breasts, growth of pubic hair, and the personality changes at puberty are related to theelin production. In the adult it causes some of the alterations in the uterus that accompany the menstrual cycle.
The corpus luteum manufactures a further hormone called progestin or progesterone. This causes further changes in the uterus in preparation for reception of a fertilized ovum. If pregnancy does not occur, the corpus luteum degenerates.

9. THE TESTES.

The testes were described in section 159, page 114. The hormones or androgens called testosterone and androsterone were listed. There are responsible for the changes occurring in the male at puberty. They stimulate the prostate gland, seminal vesicles and testes in the production of semen.

Note: Estrogen (female sex hormones) have been isolated from the male, and androgens from the female.

In cancer of the breast in the female testosterone has been injected and has caused disappearance of secondary tumors in bones, etc.

In cancer of the prostate, estrogens (female hormones) have been injected to inhibit the growth of secondary tumors. The testes have also been removed to decrease the production of male sex hormones, as they appear to stimulate the growth of prostatic cancer.

10. GASTRO-INTESTINAL SYSTEM.

The glands in the stomach, and duodenum, and the cells of the liver secrete hormones which affect other structures.

S. 165 SOME PATHOLOGICAL CONDITIONS.

Many pathological conditions are due to too little or too much secretion of the ductless glands. This may be due to underdevelopment in early life. It may be due to destruction from disease in later life, causing a decrease in secretion. Oversecretion may result from tumors or from overstimulation by one of the other ductless glands. Because some of these conditions require radiography for diagnosis, they are summarized briefly below.

PITUITARY GLAND.

(1) Giantisum is a condition resulting from an overstimulation of the anterior lobes of the pituitary gland due to a tumor in it. This occurs in younger individuals before growth is complete. It results in overgrowth of the skeleton. The subject may be seven or eight feet tall.
(2) Acromegaly is a similar condition occuring in adults. Here the hands, feet, and skull become large. Gloves and hat are found to be too small. There is tufting of the terminal phalanges. Sex glands atrophy.
(3) Pituitary dwarfism is the result of insufficient secretion of the anterior lobe of the pituitary gland in childhood. The subject may be only three or four feet in height. Mental development is normal. Sexual underdevelopment occurs. Treatment - anterior lobe extracts, if the condition is recognized early.

THYROID GLAND.

(1) Simple goiter (goitre) is an enlargement of the thyroid and may result from an inadequate supply of iodine. In certain geographical areas the iodine content of the drinking water is too low. The entire human and animal population may suffer. Iodized table salt will make up the deficiency.

(2) Cretinism is a condition caused by underdevelopment or abscence of the thyroid gland in infancy. The development and growth of the skeleton is retarded, the epiphyses appear late, dwarfism results. There is also mental underdevelopment. If the condition is recognized early and thyroid extract be given, normal development may occur.
(3) Myxedema is a similar condition occurring in adult life. It may be due to destruction of the thyroid by disease. It may be caused by the removal of too much thyroid tissue at operation. The subject becomes fat, is mentally slow, and appears lazy. Thyroid is given.
(4) Hyperthyroidism. Graves disease or exophthalmic goiter, is a condition in which there is an oversecretion of the thyroid hormone thyroxine. The gland enlarges. This disease is characterized by nervousness, tremors, rapid heart, loss of weight, protruding eyeballs, and a high basal metabolic rate.

PARATHYROID GLANDS.

(1) Hypoparathyroidism is a condition resulting from insufficient secretion of the parathyroid glands. It may follow a thyroidectomy if the parathyroids are removed by error. It is accompanied by muscular twitchings, sometimes by convulsions, with a low calcium content in the blood.
(2) Hyperparathyroidism is due to excessive secretion of the parathyroid glands from a tumor, etc. This results in an elevation of the calcium in the blood. Decalcification and cystic changes occur in bones. Calculi and calcinosis may occur in the kidneys.

SUPRARENAL GLANDS.

(1) Addison's Disease is a condition resulting from a disease in the secretion of the cortex of the suprarenal glands. It results in muscular weakness, low blood pressure and pigmentation of the skin. In addition there is an increase in the sodium and water excretion by the kidneys.
(2) Cortical tumors may occur in the young or in adult life. If the tumor is in the younger age group, there is early and marked development of the sex organs and an early appearance of secondary sexual characteristics. The epiphyses appear early, and the epiphyseal lines disappear, stunting growth. Tumors cause masculinity in the female adult and feminism in the male adult.

S. 166 APPLICATION TO RADIOGRAPHY.

Ductless glands are soft tissue structure and do not show as separate images in a film unless they are

large. Under some circumstances radiography may help:
(a) if the gland contains calcium, this will show in radiographs;
(b) if there is pressure on adjacent structures such as bones, these bones will show changes, or organs may show displacement;
(c) an increase or decrease in the secretion of a ductless gland may result in changes in the structure, density or development of bones.

Pituitary gland. This gland is not visible, but if enlarged, may cause enlargement, thinning, erosion or destruction of the sella turcica or clinoid processes. Films taken of the skull in the lateral projection may show these abnormalties.
In dwarfism films may show an early appearance of the epiphyses or premature closure of the epiphyseal lines.

Pineal gland. This gland is not visible, but if calcified, the calcium will show in films of the skull. In antero-posterior or postero-anterior views this calcification should lie in the midline. In the presence of space occupying lesions such as tumors or inflammations, the calcified pineal may be displaced away from the midline. It is obvious that films must be taken without any rotation of the head.

Thyroid gland. An enlarged thyroid gland may be outlined in films of the neck, particularly is there is calcification of it. The trachea may show displacement or constriction from a large thyroid. Retrosternal thyroid glands may be outlined in the upper mediastinum, and may also displace the trachea. In cretinism bones should show delayed development.

Parathyroid glands are not visible. Decalcification and cystic changes or punched-out areas may be outlined in bones if a parathyroid tumor be present.

Thymus gland. An enlargement of the thymus gland may occur in children and shows as an increase in the width of the superior mediastinum, above the heart. Since infants cannot be instructed to breathe in and hold it for an x-ray exposure of the chest, a broad upper mediastinum must be interpreted cautiously.

Pancreas. This gland lying behind the stomach is not visible. Enlargement of the head may cause displacement of the pylorus of the stomach or the duodenum. Calcifications in the pancreas should be visible.

Suprarenal glands. They may be outlined, if enlarged. The retroperitoneal injection of air may help to outline them. Air is injected beside the rectum. It tracks up behind the peritoneum to surround the kidneys and suprarenal glands. If the suprarenals are calcified, the calcium should be visible in films of the abdomen.
Abdominal arteriograms may help by outlining the blood vessels of the kidneys and suprarenals.

The testes and ovaries are not visible.

S. 167 TERMS USED IN DUCTLESS GLANDS.

Addison's disease
adrenal glands
adrenalin
adrenocorticotropic hormone
androgen
androsterone
anterior lobe, pituitary
basal metabolism
corpus luteum
cortex of suprarenal
cortisone
cretin
cretinism
duct glands
ductless glands
endocrine glands
epinephrin
epiphysis cerebri
estrogen
estrin, oestrin
exophthalmos
folliculin
gland
gonad
gonadotropic
Graafian follicle
hyperparathyroidism
hyperthyroidism
hypophysis cerebri
hypoparathyroidism
hypothyroidism
insulin
lactogenic
liver
medulla of suprarenal
metabolism
metabolic
myxedema
ovary
oxytoxin
pitressin
pineal gland - body
pancreas
parathyrotropic
pancreatotropic
parathyroid glands
parathormone
pituitary gland
pituitrin
posterior lobe, pituitary
progestin - progesterone
suprarenal gland
testes
testoterone
theelin
thymus
thyroid gland
thyrotropic
throxine

CHAPTER XXI. THE NERVOUS SYSTEM.

S. 168 PARTS OF THE NERVOUS SYSTEM.

I. THE CENTRAL NERVOUS SYSTEM

1. Brain: (1) -cerebrum or forebrain:
    (a) right cerebral hemisphere
    (b) left cerebral hemisphere
    (c) lobes of cerebral hemispheres;
       frontal lobe, temporal lobe,
       parietal lobe, insula,
       occipital lobe
    (d) fissures of cerebral hemispheres:
       longitudinal fissure
       central fissure
       lateral fissure
       transverse fissure
    (2) midbrain: (a) quadrigeminal bodies
              (b) cerebral peduncles
    (3) hindbrain: (a) pons
              (b) cerebellum
              (c) medulla oblongata

2. Spinal cord

II. THE PERIPHERAL NERVOUS SYSTEM.

1. Cranial nerves - twelve pairs
2. Spinal nerves - thirty-one pairs
3. Autonomic nervous system:
    (1) sympathetic or thoracico-lumbar
    (2) parasympathetic or cranio-sacral

III. MENINGES or coverings of the brain and cord

1. Pia mater
2. Arachnoid with subarachnoid space
3. Dura mater

IV. VENTRICLES or cavities of the brain

1. Lateral ventricles (two) left and right
2. Third ventricle
3. Fourth ventricle

S. 169 DEFINITIONS OF SOME TERMS.

A neuron is a nerve cell, and consists of a cell body and two sets of processes: dendrites and an axon.

Dendrites (sing. dendron) are several processes that extend out from a cell body, and carry impulses towards the cell body.

An axon is a single process extending out from the cell body, and may be two or three feet in length. It carries nerve impulses away from the cell body.

A sensory neuron (afferent neuron) is a nerve cell that conducts impulses towards or into the spinal cord to the brain. These impulses may be sensations of heat, cold, touch, pressure, pain, or of muscle position, or from the special sense organs, the eye (sight), ear (hearing), nose (smell), or the mouth (taste).

A motor neuron (efferent neuron) carries impulses from the brain down the spinal cord, or from the cord to muscles or secreting glands, or from the brain to muscles or glands.

A synapse is the point of contact of a dendron of one neuron with the axon of another neuron.

An end organ is a structure at the outer end of an axon or dendron.

(a) In sensory nerves the end organs are at the ends of dendrites, and pick up sensations of pain, heat, etc. The end organ may be a minute fiber in close contact with body cells as in the skin. It may be the expanded end such as the taste buds in the tongue. It may be a special nerve ending such as is present in the nerves of sight, hearing, etc.
(b) In motor nerves (neurons) the end organ is a flat plate on a muscle fiber, or a delicate branching of minute fibers about secretory cells of a gland.

A reflex arc is a complete circuit consisting of a sensory neuron, a connecting neuron and a motor neuron.

A reflex act. A sensory neuron carries a nerve impulse of a pain or other sensation to the spinal cord. A connecting neuron carries it to a motor neuron, which in turn conducts it to a muscle, causing that muscle to contract, e.g., a finger touches a hot stove.

A ganglion is a group of cell bodies outside of the brain or spinal cord, e.g., outside the central nervous system.

A nucleus is a group of nerve cell bodies inside of the brain or spinal cord.

A center is a group of nerve cells concerned with some specific function, e.g., respiratory center.

A plexus is a network of cell processes. Sometimes a ganglion is associated with such a plexus.

*[handwritten top:] messages to brain = afferent
" from " = efferent
down to 1st; see Vert (lumbar?)
cerebral = skull cap
parietal — visceral cranium, facial also, not skull*

S. 170 DETAILED STUDY - CENTRAL NERVOUS SYSTEM.

The entire brain is enclosed by the visceral cranium (G. encephalon - brain). It consists of a large cerebrum or forebrain, a much smaller midbrain, and the hindbrain.

The spinal cord is a continuation of the brain stem and is contained within the spinal canal of the vertebrae.

1. THE CEREBRUM.

The cerebrum or forebrain occupies the entire visceral cranium except the posterior cranial fossa. A deep fissure or groove, the longitudinal fissure lies directly under the sagittal suture of the skull and passes from front to back. It divides the cerebrum into two halves, the right and left cerebral hemispheres. The division is incomplete below. Fibers pass across from one hemisphere to the other in the inferior part below the fissure. These form the corpus callosum. A fold of dura mater, the outer brain covering called the falx cerebri, dips down into this fissure.

The outer surface of the cerebrum appears grey, as it is composed of nerve cell bodies. The outer surface is thrown into ridges called gyri or convolutions. There are grooves or hollows between these ridges called fissures or sulci, large or small.

*[handwritten:] why brain is grey = composed of nerve cell bodies
white = dendrites and axon
Folds = convolutions
grooves = fissures
sulci (chinks)*

F. 185 THE BRAIN - left lateral view -
- central sulcus
- frontal lobe
- parietal lobe
- occipital lobe
- lateral fissure
- temporal lobe
- cerebellum
- pons

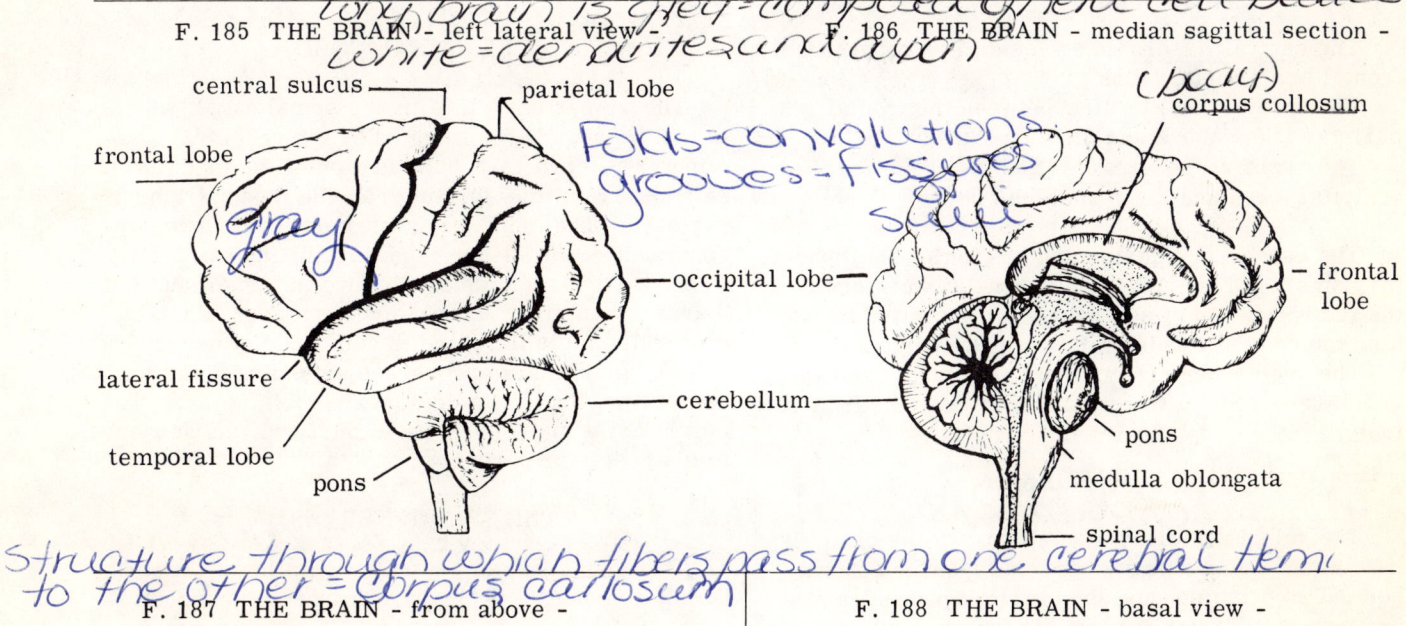

F. 186 THE BRAIN - median sagittal section -
- corpus collosum (body)
- frontal lobe
- pons
- medulla oblongata
- spinal cord

[handwritten:] Structure through which fibers pass from one cerebral hemi to the other = corpus callosum

F. 187 THE BRAIN - from above -
- Lt cerebral hemisphere
- Rt cerebral hemisphere
- frontal lobe
- central sulcus
- parietal lobe
- lateral fissure
- occipital lobe
- longitudinal fissure

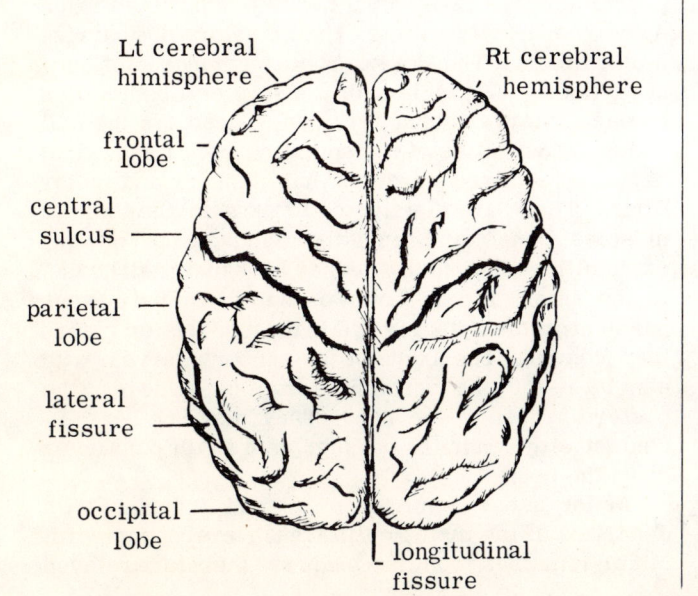

F. 188 THE BRAIN - basal view - "with origin of cranial nerves"

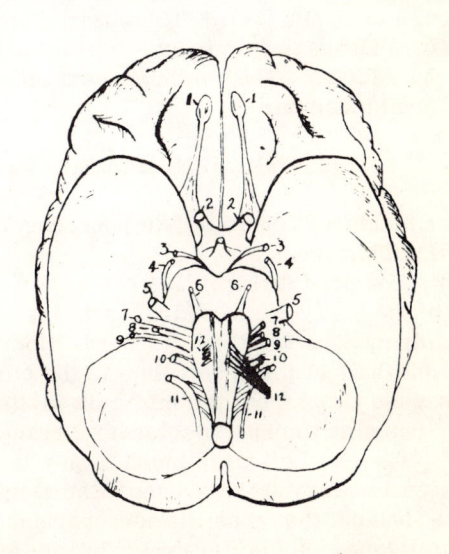

The deeper part of the cerebrum is white, as it is composed of nerve fibers. These fibers connect the different parts of one hemisphere with each other, or the right and left hemisphere, or the cerebrum to mid and hindbrain, or the cerebrum and the spinal cord.

Each cerebral hemisphere is completely divided into five lobes by deep grooves or fissures:
1. the frontal lobe lies deep to the frontal bone on each side;
2. the parietal lobe lies under the parietal bone;
3. the temporal lobe is under each temporal bone;
4. the occipital lobe lies in front of the occipital bone on each side;
5. the insula lies deep in the brain substance.

The central fissure on each side lies between the frontal and parietal lobes.

The lateral fissure lies between the frontal and parietal lobes above and the temporal lobe below.

The transverse fissure lies between the two occipital lobes and the cerebellum below.

The cerebrum contains centers for speech, hearing, smell, taste, and sight, as well as centers for the interpretation of sensations. These latter lie behind the central fissure or sulcus in the parietal lobe.

The motor centers control muscular movement, and lie in front of the central fissure in the frontal lobe.

2. THE MIDBRAIN.

The midbrain forms a small part of the brain. It lies on the under surface and rests upon the sphenoid bone. Two prominences, the cerebral peduncles, can be seen on its under surface. These are composed of the nerve fibers passing from the cerebrum to the hindbrain and spinal cord. The quadrigeminal bodies are four additional prominences on the upper surface of the midbrain. The midbrain connects the cerebrum and hindbrain.

3. THE HINDBRAIN.

The hindbrain consists of the pons, cerebellum and medulla oblongata.

(a) The pons (bridge) lies below the midbrain, in front of the cerebellum, and above the medulla. It has a prominence in front due to nerve fibers passing from one-half of the cerebellum to the other. Other fibers pass down from the midbrain to the medulla. It also contains the nuclei of several cranial nerves.

(b) The cerebellum is much larger and occupies the posterior cranial fossa, deep to the occipital bone. It lies behind the pons. It is separated from the occipital lobes of the cerebrum by the transverse fissure. The tentorium cerebelli is a fold of dura mater in this fissure. The cerebellum consists of two lateral lobes connected across the midline by a constricted part. It is connected through the pons with the brain above and the medulla below.

(c) The medulla oblongata lies below the pons, between it and the spinal cord. It lies just above the foramen magnum. Nerve fibers pass through it connecting the brain above and spinal cord below. Many of these nerve fibers cross over in the medulla to the opposite side. This explains why paralysis in the body occurs on the opposite side to a brain lesion. The nuclei of several cranial nerves lie in the medulla. Some of the vital centers such as the respiratory, cardiac, and vasomotor centers are located here.

THE SPINAL CORD.

The spinal cord lies in the spinal canal, which, it will be recalled, is formed by the vertebral foramina. The cord is a continuation of the medulla. It extends from the foramen to the second lumbar vertebra. The spinal nerves below this level are continued down as the cauda equina (horse's tail). The cord is incompletely divided into right and left halves by anterior and posterior grooves. Each lateral half is similar, and is composed of nerve cell bodies, and of nerve processes extending up or down connecting the brain and peripheral nerves. The motor cells and fibers lie in the front, the sensory in the posterior parts.

THE SPINAL NERVES.

Thirty-one pairs of spinal nerves leave the cord. One nerve passes out through an intervertebral foramen at each level on both sides. These are the peripheral nerves. Each spinal nerve is connected to the spinal cord by two roots. The anterior root carries motor fibers. The dorsal root is composed of sensory fibers. A ganglion of sensory cell bodies lies in each intervertebral foramen. These are the cell bodies of dendrites of the spinal nerves. Each spinal nerve is a mixed nerve. It has sensory and motor fibers. These are distributed to the skin, the skeletal muscles, bones, and secreting glands of the body and extremities. The motor nerves have their cell bodies in the anterior part (horn) of the cord. Their axons pass out in the spinal nerve to the muscles or glands they control. The axons of the sensory nerves, with ganglia in the intervertebral foramina, pass in by the posterior root to the cord. They may end here in contact with dendrites of other neurons or pass up or down the cord.

Motor axons from the brain end in contact with dendrites of the motor cells at each level of the cord. Motor impulses from the brain are therefore relayed

nervous are called cauda equina (horses tail)

157

F. 189 SAGITTAL SECTION OF BRAIN THROUGH MEDIAN LINE TO SHOW VENTRICLES AND MENINGES
(note - cerebrospinal fluid outlined with black dots)

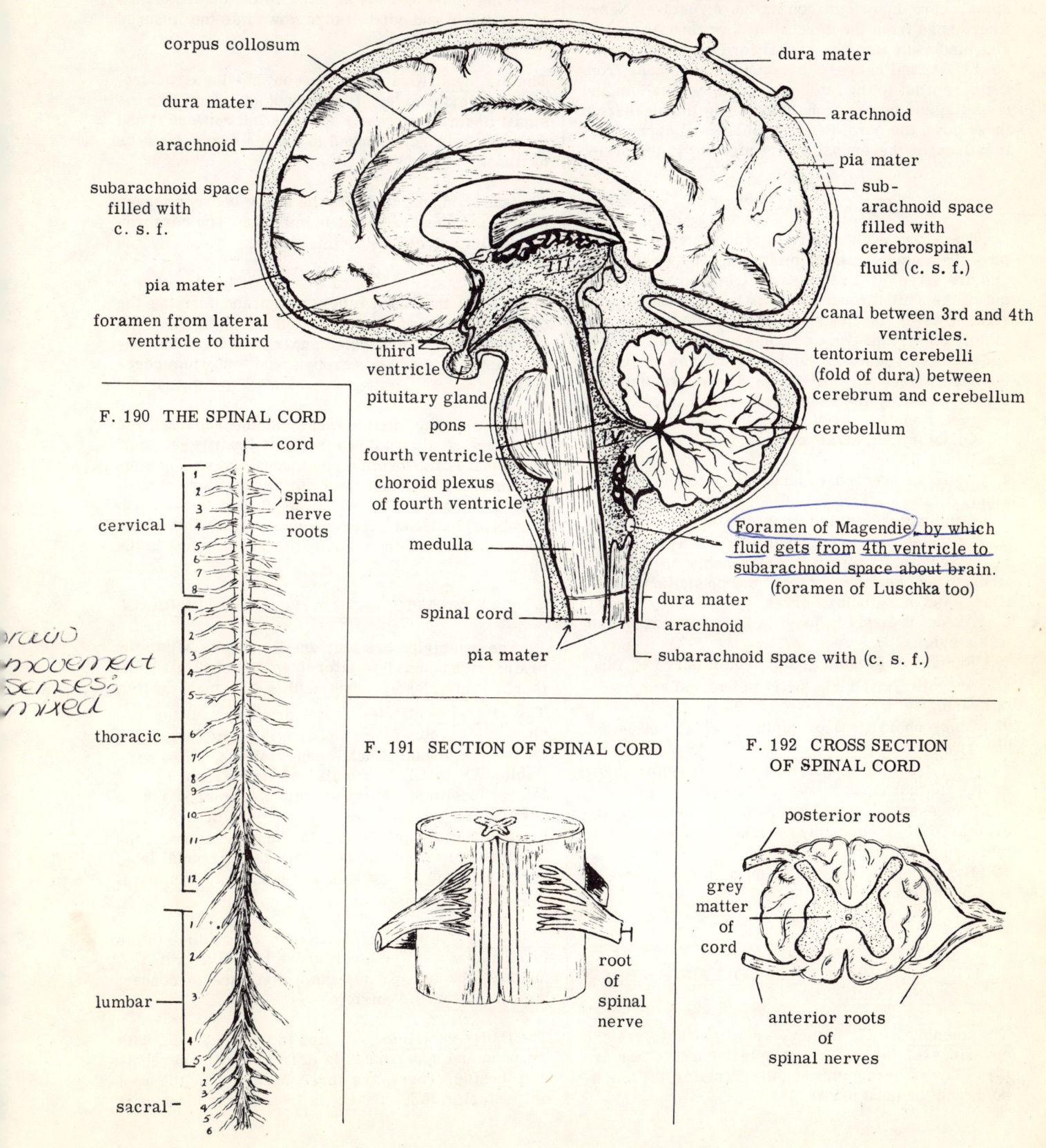

Labels:
- corpus collosum
- dura mater
- arachnoid
- subarachnoid space filled with c. s. f.
- pia mater
- foramen from lateral ventricle to third
- third ventricle
- pituitary gland
- pons
- fourth ventricle
- choroid plexus of fourth ventricle
- medulla
- spinal cord
- dura mater
- arachnoid
- pia mater
- subarachnoid space with (c. s. f.)
- dura mater
- arachnoid
- pia mater
- sub-arachnoid space filled with cerebrospinal fluid (c. s. f.)
- canal between 3rd and 4th ventricles.
- tentorium cerebelli (fold of dura) between cerebrum and cerebellum
- cerebellum
- **Foramen of Magendie, by which fluid gets from 4th ventricle to subarachnoid space about brain.** (foramen of Luschka too)

F. 190 THE SPINAL CORD

- cord
- spinal nerve roots
- cervical (1-8)
- thoracic (1-12)
- lumbar (1-5)
- sacral (1-6)

brain movement senses; mixed

F. 191 SECTION OF SPINAL CORD

- root of spinal nerve

F. 192 CROSS SECTION OF SPINAL CORD

- posterior roots
- grey matter of cord
- anterior roots of spinal nerves

*On old Olympics Towering Tops.
A French and German Viewed a Hop*

down the cord and out by two neurons, the upper and lower motor neurons.

The student should realize that the entire brain and spinal cord form one continuous structure. Nerve fibers pass from the cerebrum, down through the mid and hindbrain into the spinal cord, and are relayed out by a spinal nerve. Other motor fibers pass from the cerebrum to the midbrain, pons, cerebellum, and medulla, and new neurons may convey impulses from these down the cord. Sensory fibers will carry their impulses in the opposite direction up to the brain.

THE CRANIAL NERVES.

There are twelve pairs of cranial nerves. These have their centers in the midbrain, pons, or medulla, and are given off directly from the brain. They pass out of the skull through foramina to end in the various structures of the head and neck. Some of them are motor, some sensory, and some mixed, i.e., sensory and motor. Frequently the cranial nerves are called the first, second, third, etc. These are listed in order below together with their other names. There are two of each - a right and a left.

1. Olfactory or first cranial (pair) to the nose, smell.
2. Optic or second cranial (pair) to the eyeball, sight.
3. Oculomotor or third (pair) to some eye muscles.
4. Trochlear or fourth (pair) to one eye muscle.
5. Trigeminal or fifth (pair) sensory to the face, (tri - three, geminal - roots) the ophthalmic, maxillary, and mandibular nerves. *(eye lid)*
6. Abducent or sixth (pair) to lateral rectus muscle of the eye.
7. Facial or seventh (pair) motor nerve to face.
8. Acoustic or eighth (pair) to internal ear, nerve of hearing.
9. Glossopharyngeal or ninth (pair) to tongue and pharynx.
10. Vagus or tenth (pair) part of parasympathetic system to thorax, abdomen, and pelvis.
11. Accessory or eleventh (pair) two parts; the cranial part accompanies vagus, cervical part to muscles of the neck.
12. Hypoglossal or twelfth (pari) motor nerve to tongue and neck.

12 pairs

S. 171 THE MENINGES OR COVERINGS - BRAIN AND CORD.

The meninges (G. meninx - a membrane) are the coverings of the brain and spinal cord. There are three layers or membranes: the pia mater, the arachnoid, and the dura mater.

The pia mater (L. pia - tender, clinging or affectionate; mater - mother; clinging mother) is the inner covering. It is closely applied to the outer surface of the brain and cord. It dips down into the fissures and sulci.

The arachnoid (G. arachne - a cobweb-like structure) is the middle layer. It does not dip down into the small fissures; so that a space is left between it and the pia. It is not attached to the pia except by webs of tissue.

The subarachnoid space is the space between the pia mater and the arachnoid membrane. The cerebrospinal fluid circulated in this space.

The dura mater (L. dura - tough or hard; mater - mother) is the tough other membrane forming the outer covering of the brain and cord. In the brain there are two layers which separate to form the venous sinuses, the falx cerebri, and tentorium cerebelli.

These three membranes and the subarachnoid space are continued down from the brain to surround the spinal cord, forming continuous layers. The subarachnoid space about the brain is therefore continuous with a similar space about the spinal cord. Cerebrospinal fluid may circulate from this space overlying the brain down to the same space in the cord.

S. 172 VENTRICLES - CAVITIES OF THE BRAIN.

The ventricles are four small cavities within the brain: right and left lateral ventricles, third and fourth ventricles (L. ventriculus - a small cavity).

The lateral ventricles (pair) are two cavities, one on each cerebral hemisphere, and lie under the corpus callosum. Each opens into the third ventricle. When filled with air and radiographed in the lateral position, this ventricle resembles a hand pointing out a direction. The wrist is the posterior horn in the occipital lobe, the hand is the body, the index finger is the anterior horn in the frontal lobe, and the thumb is the inferior horn in the temporal lobe.

The third ventricle (one) lies in the midline of the forebrain at a lower level, above the sella turcica. A narrow channel passes down and back to connect it with the fourth ventricle.

The fourth ventricle (one) lies in the hindbrain, with the pons and upper medulla in front and the cerebellum behind. There are three openings in the roof or posterior thin surface, in front of the lower part of the cerebellum. These openings communicate with the subarachnoid space and allow cerebrospinal fluid to pass out into the subarachnoid space. They are called the foramina of Luschka and Magendie.

The choroid plexuses are networks of veins in the root of each ventricle. The thin lining membrane of the ventricle in this area secretes cerebrospinal fluid. The choroid plexuses may become calcified and therefore visible in films.

The cerebrospinal fluid is a clear, colorless liquid formed from blood in the choroid plexuses and secreted into the ventricles. Because all ventricles communicate, this fluid may pass down to the fourth ventricle. It passes out through the foramina in the roof of the fourth ventricle into the subarachnoid space to surround the brain and spinal cord. Blood, pus, organisms, etc., in one ventricle will therefore pass out into the subarachnoid space of the cord. The fluid in the subarachnoid space is frequently examined for these.

A lumbar puncture is a procedure consisting of inserting a long needle between the spinous processes of the two lumbar vertebrae into the subarachnoid space of the spinal cord. Clear cerebrospinal fluid will drip out through the needle and may be collected. It can be examined for pus cells, blood cells, salt content, etc. Damage to the brain with hemorrhage may result in blood cells in this fluid. Anesthetics are sometimes injected through the needle for a spinal anesthetic.

S. 173 THE AUTONOMIC NERVOUS SYSTEM.

The atonomic nervous system is listed under the peripheral nervous system, S. 168. It controls the contraction and dilatation of hollow organs having involuntary muscles in their walls. It regulates the contraction of heart muscle. It controls the activity of many secreting glands.
These structures include:
(1) the sweat glands, blood vessels, and the hair muscles of the skin;
(2) the pupils - contraction and dilatation;
(3) hollow organs - digestive tract, bile ducts and gall bladder, uterus, and uterine tubes, male reproductive ducts, ureters, bladder, bronchi, and the bronchioles; (all these contain involuntary muscle);
(4) secreting glands of the mouth, salivary glands, glands of the esophagus, stomach, small and large intestine, pancreas, uterus, vagina, testes, seminal vesicles, prostate, etc.;
(5) the heart and blood vessels including capillaries.
The central nervous system (brain and cord) controls the contraction of skeletal muscles.

The autonomic nervous system is considered separately as it is independent of cerebral control. It has centers (groups of cell bodies) in the midbrain, medulla, and in the dorsal, lumbar, and sacral regions of the cord. These control the activity of the structures outlined above. It is not possible, for example, to cause contraction of the walls of the stomach, nor secretion of the salivary glands by conscious effort.
There are two distinct parts of the autonomic nervous system: (1) the sympathetic (thoracolumbar)
(2) the parasympathetic (craniosacral).
These two divisions are antagonistic, i.e., have opposing actions. If one division causes contraction, the other causes dilatation, etc.

THE SYMPATHETIC NERVOUS SYSTEM.

1. Sympathetic ganglia. A series of ganglia (groups of cell bodies) lie on each side of the vertebral column from the skull to the coccyx. These are:
(a) three cervical ganglia on each side;
(b) ten to twelve thoracic on each side;
(c) four lumbar on each side;
(d) four to five sacral.
2. The sympathetic trunks or chains are nerve fibers connecting these ganglia. The nerve fibers pass up or down between the ganglia.
3. Centers for the sympathetic system lie in the lateral parts of the thoracic and lumbar spinal cord.
4. Preganglionic fibers are axons from these centers that pass out with the spinal nerves to reach the sympathetic ganglia. These preganglionic fibers may end in the ganglion. They may pass up or down the sympathetic trunk. They may pass completely through a ganglion and end in a visceral ganglion, e.g., to the celiac, renal, aortic, or hypogastric ganglia.

The greater and lesser splanchnic nerves are of this latter type. Their axons pass out from the fifth to the eleventh dorsal nerves, through the ganglia and form two trunks. These pass down through the diaphragm into the abdomen. They end in the ganglia of the celiac and renal plexuses.
5. Postganglionic fibers are axons which pass from the sympathetic ganglia out in one of two ways:
(a) some of them pass back to a spinal nerve and along it to supply sweat glands, vessels, or hair muscles of the skin;
(b) others pass as visceral branches to other ganglia close to the organ supplied or to the organ itself.

The cervical sympathetic ganglia receive no fibers from the cervical part of the spinal cord, but from the upper thoracic ganglia by way of the sympathetic trunks.

3 & 4 lumbar is usually where they do the spinal puncture.

6. **Plexuses.** There are three large plexuses of nerve fibers:
   (a) the cardiac above the heart;
   (b) the celiac behind the stomach where the celiac artery begins;
   (c) the hypogastric, in the lower abdomen. From these plexuses, fibers pass with blood vessels to the organs supplied.

THE PARASYMPATHETIC NERVOUS SYSTEM.

The parasympathetic or cranio-sacral nervous system supplies nerve fibers to many of the same structures as the sympathetic, particulary the viscera.

These fibers produce opposite reactions to those induced by stimulation of the sympathetic fibers. The sympathetic have their centers in the thoracic and lumbar regions of the cord. The parasympathetic centers are in the midbrain and medulla - the cranial division, and the sacrum below - sacral part. From the cranial part, fibers pass out along with the 3rd, 7th, and 9th cranial nerves to end in ganglia close to the organs they supply, in the head. The vagus, or tenth, and accessory or eleventh cranial nerves also contain parasympathetic fibers which pass down with the vagus nerves. These enter the thorax and abdomen supplying the trachea, lungs, heart, and digestive tract as far as the splenic flexure. Many of these fibers join the plexuses and pass along the blood vessels with the sympathetic fibers.

The sacral part has centers in the sacral segment of the cord. The fibers pass out with the second, third and fourth sacral nerves and form the pelvic nerve and plexus. Nerve fibers are distributed to the colon below the splenic flexure, and to the pelvic organs.

One theory of the action of the sympathetic system is that adrenalin from the suprarenal glands stimulates this system in normal life. During emergencies such as flight or fight, the secretion of adrenalin is said to be increased to further stimulate the sympathetic to help the individual overcome the emergency. Whether this theory be true or not, it can be of definite value in helping the student remember the action of the nervous system. In fright the pupils dilate, the face becomes pale, because of contraction of blood vessels. The heart rate speeds up, and the blood pressure is raised to meet the emergency. The normal digestive processes and secretions of glands stop during the emergency.

ACTION OF THE SYMPATHETIC AND PARASYMPATHETIC.

Organs	Sympathetic	Parasympathetic
pupil	dilates	contracts
bronchi	dilates	contracts
heart	rate increased	rate decreased
G. I. tract	decreased peristalsis	increased peristalsis
sphincters	contract	
glands	decrease in activity	increases secretion
uterus	decreased contractions	increases contractions
arteries	contract	dilate

S. 174 SOME ANOMALIES OF THE NERVOUS SYSTEM.

Anencephaly (adj. anencephalic): absence of a brain.

Hydrocephalus: a large head, often due to a block in the holes in the roof of the fourth ventricle. The cerebrospinal fluid cannot get out from the brain and cord. Fluid accumulates in the ventricles, which then become dilated, compressing the brain against the skull. The sutures separate, and the head enlarges. If present before birth, delivery may not be possible because of the size of the head.

S. 175 SOME PATHOLOGICAL CONDITIONS.

Encephalitis: an inflammation of the brain.

Meningitis: an inflammation of the meninges or coverings of the brain and cord. This may be due to: tuberculosis, influenza, the pneumococcus or germ that caused lobar pneumonia, etc.

Poliomyelitis (infantile paralysis): a disease in which the motor cell bodies in the anterior part of the spinal cord are affected and sometimes destroyed. If destroyed, this results in a paralysis of the muscles controlled by the axons from these cell bodies. The extent depends upon the number of cells destroyed.

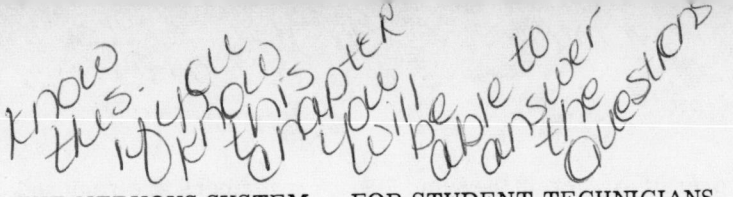

S. 176 SUMMARY OF THE NERVOUS SYSTEM - FOR STUDENT TECHNICIANS.

The summary given below should provide a student x-ray technician with sufficient knowledge to perform radiographic examinations. The foregoing sections have been included to make the Handbook complete. The student should not be burdened with these details. They may interest the graduate technician.

The unit structure of the nervous system is the nerve cell or neuron. It has a cell body and two sets of processes. The dendrites, at one end, carry nerve impulses towards the cell body. The axon, at the other end, carries impulses away from the cell body.

Motor neurons conduct impulses from the brain or cord to muscles causing them to contract, or to secreting glands causing them to secrete.

Sensory neurons carry sensations of heat, cold, touch, pressure, pain, to the cord and up to the brain. Some sensory neurons convey sensations from the eye (sight), ear (hearing), nose (smell), tongue (taste to the region of the brain where these are interpreted.

The nervous system is the control system of the human body. It consists of central and peripheral parts. The brain and spinal cord make up the central nervous system. The brain is completely enclosed by the bones of the visceral cranium. The brain includes: the cerebrum or forebrain, midbrain, and hindbrain.

The cerebrum: the large upper part is incompletely divided into two halves, the right and left cerebral hemispheres. These occupy the entire cranial cavity except the posterior cranial fossa. The cerebrum has centers controlling all mental processes, as well as motor centers to initiate muscular contraction and secretion of glands, as well as sensory centers for interpretation of sensations from the skin, muscles, joints, eyes, ears, nose, mouth, etc.

The midbrain is very small and lies below the cerebrum. It has nerve centers and conducting fibers.

The hindbrain occupies the posterior cranial fossa. It includes the pons, cerebellum, and medulla oblongata. It lies below the cerebrum with the pons in front, the large cerebellum behind, and the medulla below. These three parts contain nerve centers, nerve fibers which connect the three parts, as well as connecting fibers to the midbrain, cerebrum, and cord.

The spinal cord is a continuation downward of the medulla. It extends from the foramen magnum to the second lumbar vertebra. It ends by dividing into sacral and coccygeal nerves. These nerves spread out like a horse's tail and are called the cauda equina. The cord lies in the canal formed by the vertebral foramina.

The peripheral nervous system includes the cranial nerves, the spinal nerves, and the sympathetic and parasympathetic nervous systems, i.e., the autonomic nervous system.

Cranial nerves: twelve pairs of cranial nerves, right and left, arise from the mid and hindbrain. Ten pairs pass out through various foramina in the skull to reach the head and neck. The tenth (vagus) and the accessory (eleventh) supply parasympathetic nerves to the thoracic, abdominal and pelvic organs.

Spinal nerves: thirty-one pairs of spinal nerves are given off from the spinal cord. These leave through the intervertebral foramina. The lower cervical and first dorsal spinal nerves form large nerve trunks that pass out to the upper limbs. The dorsal spinal nerves pass around the body in grooves on the under surface of the ribs. The lumbar spinal nerves pass around the body in an obliquely downward direction. Some of these form large trunks to the lower limbs. Each spinal nerve carries sensory fibers into the cord and motor fibers out of the cord to the many structures supplied.

The autonomic nervous system: this consists of two parts: the sympathetic and parasympathetic. These are independent of brain control, although they have centers in the hindbrain and spinal cord. They supply the organs having involuntary muscles in their walls, i.e., the viscera, as well as secreting glands. Nerve fibers pass to these structures from both parts. They have opposing actions, e.g., the parasympathetic cause secretion of glands, the sympathetic inhibit secretion. The sympathetic cause contraction of blood vessels, thereby raising blood pressure, etc.

Sympathectomy is an operation wherein the sympathetic nerve fibers are removed, thereby causing blood vessels to become permanently dilated to increase the supply of blood to a limb, etc.

Vagotomy is an operation whereby the vagus nerves around the lower esophagus are removed, thereby cutting off impulses to the secreting glands of the stomach to decrease gastric secretion in ulcer cases.

The meninges are the three coverings or layers which enclose the brain and spinal cord. These are called, from within out, the pia mater, arachnoid, and dura mater.

The subarachnoid space lies between the pia mater and arachnoid layers. The cerebrospinal fluid circulates about the brain and cord in this space.

The ventricles are four cavities within the brain. The two lateral ventricles lie one in each cerebral hemisphere. They open into the third ventricle, which lies in the midline at a lower level. The fourth ventricle is in the hindbrain. It communicates with the third ventricle by a narrow channel that passes through the midbrain. The fourth ventricle has three holes (foramina) in its roof. These open into the subarachnoid space. Cerebrospinal fluid passes from the fourth ventricle out to the subarachnoid space by these three holes.

The cerebrospinal fluid is a colorless liquid that is formed in the ventricles of the brain. It passes out to the subarachnoid space through the roof of the fourth ventricle. It circulates around the brain and down the subarachnoid space of the cord to the level of the upper sacrum. In head injuries, bleeding into the ventricles or in the subarachnoid space about the brain will result in blood in the cerebrospinal fluid about the spinal cord. Infection involving the ventricles or subarachnoid space will result in white blood cells or organisms in the cerebrospinal fluid.

A lumbar puncture is a procedure consisting of inserting a long hollow needle between two adjacent spinous processes of lumbar vertebrae into the subarachnoid space to obtain cerebrospinal fluid. This is usually done between the third and fourth lumbar vertebrae. The fluid removed may be examined for blood, pus cells, organisms, or chlorides, etc.

S. 177 BLOOD SUPPLY TO THE BRAIN.

The brain is supplied by the two internal carotid arteries and two vertebral arteries. These enter the cranium through foramina at the base.

Meningeal arteries also enter through foramina and follow grooves on the inner table of the skull to supply the inner table and dura mater with blood. These grooves are often visible in radiographs and may be difficult to distinguish from fractures.

The venous sinuses of the skull are large trunk veins which drain blood from the veins within the skull. They leave the cranium as the internal jugular veins. Two, the superior and inferior sagittal sinuses, lie between the two cerebral hemispheres, and extend back to the occipital bone. They empty into two transverse sinuses. These pass around the base of the skull and form the internal jugular veins on each side. Other smaller sinuses empty into the larger sinuses as they proceed to the jugular foramina.

Grooves in the inner table accommodate the venous sinuses. These, particularly on the occipital bone, are often visible in radiographs of the skull.

S. 178 APPLICATION TO RADIOGRAPHY.

The various parts of the brain, the fluid filled ventricles, and the spinal cord are not visible as separate images in skull films. The pineal gland, if calcified, does show; and the calcification should be in the midline, if views are taken correctly.

Expanding lesions in the brain, inflammations, tumors, and blood clots will not often be visualized. These space-occupying lesions may press upon the ventricle, deforming or displacing them. It is necessary to use an opaque or lucent medium to outline the ventricles.

They may displace the pineal gland from the midline; and if the pineal gland be calcified, its displacement may be seen.

They may cause thinning of the cranium, or destruction of bone from pressure.

If there is calcification in a tumor or its blood vessels, this should be apparent in films.

Tumors may cause displacement of blood vessels or they may have a rich blood supply. Arteriograms may demonstrate these changes.

Tumors of the pituitary gland should cause enlargement, or destruction of the sella turcica, or erosion of the clinoid processes, demonstrable by x-ray.

Ventriculography is a procedure consisting of making a small hole in the cranium and inserting a long needle into the lateral ventricles. Air is injected through the needle after removal of the fluid, to fill the cavities, and outline deformities or displacement due to space occupying lesions. Films are then taken to outline the ventricles.

Encephalography is a procedure that consists of doing a lumbar puncture, with the patient sitting upright, the withdrawal of spinal fluid, and its replacement by air. This air rises up in the subarachnoid space to surround the brain, and by passing through the openings in the fourth ventricle, to outline the ventricles as well. Films are taken of the skull to show the ventricles, Encephalogram - the films.

Cerebral arteriography consists of injecting opaque dye into one of the internal carotid arteries in the neck to outline the blood vessels on that side of the brain. Films are then taken. The vessels may be displaced, or may be thinned out, or may be too numerous. There may be dilatation if an aneurysm be present.

Myelography is a procedure whereby a lumbar puncture is done, and a small quantity of opaque dye is injected into the subarachnoid space. Under fluoroscopic control, and by tilting the table, the fluid may be moved up or down to outline deformities. Myelogram - the films.

Tumors involving the cord, or a rupture of a nucleus pulposus result in deformity of the column of opaque dye. The extent and location of these lesions may be determined by a myelogram.

Successful ventriculograms, encephalograms, myelograms or cerebral arteriograms depend upon the type of films obtained by the technician. Careful centering and correct technic are essential, and some experience is necessary.

S. 179 TERMS USED IN CHAPTER XXI.

anencephaly
abducent nerve
accessory nerve
acoustic nerve
arachnoid
autonomic nervous system
axon

cell body
center
central nervous system
cerebellum
cerebellar (adj.)
cerebrum
cerebral (adj.)

F. 193 VENTRICLES OF BRAIN
- sagittal section through median line -

Lateral ventricle shown with black dots

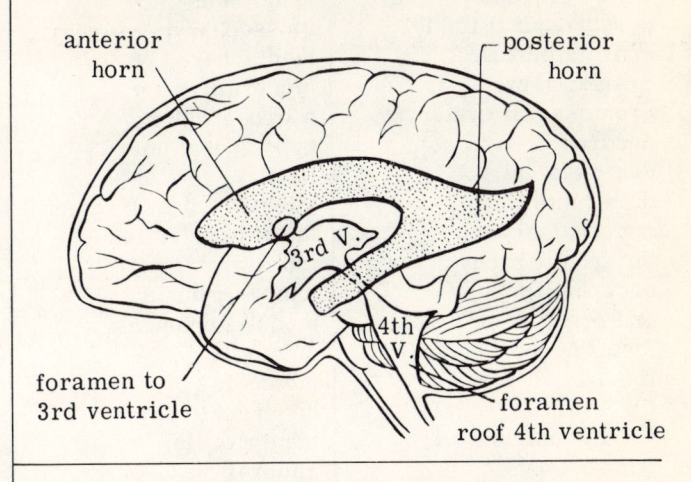

F. 194 LATERAL VENTRICLES - frontal view -

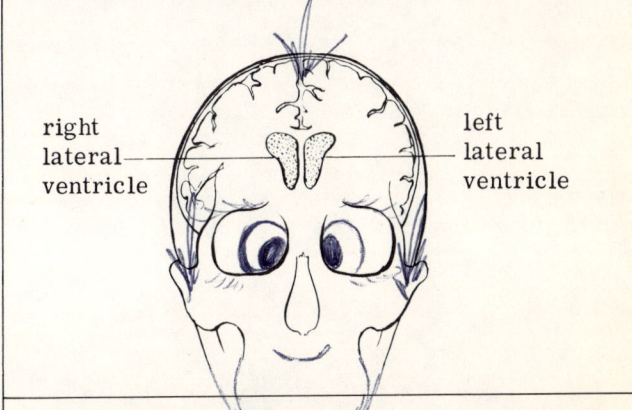

F. 195 MYELOGRAM - dark shadow represents opaque medium injected

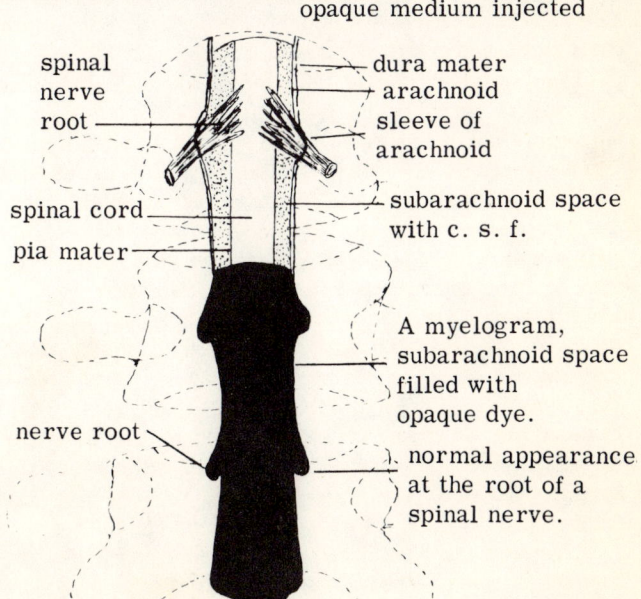

cerebral arteriography
cerebral peduncles
cerebral hemispheres
cerebrospinal fluid
choroid plexus
cranial nerve
craniosacral system
dendron
dentrites (pl.)
dura mater
encephalogram
encephalography
encephalitis
end organ
facial nerve
fissure
forebrain
fourth ventricle
frontal lobe

ganglion
ganglia (pl.)
ganglionic (adj.)
glossopharyngeal nerve
hemisphere
hindbrain
hydrocephalus
hypoglossal nerve
insula
intervertebral foramen
lateral ventricles
lobes
lumbar puncture
medulla oblongata
meninges
meningitis
meningeal (adj.)
meningocele
midbrain
motor nerve

myelogram
myelography
nerve cell
nervous system
neuron
nucleus
occipital lobe
oculomotor nerve
olfactory nerve
optic nerve
parasympathetic
parietal lobe
peripheral nerves
pineal gland
plexus
poliomyelitis
pons
quadrigeminal bodies
reflex arc
sensory nerve

spinal cord
spinal canal
spinal nerve
subarachnoid space
subdural space
sympathetic nervous
 system
synapse
temporal lobe
third ventricle
thoracic-lumbar system
trigeminal nerve
trochlear nerve
vagus nerve
ventricle
vertebral canal
ventriculography
vertebral foramen
vertebral foramina (pl.)

CHAPTER XXII. THE SPECIAL SENSES. 11/6/73.

S. 180 THE PARTS OF THE EYEBALL.

1. Coats:
   (1) fibrous (outer) layer
       (a) sclera
       (b) cornea
   (2) vascular (middle) layer
       (a) choroid
       (b) ciliary body
       (c) iris and pupil
   (3) retina (inner or nervous layer

2. Refracting media:
   (1) aqueous humor
   (2) lens and capsule
   (3) vitrous body or humor

3. Muscles:
   (1) iris (a) constrictor of pupil
              (b) dilator of pupil
   (2) lens - ciliary muscles

S. 181 DETAILED STUDY OF THE EYEBALL.

The eyeball occupies the anterior part of the orbit. It is spherical in shape, except at the front where it bulges anteriorly. It measures almost one inch in diameter. It has three coats or coverings: the fibrous or outer layer, the vascular or middle layer, and the retina or inner layer.

1. The coats of the eyeball.

(1) The outer layer is fibrous tissue and includes:
   (a) the sclera which covers the posterior five-sixths of the eyeball and is white; (look at the eye);
   (b) the cornea which covers the anterior one-sixth. It is transparent so that light may pass through it.

(2) The vascular or middle layer is rich in blood vessels.
   (a) The choroid coat is the posterior two-thirds of the middle layer, and is inside the fibrous layer.
   (b) The ciliary body is a thickened ring in front of the choroid proper. It contains the ciliary muscle consisting of circular and radiating fibers. This muscle is attached to the ligament of the lens and regulates the convexity of the lens.
   (c) The iris is the colored membrane that surrounds the pupil. Pigment in the iris determines the color of the eye. The iris contains circular and radiating muscle fibers: the constrictor and dilator of the pupil. The pupil is the circular hole in the center of the iris, and appears black. It contracts in bright light or for close vision, and dilates in dim light or for distant vision.

(3) The retina is the inner coat. It actually consists of ten layers, only one of which will be considered here: the visual layer.
   (a) The rods and cones make up the visual layer. These are the receptors for sensations of light and color. The cones are adapted for bright light and color. The rods are sensitive to dim light. Cones are most numerous in the retina directly opposite the pupil. Rods are much more numerous and lie in

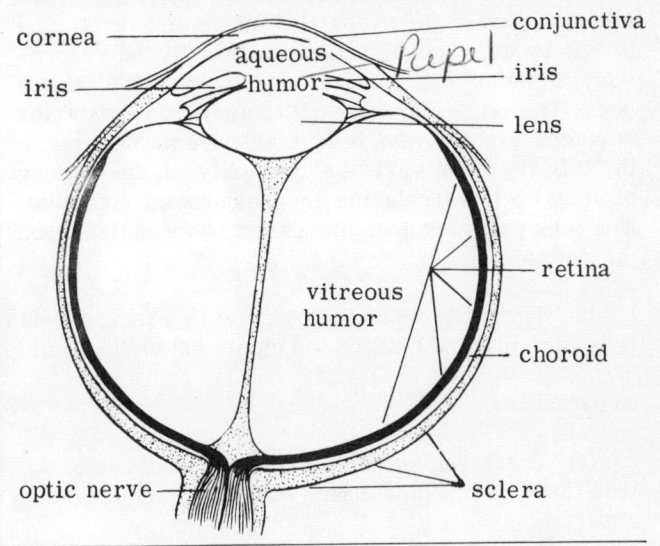

F. 196 THE EYEBALL - viewed from above -

labels: cornea, iris, aqueous humor, conjunctiva, pupil, iris, lens, vitreous humor, retina, choroid, optic nerve, sclera

---

F. 197 THE EYE BALL - viewed from one side -

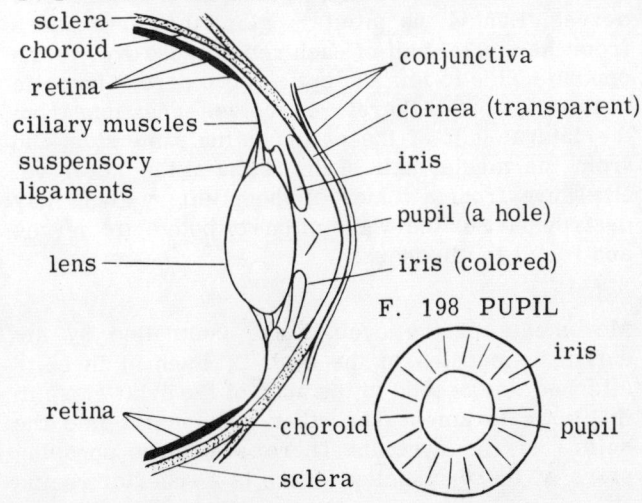

labels: sclera, choroid, retina, ciliary muscles, suspensory ligaments, lens, retina, conjunctiva, cornea (transparent), iris, pupil (a hole), iris (colored), choroid, sclera

F. 198 PUPIL

labels: iris, pupil

the peripheral part of the retina. These visual cells contain visual purple which fades with exposure to light and regenerates with rest. Waves of light or color cause some chemical changes in the visual cells, which then transmit sensations along the optic nerve to the visual center in the forebrain. The brain interprets these sensations.

(b) The several other layers of the retina are complicated, and will not be considered here.

2. The refracting media.

The refracting media fill the cavity of the eyeball, and are transparent so that light may pass through them to reach the retina.

(1) The aqueosus humor lies behind the cornea, (transparent) in the anterior part of the eyeball. It is thin and clear.

(2) The lens and its capsule lie vertically in the anterior part of the eyeball behind the aqueosus humor. It is attached along its margin to the suspensory ligament of the lens and by it to the ciliary body. The lens is biconvex; its anterior and posterior surfaces are convex. It is transparent. Muscles in the ciliary body vary the convexity of the lens by pulling upon or relaxing the suspensory ligament. The lens provides accommodation to focus light upon the retina.

(3) The vitreous body or humor is a transparent jelly-like material filling the cavity behind the lens.

3. Muscles.

(1) The muscles of the iris, and (2) those of the lens have been discussed with the iris and lens above.

The optic nerves pass back through the optic foramina to the cranial cavity, forming the second cranial nerves. Behind the pituitary gland the nerve fibers from the medial half of each retina cross over to the opposite side to join the optic nerve here. The optic nerve on one side therefore receives sensations from the lateral half of the retina on the same side, and from the medial half of the retina of the other eye. Pressure from a tumor of the pituitary gland may destroy part or the whole of one or both optic nerves and result in blindness.

Movements of the eyeball are controlled by six extrinsic muscles of the eyeball. Each of these is attached at one end to the apex of the orbit close to the optic foramen. The other end inserts into the sclera of the eyeball. There are three opposing pairs of these muscles. There is a superior rectus muscle attached to the upper surface of the eyeball. Contraction of this muscle turns the eye upward. The opposing inferior rectus is attached to the under surface, and turns the eye downward. The medial rectus on the medial side and the lateral rectus on the lateral side turn the eye in or out. The superior oblique muscle attached to the top of the eyeball rolls the eyeball inward. The inferior oblique muscles below the eyeball rolls the eye out.

These muscles receive motor fibers from the oculomotor (3rd), or trochlear (4th), or abducent (6th), cranial nerves, through the apex of the orbit.

The nerve control is so arranged that both eyes move in the same direction at the same time, up, down or to the left or right.

This does not apply to convergence, in which both eyes turn inward to view some close object. Strabismus (squint or crossed eyes) is due to weakness of one muscle or its nerve control.

The eyelids protect the eyes and cover them during sleep. The external canthus is the point at the outer border where the two eyelids meet. This is sometimes used as a landmark for the radiographic base line.

The conjunctiva is the thin membrane that covers the inner surfaces of the eyelids and is reflected over the front of the eyeball where it is transparent.

The lacrimal or tear gland lies behind the outer part of the supra-orbital margin of each orbit. It secretes through several ducts which open on the conjunctiva. Tears lubricate the eyeball.

A small opening is present on the free surface of each eyelid close to its medial end (puncta). This opening leads into a small lacrimal duct. The two ducts pass medially to end in a small sac, the lacrimal sac. A nasolacrimal duct passes down a groove and opening on the lacrimal bone to reach the nasal cavity on each side. One of these ducts may become obstructed. Opaque media may be injected to outline the ducts. Tears should enter the nose by the lacrimal duct system.

S. 182 APPLICATION TO RADIOGRAPHY.

1. The lacrimal duct may be injected with opaque dye through the puncta to outline an obstruction in it.

2. In case of impending blindness, or diplopia (seeing double) films may be required to show the optic foramen. This requires special views. (See skull).

3. In other cases of blindness films of the sella turcica may be required to diagnose or exclude a tumor of the pituitary gland.

4. In injuries to the eye a piece of metal may be driven into the orbit or eyeball. If in the eyeball the foreign body will change its position with movement of the eye. Films may be taken to determine if an opaque foreign body be present and to locate it.

S. 183 APPLICATION to FLUOROSCOPY - Dark Adaptation.

A fluoroscopic screen contains calcium tungstate crystals. These crystals are lighted up or illuminated when the undertable x-ray tube is energized. The degree of illumination of this screen is very faint if compared to that of an ordinary desk lamp. This may be demonstrated by having someone step on the fluoroscopic foot switch, leaving the overhead room light turned on. It will be impossible to see any light on the screen. When a patient's body is interposed between the x-ray tube and the screen, the illumination is further decreased. This varies with the thickness and density of the part of the body fluoroscoped.

A radiologist who goes from a well-lighted room into the fluoroscopic room will see images on the screen very faintly or not at all. The eyes must be prepared or accommodated by dark adaptation. The rods of the retina take over vision in very dim lighting. The cones are insensitive to such faint illumination. The preparation consists of a period of resting the rods of the retina. The longer the period of rest the more acute vision of faint light becomes. This was formerly accomplished by sitting in a room in complete darkness and by wearing smoked goggles between fluoroscopic examinations. Later it was decided that, since the rods of the retina are insensitive to colored light, the same accommodation could be obtained by wearing red goggles for a period of time. The radiologist could sit in a room with ordinary lighting. The red goggles filtered out all but red light. The rods were supposed to be insensitive to red light. More recently the insensibility of rods to red light has been questioned. It has been suggested that prepartion should include the wearing of red goggles in ordinary light with a further short period spent in a completely darkened room (Riebel). In addition, if red goggles are worn between fluoroscopic examinations, a short period should be spent in a completely darkened room before the next examination is attempted. If the eyes are exposed to bright light such as that of viewing boxes, the dark adaptation is very quickly lost. Then the dark adaptation must be repeated.

A technician assisting a radiologist at fluoroscopy may wonder why the radiologist can see images that are not visible to her. The radiologist's eyes are not better, but he knows what to look for, and in addition his eyes are adapted. Technicians often become impatient when the radiologist "wastes" a lot of time getting ready for fluoroscopy. This is not wasted time but a very necessary preparation.

F. 199 OPTIC NERVES - crossing or decussation -

- viewed from above -

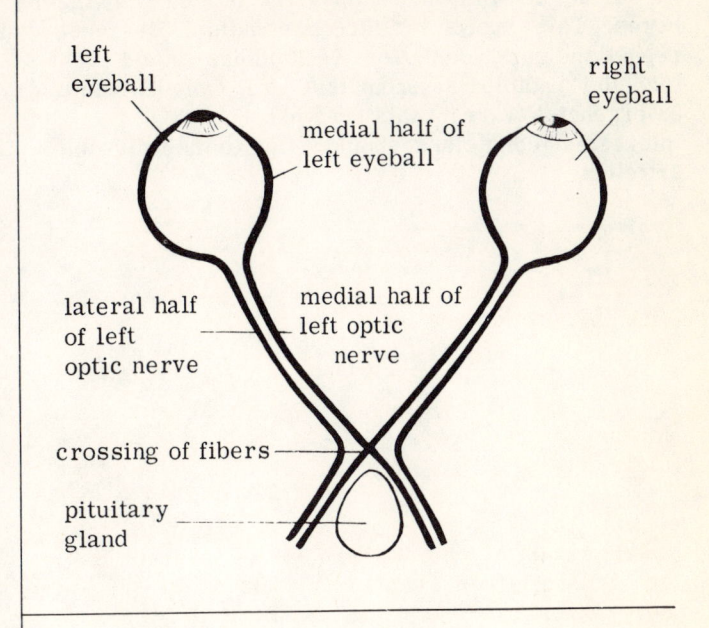

F. 200 MUSCLES OF THE EYEBALL - lateral view -

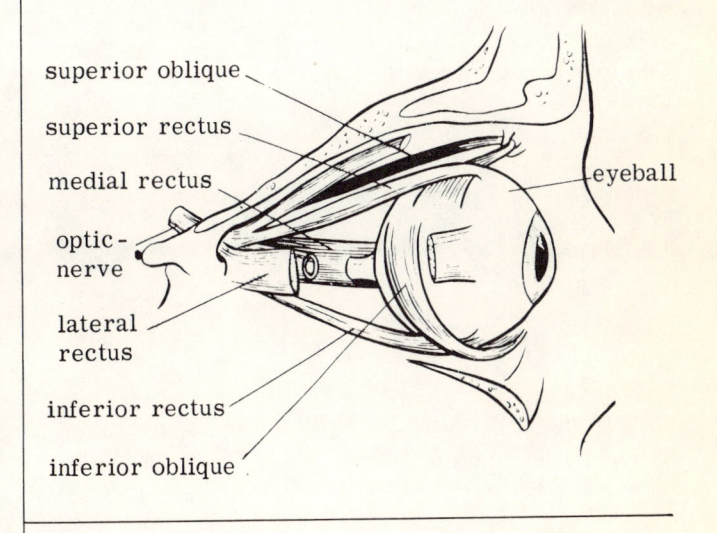

F. 201 LACRIMAL (TEAR) GLAND and DUCTS

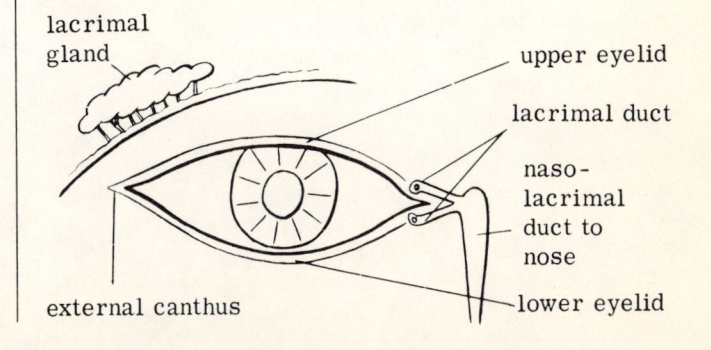

A radiologist, on the other hand, may become annoyed when doctors or technicians ask him to examine films between fluoroscopic examinations. He must do this using brightly lighted viewing boxes. This spoils his accommodation. He must repeat the dark adaptation. Technicians should protect the radiologist from this evil. Only extreme emergencies warrant this practice.

Interested technicians should refer to the following articles:

1. Fluoroscopes and fluoroscopy by Chamberlain, W. E. in Radiology, Vol. 38, 1942.

2. Efficiency of Red Goggles by Riebel, F. A. in American Journal of Roentgenology, Vol. 70, 1953.

3. The Uses of the Eyes in X-Ray Diagnosis, by Riebel, F. A. in Radiology, Vol. 70 1958.

S. 184 THE EAR - IMPORTANT PARTS.

1. External ear: (1) auricle or pinna
                  (2) external auditory meatus.
                  (3) tympanic membrane or ear drum

2. Middle ear or tympanic cavity:
   (1) auditory ossicles:
       (a) malleus or hammer
       (b) incus or anvil
       (c) stapes or stirrup
   (2) openings:
       (a) to external auditory meatus
       (b) to auditory (Eustachian tube)
       (c) to mastoid antrum, cells
       (d) to cochlea of internal ear
       (e) to vestibule of internal ear

3. Internal ear: (1) osseous labyrinth:
                      (a) vestibule
                      (b) cochlea
                      (c) semicircular canals
                  (2) membraneous labyrinth: as above
                  (3) hair cells, organ of hearing to cochlear part of the acoustic or eighth cranial nerve
                  (4) hair cells of semicircular canals to the vestibular branch of the acoustic nerve.

S. 185 BRIEF STUDY OF PARTS OF THE EAR.

The cartilaginous auricle, and the external auditory meatus, the parts of the external ear, have been described with the skull. The ear drum or tympanic membrane lies at the inner end of the external auditory meatus and separates it from the middle ear. The function of the external ear is to conduct sound vibrations or waves to the ear drum or tympanic membrane. The drum then vibrates.

The middle ear is a very small cavity within the petrous part of the temporal bone. There are five openings in its walls.

The cochlear opening lies between the middle ear and cochlea of the internal ear. This opening is closed.

The vestibular opening connects the cavity of the middle ear with the vestibule of the inner ear. This also is closed by a membrane.

There is an opening into the mastoid antrum and the mastoid cells. Infection of the middle ear (otitis media) may pass into the mastoid cells (mastoiditis).

The auditory or Eustachian tube from the nasopharynx also opens into the middle ear. Air from the throat may pass up into the middle ear. Air pressure on the inside and outside of the ear drum is kept equal by the auditory tube. The drum does not bulge in nor out. Infection also may pass up through the auditory tube from the throat to involve the middle ear.

The other opening between the external and middle ear is covered by the ear drum or tympanic membrane.

Three minute bones, the ossicles, form a system of levers in the middle ear. The malleus or hammer is attached at one end to the ear drum. The other end is in contact with one end of the incus or anvil. The opposite end of the incus is attached to one end of the stapes or stirrup. The other end of the stapes fills the vestibular opening of the internal ear. Sound vibrations are transmitted through the ear drum to the malleus. The vibrations are carried and magnified by the three ossicles to the vestibule of the internal ear.

The internal ear lies within the petrous part of the temporal bone. It is less than one inch in size. Because its anatomy is complicated, only a brief summary will be given here. A series of bony chambers form an osseous labyrinth composed of three parts: a vestibule, a cochlea, and three semicircular canals. Inside the bony labyrinth a further membranous lining conforms to the shape of the bony structures. Lymph fills the cavity. The cochlea is shaped like a snail. In its membrane are hair cells. These receive the vibrations of sound transmitted to the vestibule. The cochlear branch of the acoustic or eighth cranial nerve carries these sensations to the brain where they are interpreted.

The semicircular canals are three half circles filled with lymph and forming part of the bony labyrinth. These canals are placed at angles to each other. A change in position of the head causes changes in the fluid within these canals. Hair cells within them transmit sensations to the vestibular branch of the acoustic nerve and hence to the brain. The position of the head is thereby determined.

The acoustic or eighth cranial nerve passes into the internal auditory meatus through the internal auditory foramen on the posterior surface of the petrous part of the temporal bone. This sensory nerve consists of two parts. The cochlear part is concerned with hearing. The vestibular part is concerned with body equilibrium and the position of the head.

An acoustic neuroma involving the acoustic nerve may cause erosion of the internal auditory opening. This may be apparent in special views on this area.

170

F. 202 THE EAR - external - middle - internal -

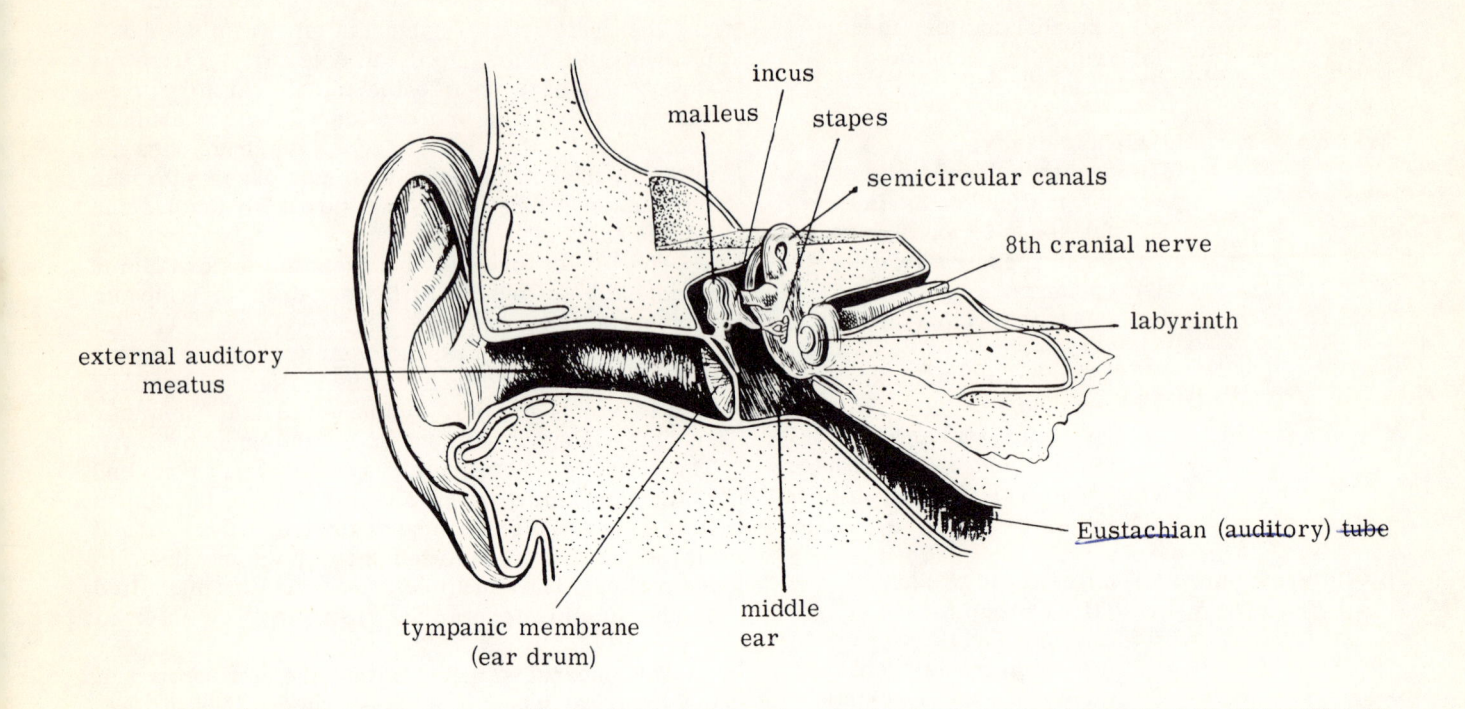

Handwritten note: 1. malleus 2. stapes 3. incus

Labels: incus, malleus, stapes, semicircular canals, 8th cranial nerve, labyrinth, external auditory meatus, Eustachian (auditory) tube, tympanic membrane (ear drum), middle ear

F. 203 BRAIN - basal view - to show origin of olfactory nerve (smell), optic nerve (sight).

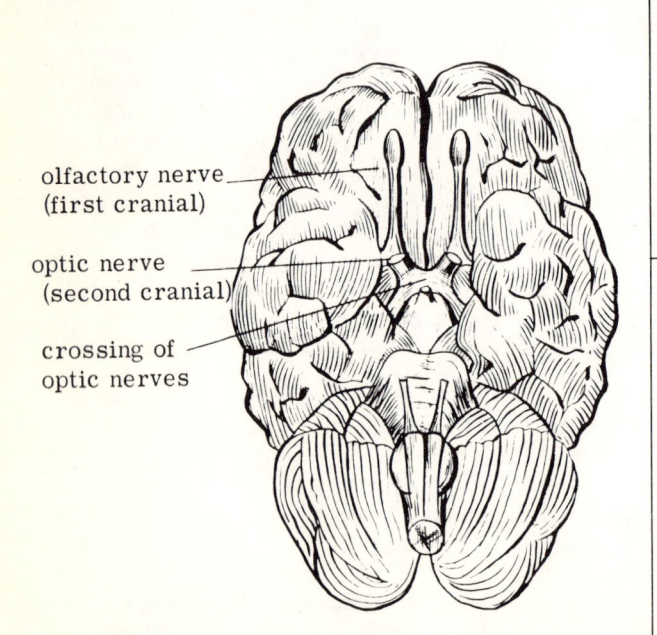

Labels: olfactory nerve (first cranial), optic nerve (second cranial), crossing of optic nerves

F. 204 OLFACTORY NERVE and END ORGANS OF SMELL

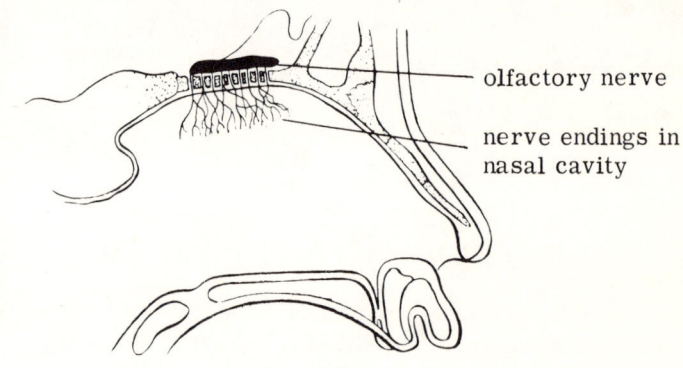

Labels: olfactory nerve, nerve endings in nasal cavity

F. 205 TASTE BUDS OF TONGUE

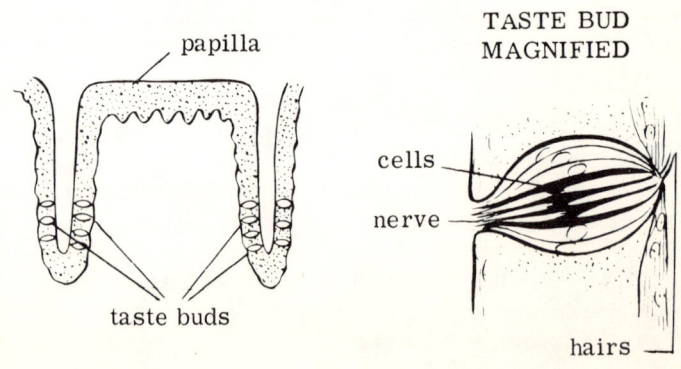

Labels: papilla, taste buds

TASTE BUD MAGNIFIED

Labels: cells, nerve, hairs

S. 186 THE END ORGANS OF SMELL.

The olfactory or first cranial nerves are concerned with smell. Minute fibers of these nerves leave the cranium through small openings in the cribriform plate of the ethmoid bone to enter the nasal cavities. These fibers end in hair cells in the lining membrane of the upper part of each nasal fossa. Particles of many substances in the form of gas reach these hair cells. They cause some chemical changes in the hair cells. Impulses are transmitted by the olfactory nerves to the brain from these hair cells and are interpreted as the odor of some specific substance. These nerve endings become fatigued readily so that obnoxious odors after a time fail to stimulate them.

S. 187 THE END ORGANS OF TASTE.

Fibers from the seventh and ninth cranial nerves carry taste fibers to the tongue. On the upper surface of the tongue many minute projections called papillae are present. Some of these contain taste buds. These taste buds are oval bodies composed of long cells having hairs at their surfaces. Taste is concerned primarily with four taste sensations: salty, sweet, sour, and bitter. These substances in solution cause chemical changes in cells of the taste buds. The stimulus produced by these changes is transmitted by the olfactory nerves to the brain for interpretations.

Taste differentiation is limited. Actually there is usually a combination of taste and smell. Patients with head colds often complain that they cannot taste their food. Actually their sense of smell is diminished by the head cold, and they cannot smell.

CHAPTER XXIII. CONTENTS OF THE BODY CAVITIES.

S. 188 See body cavities, section 15, page 15.

I. THE HEAD
1. Visceral cranium: brain, pituitary and pineal glands
2. Orbits
3. Nasal cavities, nasopharynx, paranasal sinuses
4. Mouth
5. External and internal auditory meatuses

II. THE NECK
1. Pharynx or throat
2. Larynx or voice box
3. Upper trachea
4. Thyroid cartilage or Adams's apple
5. Thyroid gland
6. Parathyroid glands
7. Blood and lymph vessel

III. CONTENTS OF THE CHEST OR THORAX.
1. Right Lung
2. Left lung
3. Mediastinum, containing:
   (1) trachea or windpipe
   (2) esophagus or gullet
   (3) thymus gland
   (4) aorta, ascending, arch, descending
   (5) superior vena cava,
   (6) inferior vena cava, thoracic part
   (7) phrenic and vagus nerves, a pair of each
   (8) heart
   (9) lung roots (two), each consisting of:
       (a) a main bronchus
       (b) a pulmonary artery
       (c) bronchial arteries, several
       (d) two pulmonary veins
       (e) bronchial veins
       (f) lymph nodes or glands
   (10) other lymph nodes, and the thoracic and right lymph ducts
   See mediastinum - section 111, page 85.

IV. CONTENTS OF THE ABDOMEN
1. Digestive system:
   (1) stomach
   (2) small intestine
   (3) colon, except pelvic colon
2. Accessory digestive ograns:
   (1) liver
   (2) gall bladder
   (3) bile ducts

3. Urinary system:
   (1) kidneys, right and left
   (2) upper ureters, including renal pelves
4. Glands:
   (1) suprarenal or adrenal glands
5. Vessels:
   (1) abdominal aorta and branches
   (2) inferior vena cava and its branches
   (3) portal vein and branches
   (4) lymph nodes, vessels, thoracic duct
6. Nerves:
   (1) sympathetic, (2) parasympathetic

V. CONTENTS OF THE PELVIS.
1. Digestive system:
   (1) pelvic colon
   (2) rectum
   (3) ileum, usually
   (4) cecum and appendix, sometimes
2. Urinary system:
   (1) lower ureters
   (2) urinary bladder.
3. Female genitals:
   (1) broad ligament
       (a) uterus
       (b) uterine tubes
       (c) ovaries
   (2) vagina
4. Male genitals:
   (1) parts of seminal ducts
   (2) seminal vesicles
   (3) prostate gland

VI. LOCATION OF ABDOMINAL ORGANS

See section 133, page 98; divisions of the abdomen, and variations in positions of organs.

1. THE RIGHT UPPER QUADRANT; R. U. Q. or U. R. Q.

   (1) duodenum, superior, descending, horizontal
   (2) part of the small bowel
   (3) upper ascending colon, cecum sometimes
   (4) right half of transverse colon
   (5) liver, greater part of
   (6) gall bladder
   (7) bile ducts
   (8) head of pancreas
   (9) end of pancreatic duct
   (10) right suprarenal gland
   (11) right kidney
   (12) upper right ureter, and right renal pelvis
   (13) blood and lymph vessels

2. THE RIGHT LOWER QUADRANT;
   R. L. Q. or L. R. Q.

   (1) lower ascending colon, usually
   (2) cecum, usually
   (3) appendix, usually
   (4) right ureter, mid part
   (5) terminal ileum
   (6) blood and lymph vessels

3. THE LEFT UPPER QUADRANT;
   L. U. Q. or U. L. Q.

   (1) duodenum ascending part
   (2) part of small intestine
   (3) upper descending colon
   (4) left half of transverse colon
   (5) spleen
   (6) liver, a small part of
   (7) left suprarenal gland
   (8) left kidney
   (9) upper left ureter and left renal pelvis
   (10) blood and lymph vessels

4. THE LEFT LOWER QUADRANT; L. L. Q.

   (1) lower descending colon
   (2) part of pelvic colon sometimes
   (3) small intestine, part of ileum
   (4) left ureter, mid part
   (5) blood and lymph vessels

The student should compare the contents of:
the right and left upper quadrants;
the right and left lower quadrants.

In F. 206, opposite, the anterior walls of the chest and abdomen have been removed to show the underlying structures.

The student should first locate the bony landmarks. The curved lines below the middle of the drawing represent the costal margins, with the xiphoid process projecting down in the median line. The iliac crests are also outlined.

The diaphragm should be located, and its shape and position studied. The center of the dome on each side lies at a definitely higher level than the lateral margins. The attachments to the chest wall at the front and back are also much lower than the dome. Because of this arrangement the bases of the lungs extend down over the dome at the front, laterally, and behind. The abdominal organs immediately below the diaphragm are actually within the thoracic walls. On the right side they may reach the nipple.

In the drawing, the liver, stomach, and spleen occupy most of the upper abdomen. The twenty-three feet of small bowel are coiled up in the lower abdomen and pelvis, obscuring many abdominal organs. Only part of the colon is visible.

The deeper structures such as the kidneys, ureters, pancreas, suprarenal glands, and the abdominal aorta, and inferior vena cava are all hidden by the structures in front of them.

The diagram illustrates the futility of attempting to show all the contents of the abdomen in a single drawing. It would be much more logical to use separate drawings to outline the different organs. The student should use the blank outlines provided, and others, if necessary, for this purpose.

F. 206 ORGANS VISIBLE IN THORAX AND ABDOMEN FOLLOWING REMOVAL OF ANTERIOR WALL

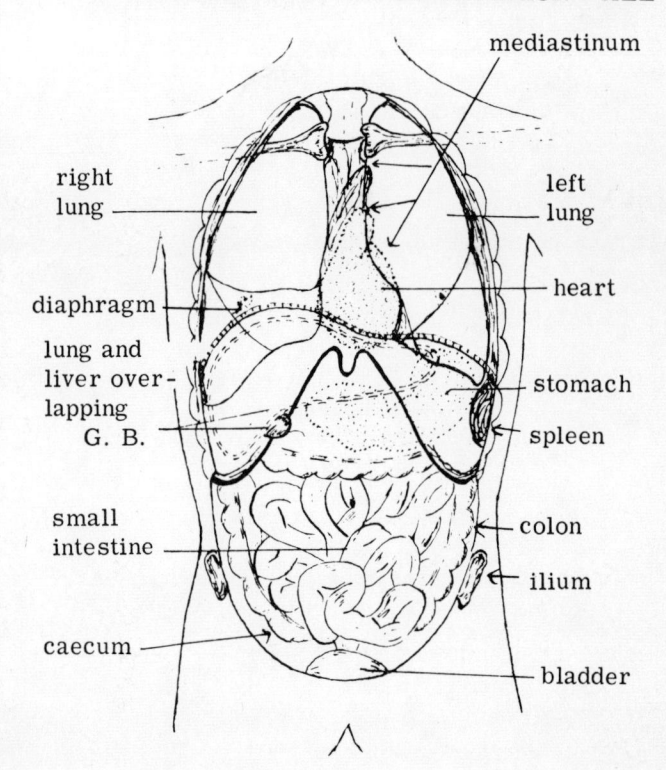

174

F. 207 BLANK OUTLINES - fill in -

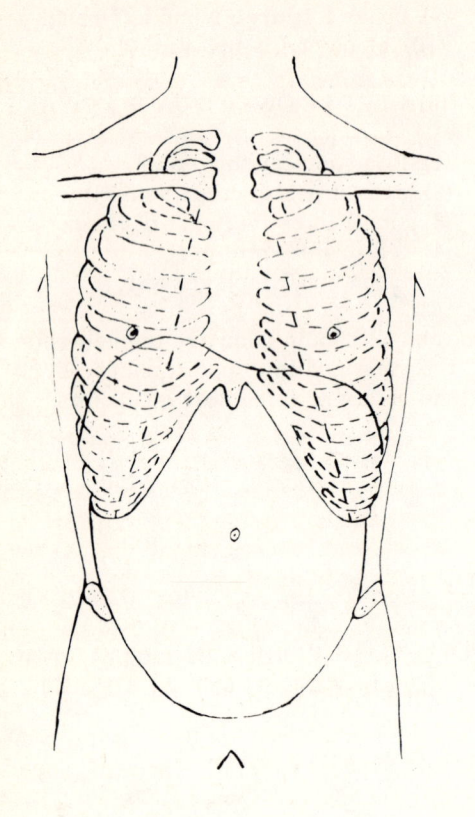

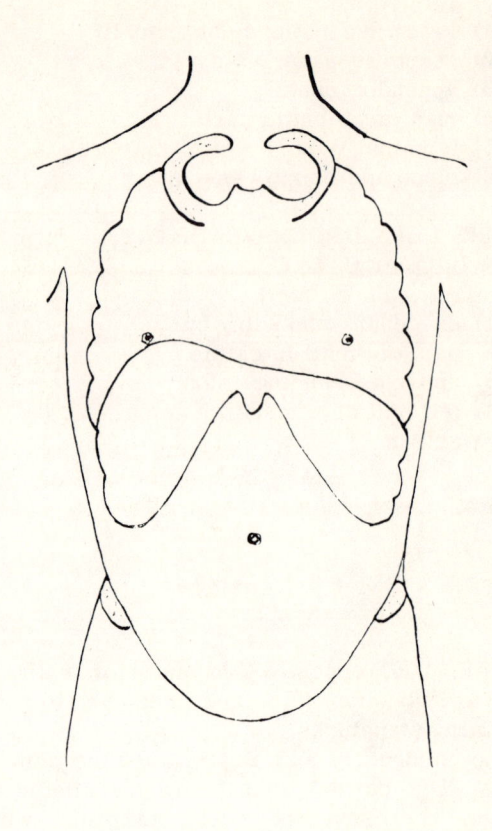

CHAPTER XXIV. INSTRUCTIONS FOR WRITING EXAMINATIONS.

S. 189 EXAMINATIONS.

For final examination each student is usually supplied with a booklet containing the questions and diagrams. The student writes the answers in this booklet and returns it to the presiding examiner.

For tests given during the course a list of questions is often written on the blackboard, or the student is given a question paper. The student must write the answers on foolscap or other paper and return these to the examiner. The remarks below are applicable to both these methods.

Each student writing examinations may be given a copy of the following instructions. Some time may profitably be spent in class discussing answer papers.

INSTRUCTIONS RE EXAMINATIONS - READ CAREFULLY.

1. If you are assigned an examination or code number, enter this number on your answer booklet or on each page, if loose pages are used. Do not enter your name nor any other identification marks.

2. Number each page of your answer papers consecutively: 1,2,3, etc., if loose pages are used.

3. Write your answers on one side of each page only, if foolscap or other loose pages are used.

4. If pads of foolscap are used, tear the pages apart.

5. Number each question or part of a question on your answer paper exactly as it is on the question paper.

6. Do everything possible to make your answer paper easy to mark - by the arrangement - numbering of pages and questions - and neatness. Do not antagonize the examiner by making marking difficult for him.

OTHER INSTRUCTIONS.

1. Read carefully the entire examination paper for each subject before you start to answer the questions.

2. Answer first those questions which you feel you know best.

3. Divide the time allowed by the number of questions asked, in order to determine how much time you should spend in answering each question. If marks are stated, you must also take the value of each question into consideration.

4. Before answering a question read that question carefully, then limit your answer to the subject matter asked for. Do not try to show that you have extra knowledge by adding material that is not required in answering the question.

5. Before writing your answer go over carefully in your mind those points you want to include in your answer. Arrange them in your mind in some systematic order. Then write down everything about each point so that you do not jump from one thing to another.

6. Leave a space after your answer so that you may add to it if time permits and you think of something further.

7. Distinquish carefully between questions asking for DEFINITIONS and DESCRIPTIONS:
(a) a definition should be short and to the point;
(b) a description requires a detailed answer.
When giving definitions be sure to write down on your answer paper the term you are defining. Leave a line between each definition.

8. If a list of names is asked for, write them down one under the other, not on one line. This will make marking much easier for the examiner.

9. DRAWINGS and DIAGRAMS: make these large. Do not economize on paper. Do not put labels on top of a drawing, but to one side, with a line or arrow to indicate that part in a drawing.
Distinguish between a question asking for a drawing only, and one in which you are asked to describe something and illustrate with a drawing.

10. If you are not satisfied with an answer, and if time permits, start over and answer it to your satisfaction.

Note: when candidates are assigned examination or code numbers, the examiner does not know the name of the candidate whose paper he is marking.

The following form may be used by instructors giving examinations. Forms may be printed and perforated. The student becomes accustomed to the procedure. The examiner correcting the papers will do so with no knowledge of the identity of the candidate.

Candidate's examination (code) number	Candidate's examination (code) number . . . .
Candidate's name	Candidate's name . . . .
Hospital or office	Hospital or office . . . .
Subject . . . . .Date	Subject . . . . .Date . . . .
The candidate must enter the code number on the front of the examination booklet, or on each page, if loose pages are used.	
	The candidate must tear off and return this half to the presiding examiner, who will place it in an envelope and seal.
DO NOT ENTER YOUR NAME NOR ANY OTHER IDENTIFICATION MARK ON THE ANSWER PAPER. Candidates who disregard this injunction will be disqualified.	
	The examiner who marks the papers will do so with no knowledge of the identity of the student.
The candidate should retain this half.	

CHAPTER XXV. REVIEW OF ANATOMY AND PHYSIOLOGY.

The following questions may be used as a guide for review. Many similar questions could be added.

S. 190 Explain the modified meaning of the following words.
as a result of the prefix used, e.g., parathyroid - beside the thyroid:

intracranial	interphalangeal
paravertebral	supraclavicular
intervertebral	hemithorax
subdural	pericardial
unilateral	intravenous
retroperitoneal	epicondyle
suboccipital	infra-orbital
bicuspid	submental
metatarsal	surprarenal
intrauterine	perirenal
subdiaphragmatic	supracondylar
retrosternal	subcapital
supraspinatus	intertrochanteric
infraspinatus	subacromial
supra-orbital	perinephritic
intrathoracic	intercondylar
bilateral	intratracheal
submandibular	intra-abdominal
metacarpal	epigastric
microcephalic	hypogastric
macrocephalic	intercostal
anencephalic	intercarpal
subarachnoid	intrathoracic

S. 191 Name the prefix having the opposite meaning to the following:

a or ab	ex	pre
an	hyper	intra
ante	infra	
ecto	macro	

S. 192 Explain the modified meaning of the following words as a result of the suffix added, e.g., condyloid - like a condyle:

malleus	bacteriology
pedicle	nephroptosis
capitulum	broncholith
ossicle	cholecystectomy
meningocele	cholecystotomy
appendicitis	cholecystostomy
osteoma	cholecystitis
diverticulosis	malleolus

S. 193 Name the term having the opposite meaning to, e.g., medial - lateral;

anterior	extrinsic
dorsal	cephalad
superior	supine
internal	longitudinal
proximal	vertical
parietal	major - greater
cephalic	flex
invert	adduct

S. 194 Define and give an example of the following terms which are frequently used in describing parts of the body:

body	fossa
cornu	condyle
ala	sinus
shaft	foramen
meatus	neck
ramus	fissure
epicondyle	process
capitulum	sulcus
lumen	symphysis

S. 195 Describe the structure of a long bone.

S. 196 Describe the following terms which are used to describe bone development:

epiphysis	epiphyseal line
diaphysis	primary center of ossification
metaphysis	secondary center of ossification

S. 197 Name the bones and joints which form the following:

(1) the shoulder girdle and upper extremity
(2) the pelvis and lower extremity
(3) the cerebral cranium
(4) the visceral cranium, or bones of the face
(5) the vertebral column
(6) the thorax

S. 198 Name the bony prominences that can be felt or seen about the following:

shoulder joint
elbow
wrist
sternum
posterior neck
vertebrae
ilium
hip
knee
ankle

S. 199 Name the bone or bones having the following:

styloid process
epicondyle
condyle
malleolus
facet (3 examples)
trochanter
tuberosity
spinous process
capitulum
coracoid process
coronoid process
olecranon fossa
intercondyloid fossa
coronoid fossa
intercondyloid eminence
olecranon

S. 200 What part of what bones form the following joints:

acromio-clavicular joint
shoulder joint
elbow joint
wrist joint
carpometacarpal joint
metacarpo-phalangeal
interphalangeal joint
lumbosacral or sacro-
 vertebral
sacroiliac joint
hip joint
knee joint
ankle joint
metatarso-phalangeal
tarsometatarsal joint
subastragaloid joint

S. 201 Give the medical term for:

skull
upper jaw
lower jaw
shoulder blade
collar bone
arm
arm bone
forearm
wrist
finger
breast bone
hip bone
thigh bone
calf bone
shin bone
ankle
arm pit
groin

S. 202 Landmarks and bony prominences.

The structures listed below are used as landmarks in radiography, or are often specifically requested on x-ray requisitions. Locate these on your body and name the bone of which each forms a part:

external occipital protuberance
glabella
supra-orbital margin or border
infra-orbital margin or border
angle of mandible
external auditory (acoustic) meatus
mastoid process
temporo-mandibular joint
vertebra prominens
spinous process of vertebrae
suprasternal (jugular) notch
sternal angle
xiphisternal junction
costal margin
tip of acromion
spine of scapula
inferior angle of scapula
lateral epicondyle of humerus
medial epicondyle of humerus
olecranon
head of radius
styloid process of radius
styloid process of ulna
pisiform bone
crest of ilium
anterior superior spine of ilium
greater trochanter of femur
symphysis pubis
pubic arch
lateral epicondyle of femur
medial epicondyle of femur
lateral condyle of femur
medial condyle of femur
lateral condyle of tibia
medial condyle of tibia
tibial tuberosity
head of fibula
medial malleolus
lateral malleolus
calcaneal tuberosity
tuberosity of tarsal navicular
tuberosity of fifth metatarsal

S. 203 Define and locate the following structures:

hypophysis cerebri
pineal gland
paranasal sinuses
mastoid cells
pituitary gland
external or lateral canthus
radiographic base line
orbit
parotid glands and ducts
odontoid process
thyroid cartilage
styloid process of temporal bone
larynx
trachea
submandibular glands and ducts
sublingual glands and ducts
mediastinum

thymus gland	cecum	
hilum (hilus) of lung	appendix	
root of lung	spleen	
esophagus	ovary	
liver	Fallopian tubes	
gall bladder	uterus	
cystic duct	cervix uteri	
hepatic duct	broad ligament	
common duct	prostate gland	
pancreas	seminal vesicles	
suprarenal gland	bladder	
ureters	urethra	
portal vein	uterine tubes	
kidneys	testes	

S. 204 State the adjective formed from the following, and the noun (name) in common use instead of the one given:

os (2 meanings)	cholecyst
mentum (2 meanings)	ren
pulmon	nephros
pneumon	phleb
pneuma	phren
hepar	metra
cardia (kardia)	hystera
gaster	choledoch

S. 205 Questions relating to systems other than the skeletal.

1. Compare skeletal and visceral muscles.

2. Why are the following muscles important to the radiological technician?
   a. the psoas major muscles
   b. the spinatus muscles
   c. the pectoralis major muscles
   d. the diaphragm.

3. Name the constituents of the blood.

4. Name the various divisions of the circulatory system.

5. Describe the heart under the following headings:
   a. walls or coverings
   b. chambers
   c. openings
   d. valves

6. Trace the systemic, pulmonary and portal circulations from the heart back to the heart.

7. Name the parts of the respiratory system including the respiratory passages.

8. Name the main divisions of the digestive system, and list the parts of each division.

9. Name the accessory organs of digestion.

10. Name the parts of the urinary system and illustrate with a LARGE drawing.

11. Name the parts of the female reproductive system and illustrate with a labelled drawing (LARGE).

12. Name the parts of the male reproductive system under the headings: glands, ducts.

13. Name the endocrine (ductless glands) and locate each in the body. (Start at the top or bottom).

14. Name the meninges of the brain and spinal cord. What is the subarachnoid space?

15. Name the ventricles of the brain. What do they secrete? Where does this circulate?

16. Name the parts of the nervous system under the headings: central, peripheral.

S. 206   Questions on function or physiology.

1. What is meant by: muscle tone, muscle spasm, paralysis of muscle?

2. State the functions of: (a) blood plasma; (b) red blood cells; (c) white blood cells; (d) platelets.

3. What is hemoglobin?

4. State the functions of: (a) the heart; (b) the arteries; (c) the capillaries; (d) the veins.

5. What are the functions of the respiratory system?

6. State the functions of:

(a) the mouth	(d) the colon	(g) the gall bladder
(b) the stomach	(e) the appendix	(h) the pancreas
(c) the small intestine	(f) the liver	(i) the anal sphincter

7. Name the functions of: (a) the kidneys; (b) the ureters; (c) the urinary bladder; (d) the urethra.

8. What is a ductless gland? How does a ductless gland function? Illustrate by examples.

9. What structures do the autonomic nervous system control?

10. What division of the brain controls skeletal muscles? Why are they called voluntary?

S. 207   What organs or other structures may be visualized by the following radiographic procedures?

myelography	cardiography	intravenous pyelography (urography)
encephalography	bronchography	retrograde pyelography (urography)
ventriculography	sialography	cystography
arteriography	cholecystography	urethrography
venography	cholangiography	uterosalpingography
cerebral angiography	arthrography	

S. 208   Define the following:

pericardium	costophrenic sinus (sulcus)	pedicle of kidney
pleura	aorta	renal tubule
peritoneum	pulmonary artery	ureteral orifices
synovial membrane	pulmonary veins	uretero-pelvic junction
bursa	superior vena cava	external os of cervix uteri
muscle tendon	inferior vena cava	internal os of cervix uteri
aponeurosis	portal vein	ovum
tendon sheath	lymph nodes	ovulation
mediastinum	lumen	fertilization
lung root	mesentery	corpus luteum
hilum of lung	omentum	Graafian follicle
plerual cavity	peristalsis	spermatozoon
thoracic duct	sphincter	androgen
right lymph duct	stenosis	estrogen
systole	islets of Langerhans	neuron
diastole	sphincter of Oddi	
respiration	digestion	
inspiration	absorption	
expiration	hilum of kidney	

S. 209   Where are the following sphincters located?

anal sphincters   cardiac sphincter   sphincter of Oddi
ileo-cecal valve   pyloric sphincter   bladder sphincter

S. 210   Make and label a diagram of the following:

stomach   esophagus   heart
bile ducts   pancreas   suprarenal glands
colon   duodenum   diaphragm

INDEX - DRAWINGS and DIAGRAMS are listed as F. 1, p. 8, etc.

Abdomen, divisions of, 125 (F. 151, F. 152, p. 127)
abdominal cavity, 125 (F. 156, p. 129)
abduct, 13
abduction, 13
absorption, of food, 132
accessory nasal sinuses, 84 (F. 104, p. 88)
accessory organs of digestion, 130
acetabulum, 46 (F. 40, p. 47)
acoustic nerve, 169
acromegaly, 152
acromion, 36
Adam's apple, 121
Addison's Disease, 152
adduct, 13
adduction, 13
adenoids, 121
adipose tissue (fat), 17 (F. 7, p. 15)
adjectives, 9
adrenal glands, 151 (F. 168, p. 138)
adrenalin, 151
afferent neuron, 154
agranulocytosis, 106
ala, 29
alimentary canal or tract, 126
alveolar process of:
    mandible, 80
    maxilla, 78
alveoli of lungs, 122
amino acids, 133
ampulla of Vater, 132
anal canal, 130
anatomical position, 11 (F. 1, p. 10)
anatomy, definition, 6
androsterone, 151
anemia, 106
aneurysm, 115
angiography, 115
angle of mandible, 80 (F. 95, F. 96, p. 80)
ankle, bones of, 51 (F. 47, F. 48, F. 49, p. 52)
ankle joint, 53 (F. 45, F. 46, p. 49) (F. 53, p. 55)
anterior, 12
anterior clinoid processes, 75
anterior pituitary, 150
antrum of Highmore, 78
anus, 130
aorta, 110 (F. 136, p. 110)
appendiceal abscess, 134
appendix, 130 (F. 163, p. 131)
application anatomy to radiography, 24
arachnoid, 158 (F. 189, p. 157)
arches of foot, 54
areola of breast, 144
areolar connective tissue, 17
arm, bones of, 37 (F. 26, p. 38)
arrector muscle of hair, 27 (F. 16, p. 27)
arteries, systemic, 109 (F. 143, p. 118)
arterioles, 110
arteriogram, 115
arteriography, 115
artery, 109
arthrogram, 93
arthrography, 93
articular cartilages, 92

articulation, definition, 29
astragalus (talus), 51 (F. 47, p. 52)
ascending colon, 130 (F. 162, p. 131)
atelectasis, 123
atlas, 61
atlas joint (F. 66, p. 62)
atresia, 133
atrioventricular valves, 109
atrioventricular septum, 109
atrium of heart, 109 (F. 130, p. 108)
auditory ossicles, 81, 169 (F. 202, p. 170)
auditory tube, 121 (F. 202, p. 170)
autonomic nervous system, 159, 161
axis, 61 (F. 57, p. 59; F. 66, p. 62)
axon, 154
basal foramina of skull, 82, 87
basophil cell, 105 (F. 127, p. 106)
back, muscles of, 102 (F. 123, p. 101)
barium sulphate, 23
biceps (brachii) muscle, 102 (F. 119, p. 99; F. 125, p. 101)
bicuspid teeth, 81 (F. 97, p. 80)
bile ducts, 132 (F. 166, p. 132)
bladder, urinary, 139 (F. 168, F. 170, F. 171, p. 138)
blood cells, 105, 106 (F. 127, p. 106)
blood, functions of, 105
blood plasma, 104
blood vessel, structure, 112
body, definition, 29
body cavities, 19, 172 (F. 8, p. 18; F. 206, p. 173)
body of stomach, 128 (F. 159, p. 129)
body thickness and radiography, 22
body of uterus, 143 (F. 174, p. 143)
body of vertebra, 60 (F. 56 to 61, p. 59)
bone cells, 17 (F. 7, p. 15)
bones, classification, 30
bones, development of, 32 (F. 19, p. 31; F. 56 to 61, p. 59)
bone marrow, 31
bones - long, 31 (F. 17, p. 30)
bone, structure, 31 (F. 18, p. 30)
bones of:
    cranium, 72, 73, 75, 78, 80, 81
    ear, 81, 169
    face, 72, 78
    lower extremity, 45 to 51 (F. 39, p. 45)
    upper extremity, 34 (F. 24, p. 34)
    shoulder girdle, 34
    pelvis, 45, 46, 48 (F. 40, p. 47)
    thorax, 67 (F. 70, p. 66)
    vertebral column, 60 (F. 55, p. 58)
bony prominences, defined, 29
brachialis muscle, 102 (F. 125, p. 101)
brain, 154 (F. 185, F. 186, F. 187, F. 188, p. 155)
breast bone, 67 (F. 70, F. 71, F. 72, p. 66)
breasts - female, 144 (F. 177, p. 144)
breathing, 123
bregma, 85
broad ligament, 142
bronchi, 122 (F. 148, p. 120)
bronchial arteries, 123
bronchiectasis, 123
bronchioles, 122
bronchography, 124
broncho-pulmonary segments, 122

bursa, at knee (F. 116, p. 94)
caecum, see cecum, 130 (F. 163, p. 131)
calcaneus, 51 (F. 47, F. 48, F. 49, p. 52)
calculi in kidney, 140
cancellous bone, 31 (F. 18, p. 30)
canine teeth, 81 (F. 97, p. 80)
capillaries, 110
capitate bone, 40 (F. 31, p. 39)
capitulum of humerus, 37 (F. 26, p. 38)
capitulum of mandible, 81 (F. 95, p. 80)
carbohydrates, 133
carbon dioxide, 104
cardiac muscle - myocardium, 107
cardiography, 115
carpal bones, 40 (F. 31, p. 39)
cartilage, 17 (F. 7, p. 15)
cauda equina, 56
caudad, 12
caudal, 12
cavities of body, 19, 172
cecum, 130 (F. 163, p. 131)
celiac axis, 117
cell, structure of, 16 (F. 5, p. 15)
cell body, 16 (F. 5, p. 15)
cell constituents, 16 (F. 5, p. 15)
cell division, 16 (F. 6, p. 15)
cell membrane, 16 (F. 5, p. 15)
cell processes, 16
central fissure of brain, 156
centrosome, 16
cephalad, 12
cephalic, 12
cerebellum, 156
cerebrum, 155, 161
cerebral arteriography, 163
cerebral hemisphere, 156
cerebrospinal fluid, 159, 162
cerebral cranium, 73
cervical vertebrae, 61 (F. 58, p. 59)
cervix of uterus, 143
chambers of heart, 109 (F. 130, p. 108)
chest, 107 (F. 147, p. 120)
cholecystogram, 135
cholecystography, 135
cholelithiasis, 134
cholangiogram, 136 (F. 167, p. 135)
cholangiography, 136
choroid coat eyeball, 165 (F. 196, F. 197, p. 165)
chromatin, 16
chromosomes, 16
circulation:
    fetal, 114
    portal, 114 (F. 138, p. 113)
    pulmonary, 113 (F. 138, p. 113)
    systemic, 113 (F. 138, p. 113)
circulatory system, 107
circumduct, 13
circumduction, 13
classification of bones, 30
clavicle, 36 (F. 25, p. 36)
clinoid processes, 76
coccyx, 63 (F. 65, p. 61)
colon, 130 (F. 162, p. 131)
common bile duct, 132 (F. 166, p. 132)
conchae, 80
condyle - definition, 29
condyle of fumur, 50 (F. 42, p. 49)
condyle of mandible, 80 (F. 95, p. 80)
condyle of tibia, 50 (F. 43, p. 49)

congenital anomalies defined, 20
connective tissue, 17 (F. 7, p. 15)
contents of body cavities, 172 (F. 206, p. 173)
contrast media, 23
convolutions of brain, 155
coracoid process of scapula, 36 (F. 25, p. 36)
cord, spermatic, 147
cord, spinal, 156 (F. 190, p. 157)
corium, 26
coronal plane, 12
cornu - definition, 29
coronary arteries, 109
corpus callosum, 155
corpus luteum, 142, 151 (F. 176, p. 143)
corpuscle of blood, 104 (F. 127, p. 106)
corpuscles of kidneys, 140 (F. 173, p. 138)
cortex of bone, 31 (F. 18, p. 30)
costa (rib), 68 (F. 70, F. 73, p. 66)
costal cartilages, 68 (F. 70, p. 66)
coverings of brain and cord, 158 (F. 189, p. 157)
covering of heart, 107 (F. 132, p. 108)
cranial fossae, 82, 87
cranial nerves, 158
cranium, bones of, 72 (F. 79, F. 80, p. 71)
craniosacral nervous system, 160
crest, 29
crest of ilium, 47 (F. 41, p. 47)
cretinism, 152
cribriform plate of ethmoid, 76
cuboid bone, 53 (F. 47, p. 52)
cuneiform bones, 53 (F. 47, p. 52)
cystic duct, 132 (F. 166, p. 132)
cystography, 141
cystogram, 141
cytoplasm, 16
dark adaptation of eyes for fluoroscopy, 167
deltoid muscle, 102 (F. 119, p. 98; F. 125, p. 101)
dendrites, 154
density, 22
density of tissues and organs, 22
density and radiography, 22
dentine of tooth, 82 (F. 99, p. 82)
dermis, 26 (F. 13, p. 25)
descending colon, 130
descent of testes, 148 (F. 180, p. 147)
descriptive names in anatomy, 9
development of gut, 126
developmental anomalies, 20
diaphragm, 100 (F. 121, F. 122, p. 99)
diaphysis of bone, 32 (F. 19, p. 31)
digestion, 132
digestive system, 136 (F. 152, p. 127)
distal, 12
diverticula, 134
divisions of abdomen, 125 (F. 133, p. 108)
divisions of body, 19 (F. 8, p. 18)
dorsal, 12
dorsal vertebrae, 60 (F. 59, F. 61, p. 59)
dorsum sella, 76
ducts:
    bile, 132
    ejaculatory, 147
    hepatic, 132
    pancreatic, 132
    parotid, 127
    sublingual, 128
    submandibular or submaxillary, 127
    seminal, 147
ductless glands (endocrine), 149

ductus arteriosus, 114 (F. 140, p. 116)
ductus deferens, 147
duodenum, 128 (F. 165, p. 131)
dura mater, 158 (F. 189, p. 157)
dwarfism, 152
ear, bones of, 81 (F. 202, p. 170)
ear-drum, 169 (F. 202, p. 170)
ectoderm, 20 (F. 10, p. 20)
ectopic kidney, 140
efferent neurons, 154
ejaculatory ducts, 147
elastic tissue, 17
elbow joint, 42 (F. 29, p. 38; F. 36, p. 41)
embolus, 115 (F. 142, p. 116)
embryo, 20, 115 (F. 142, p. 116)
empyema, 123
encephalogram, 163 (F. 193, F. 194, p. 163)
encephalography, 163
endocardium, 107 (F. 193, F. 194, p. 163)
endocrine glands, 149
end organs, 154
endothelium, 17
ensiform process, 67 (F. 70, p. 66)
entoderm, 20 (F. 10, p. 20)
enzymes, 133
eosinophil cells, 105 (F. 127, p. 106)
epicondyles, definition, 29
epicondyles of femur, 50 (F. 42, p. 49)
epicondyles of humerus, 37 (F. 26, p. 38)
epidermis, 25 (F. 14, p. 25)
epididymis, 147 (F. 178, p. 146)
epiglottis, 121
epinephrin, 151
epiphyses of bone, 32 (F. 19, p. 31; F. 20 to F. 23, p. 33)
epiphysis cerebri, 150
epistropheus (axis), see axis, 61
epithelial tissue, 17 (F. 7, p. 15)
epithelium, 17 (F. 7, p. 15)
erythrocytes, 105 (F. 127, p. 106)
esophagus, 128 (F. 158, p. 129)
estrin, oestrin, 151
estrogens, 152
ethmoid bone, 76 (F. 88, p. 77)
ethmoidal sinuses, 78 (F. 104, p. 88)
Eustachian Tube, 121 (F. 202, p. 170)
eversion, 13
evert, 13
examinations - writing, 175
excretory organs, 139
expiration, 123
external, 12
external auditory meatus, 76, 169 (F. 202, p. 170)
external genitals, 143
extend, 13
extension, 13
extremities:
       bones of lower, 45 (F. 39, p. 45)
       bones of upper, 34 (F. 24, p. 34)
external canthus of eye, 75 (F. 101, p. 88)
external occipital protuberance, 75 (F. 83, p. 74)
extrinsic, 12
eyeball, 165 (F. 196, F. 197, p. 165)
eyelids, 166
facial bones, 72, 78 (F. 84, p. 74) etc.
false pelvis, 48
fascia, 95
fat cells, 16 (F. 7, p. 15)
fats in food, 133
female reproductive organs, 142 (F. 174, p. 143)

female breast, 144 (F. 177, p. 144)
femur, 50 (F. 42, p. 49)
fertilization, 20 (F. 9, F. 10, p. 20)
fetal circulation, 114
fetus, 20
fibrous tissue, 17
fibula, 51 (F. 43, p. 49; F. 50, p. 53)
finger joints (interphalangeal), 42 (F. 37, p. 41)
fingernails, 26 (F. 15, p. 26)
fissure, definition, 29
fissures of brain, 155
flex, 13
flexion, 13
flexures: (F. 162, p. 131)
       hepatic flexure, 130
       left colic flexure, 130
       right colic flexure, 130
       splenic flexure, 130
fluoroscopy, 167
follicles, Graafian, 142, 151 (F. 9, p. 20; F. 176, p. 143)
folliculin, 151
fontanels, 84 (F. 100, p. 88)
food, 133
food absorption, 132
foot, bones of, 45, 51 (F. 47, F. 48, F. 49, p. 52)
foramen, definition, 29
foramen of Luschka, 159
foramen Magendie, 159
foramen magnum, 75 (F. 83, p. 74)
foramen, mental, 81
foramen of Munro, 159
forearm, bones of, 37
forefoot, bones, joints (F. 54, p. 55)
fossa, definition, 29
fossa, coronoid of humerus, 37
fossa, olecranon of humerus, 37
frontal bone, 72, 75 (F. 81, p. 74)
frontal plane, 12
frontal sinuses, 72, 84 (F. 104, p. 88)
fourth ventricle of brain, 158 (F. 189, p. 157)
functions of:
       blood, 104 - 105
       bone, 29
       circulatory system, 112
       digestive system, 132
       kidneys, 139
       muscles, 95
       respiratory system, 123
       skin, 27
fundus of stomach, 128 (F. 159, p. 129)
fundus of uterus, 143 (F. 174, p. 143)
gall bladder, 132 (F. 166, p. 132)
gall stones (cholelithiasis), 134
ganglion, 154
gaster, see stomach, 128 (F. 159, p. 129)
gastric, see stomach, 128 (F. 159, p. 129)
germ layers, 20 (F. 10, p. 20)
giantism, 152
glabella, 75
gladiolus of sternum, 67
glands with ducts, 149
glands, ductless, 149
glands of internal secretion, see ductless glands, 149
glenoid cavity, 36 (F. 25, p. 36)
goiter, 152
glomerulus of kidney, 140
gonads, see reproductive,
Graafian follicles, 142, 151 (F. 9, p. 20; F. 176, p. 143)
granular layer of skin, 25

granulocytes of blood, 104 - 105
grey matter of brain, 155
greater, 12
greater:
    multangular bone, 40
    trochanter of femur, 50
    tubercle of humerus, 37
    wing of sphenoid, 76
gristle, see cartilage
groove or sulcus, definition, 29
hair, 26 (F. 16, p. 27)
hamate bone, 41 (F. 31, p. 39)
hand, bones of, 40
heart, 107 (F. 128, F. 129, F. 130, F. 131, p. 108)
heel bone, see os calcis
hemoglobin, 105
hepar, see liver
hepatic duct, 132 (F. 166, p. 132)
hepatic flexure, 130 (F. 162, p. 131)
hepatic vein, 111
hernia, 133
hindbrain, 156, 161
hip bones, 46 (F. 41, p. 47)
hip joint, 53 (F. 51, p. 55; F. 110, p. 91)
horizontal, 12
horizontal plane, 12
hormones, 149
horny layer of skin, 25
horseshoe kidney, 140
humerus, 37 (F. 26, p. 38)
hydrocephalus, 160
hyoid bone, 81 (F. 98, p. 80)
hyperthyroidism, 152
hyperparathyroidism, 152
hypogastric region, 125
hypoparathyroidism, 152
ileocecal valve, 130
ileum, 130
ilium, 46 (F. 41, p. 47)
image magnification, 24 (F. 12, p. 23)
incisor teeth, 81 (F. 97, p. 80)
incisura angularis of stomach, 128
incus, 81, 169 (F. 202, p. 170)
inferior, 12
inferior concha, 80
inferior vena cava, 111 (F. 136, p. 110)
infarct, 115
infra-orbital border, 78 (F. 80, p. 71)
innominate bone, 46 (F. 41, p. 47)
inspiration, 123
intercostal muscles, 100 (F. 120, p. 99)
interarticular joints, 63 (F. 67, p. 62; F. 109, p. 91)
internal, 12
internal auditory meatus, 76, 169
internal ear, 169 (F. 202, p. 170)
internal os of cervix, 143 (F. 174, p. 143)
intervertebral joints, 63 (F. 68, p. 62; F. 108, p. 91)
intestines, 128, 129
intracranial grooves, 83, 87
intravenous urography (pyelography), 141
intrinsic, 12
inversion, 13
involuntary muscle, 17 (F. 7, p. 15)
intravenous urogram, 141
invert, 13
inversion, 13
iodine, 23
iris, 165 (F. 198, p. 165)
iron, see hemoglobin

ischium, 46 (F. 41, p. 47)
islands of Langerhans, 132, 151
jaundice, 134
jejunum, 130
joints, classification, 92 (F. 105 to F. 112, p. 91)
joints of:
    lower extremity, 55 (F. 51 to F. 54, p. 55)
    upper extremity, 42 (F. 35, F. 36, F. 37, p. 41)
    skull, 83
    thorax, 67, 68
    vertebrae, 60, 63 (F. 66 to F. 69, p. 62)
jugular notch, 67
kidneys, 139 (F. 168 to F. 172, p. 138)
knee joint, 53 (F. 44, F. 45, p. 49; F. 52, p. 55)
lacrimal bones, 78 (F. 80, p. 71)
lacrimal gland and ducts, 166 (F. 201, p. 167)
lambda, 73, 85
lambdoidal suture, 84
laminae of vertebra, 60
landmarks of:
    lower extremity, 54
    upper extremity, 42
    thorax, 69
    vertebrae, 63
larynx, 121 (F. 150, p. 121)
lateral, 12
lateral fissure of brain, 156
lateral ventricles of brain, 158 (F. 193, F. 194, p. 163)
layers of skin, 25
left colic flexure, 130 (F. 162, p. 131)
legs, bones of, 45 (F. 39, p. 45)
lens, eye, 166
lesser, 12
lesser:
    multangular bone, 40
    trochanter of femur, 50
    tubercle of humerus, 37
    wing of sphenoid, 76
leucocytes, 105
leucocytosis, 106
leucopenia, 106
ligaments, 92
lists of words:
    blood, 105
    circulatory system, 107, 116
    digestive system, 126, 136
    ductless glands, 149, 153
    female reproductive, 145
    lower extremity, 56
    male reproductive, 148
    muscular system, 103
    nervous system, 163
    respiratory system, 124
    skin, 28
    skull, 89
    thorax, 69, 107
    upper extremity, 43
    vertebrae, 60, 64
    urinary system, 139, 141
liver, 132 (F. 164, p. 131)
lobes of lungs, 122 (F. 146, p. 120)
location of organs, 172
long bones, 30 (F. 17, p. 30)
longitudinal, 12
lower extremities, bones of, 45
lumbar puncture, 159, 162
lumbosacral joint, 63 (F. 69, p. 62)
lumbar vertebrae, 62 (F. 60, p. 59)
lumen, definition, 29

lunate bone, 40 (F. 31, p. 39)
lungs, 121 (F. 146, F. 147, F. 148, p. 120)
Luschka, foramen of, 158, 159
lymph ducts, 112 (F. 137, p. 113)
lymph glands, 111
lymph nodes, 111
lymph vessels, 111
lymphatic system, 111
lymphocytes, 105 (F. 127, p. 106)
Magendie, foramen of, 158, 159
magnification of image, 24 (F. 12, p. 23)
major, 12
malar bones, 78 (F. 90, p. 79)
male reproductive organs, 146 (F. 178, p. 146)
malleolus fibula, 51
malleolus tibia, 50, 51
malleus, 81, 169 (F. 202, p. 170)
mammary glands, 144
mammectomy, 145
mandible, 73, 80, 87 (F. 95, F. 96, p. 80)
mandibular foramen, 81
mandibular notch, 81 (F. 95, p. 80)
manubrium of sternum, 67 (F. 71, p. 66)
marrow of bone, 31
mastoid process, temporal bone, 76
maxillae, 72, 78, 85 (F. 89, p. 79)
maxillary sinuses, 78, 84 (F. 104, p. 88)
meatus, definition, 29
meatus, external auditory, 76
meatus, internal auditory, 76
meatus, internal acoustic, 76
medial, definition, 12
mediastinum, 107
median line, 11 (F. 1, p. 10)
medulla oblongata, 156 (F. 189, p. 157)
medulla of bone, 31 (F. 18, p. 30)
membranes of brain and cord, 158
meninges of brain and cord, 158, 162 (F. 189, p. 157)
meningitis, 160
menstrual cycle, 142
mesentery, 126
mesoderm, 20 (F. 10, p. 20)
mesothelium, 17
metacarpal bones, 41 (F. 31, p. 39)
metacarpus, 40
metaphysis of bone, 32 (F. 19, p. 31)
metatarsal bones, 53 (F. 47, p. 52)
metatarsus, 53
metabolism, 151
midbrain, 156, 161 (F. 189, p. 157)
middle ear, 169 (F. 202, p. 170)
mid-sagittal, definition, 11
milk, 144
minor, definition, 12
mitosis, 16 (F. 6, p. 15)
mitotic figures, 16 (F. 6, p. 15)
molar teeth, 81 (F. 97, p. 80)
monocytes, 105 (F. 127, p. 106)
Munro, foramen of, 159
motor neurons, 154, 161
mouth, 127 (F. 155, p. 129)
mucous membrane, 17
muscles of eyeball, 166 (F. 200, p. 167)
muscle tissue, 17 (F. 7, p. 15)
muscle, skeletal, 95 (F. 113, p. 94)
    classification, 94
    distribution, 96
    structure, 95
    function, 95
    paralysis, 96
    spasm, 96
myelogram, 163 (F. 195, p. 163)
myelography, 163
myocardium, 107 (F. 132, p. 108)
myxedema, 152
nails, 26 (F. 15, p. 26)
nasal bones, 78 (F. 80, p. 71)
nasal fossae (cavities), 75, 85, 121 (F. 94, p. 79; F. 155, p. 129)
nasal septum, 75 (F. 93, p. 79)
nares, 121
nasopharynx, 121 (F. 145, p. 120)
navicular (scaphoid) bone - carpal, 41 (F. 31, p. 39)
navicular (scaphoid) bone - tarsal, 51 (F. 47, p. 52)
neck, definition, 29
nephritic, 140
nephros (kidney), 140
nerve fibers, 154
nerves, cranial, 158 (F. 188, p. 155)
nerves, peripheral, 156
nerves, spinal, 156 (F. 190, p. 157)
nervous system, 154
nervous system, summary, 161 etc.
neuron, afferent, 154
neuron, efferent, 154
neutrophil cells, 105 (F. 127, p. 106)
nipple of breast, 144 (F. 177, p. 144)
nodes, lymph, 112
nose, 121
nostrils, 121
nucleus of a cell, 16 (F. 5, p. 15)
nucleus pulposus, 63 (F. 68, p. 62)
objectives, course in anatomy, 6
obturator foramen, 46
occipital bone, 72, 73 (F. 83, p. 74)
occipital condyles, 75
odontoid process, 61 (F. 66, p. 62; F. 57, p. 59)
oestrin, estrin, 151
olecranon, 40 (F. 33, p. 40)
olfactory nerve, 171 (F. 203, p. 170)
omentum, 126
opaque media, 22, etc.
openings of heart, 109
opposites - listed, 12
optic foramen, 76, 85
optic nerve, 166 (F. 199, p. 167; F. 203, p. 170)
oral cavity (mouth), 127
orbit, 75, 85
organs, definition, 17
origin of anatomical names, 9
oropharynx, 121 (F. 145, p. 120)
os, definition, 29
os calcis, 51
os coxae (innominate bone), 46 (F. 41, p. 47)
os magnum (capitate), 40 (F. 31, p. 39)
osseous tissue, 17 (F. 7, p. 15)
ossicles of ear, 81 (F. 202, p. 170)
ossification of bones, 32
ovary, 142, 151 (F. 9, p. 20; F. 174, F. 176, p. 143)
ovum, 19, 142 (F. 9, p. 20)
oxygen, 104
palate, 78, 121 (F. 91, p. 79)
palatine bones, 78 (F. 92, p. 79)
palmar, definition, 12
pancreas, 130, 151 (F. 165, p. 131)
pancreatic duct, 132 (F. 165, p. 131)
papillae of skin, 25
papillary layer of skin, 26
paranasal sinuses, 73, 84 (F. 104, p. 88)

parasympathetic nervous system, 160
parathormone, 151
parathyroid glands, 151 (F. 182, p. 150)
parenchyma, definition, 17
parietal bones, 75 (F. 82, p. 74)
parietal, definition, 12
parietal pericardium, 109 (F. 132, p. 108)
parietal peritoneum, 126
parietal pleura, 123 (F. 146, p. 120)
parotid glands, 126 (F. 157, p. 129)
parotid ducts (Stenson's), 126 (F. 157, p. 129)
parts or divisions of:
    bone, 30 etc.
    blood, 104
    cell, 16
    circulatory system, 107
    digestive system, 126
    ductless glands, 149
    eyeball, 165
    joints, 92
    lower extremity, 45
    muscles, 94
    nervous system, 154
    reproductive, female, 142
    reproductive, male, 148
    respiratory system, 121
    skin, 25
    skull, 72
    thorax, 67
    upper extremity, 35
    urinary system, 139
    vertebral column, 60
patella, 50 (F. 42, p. 49)
pathology, definition, 6
pectoralis major muscle, 100 (F. 119, p. 99; F. 125, p. 101)
pedicles of a vertebra, 60
pelvic cavity, 19, 46, 172
pelvic colon (sigmoid), 130
pelvic inlet, 48
pelvic outlet, 48
pelvis, 46, 48 (F. 40, p. 47)
pelvis of kidney, 139
penis, 147
pericardium, 109
peridental membrane, 82
peripheral nervous system, 154, 161
peristalsis, 126
periosteum, 31 (F. 18, p. 30)
peritoneum, 126 (F. 153, F. 154, p. 127)
petrous part, temporal bone, 76
phalanges of foot, 53
phalanges of hand, 41
pharynx, 121, 128 (F. 145, p. 120; F. 155, p. 129)
phlebitis, 115
physiology, definition, 6
pia mater, 158 (F. 189, p. 157)
pineal gland or body, 150
pisiform bone, 41 (F. 31, p. 39)
pitocin, 150
pitressin, 150
pituitary dwarfism, 152
pituitary gland, 149 (F. 181, p. 150)
pituitrin, 150
planes, definition, 11
plantar, definition, 12
platelets, 106
pleura, 123 (F. 146, p. 120)
pleural cavity, 123 (F. 146, p. 120)
pleurisy, 123

plexus of nerves, 160
plural forms, 9
pneumoarthrography, 93
pneumothorax, 123
polycystic kidneys, 140
polycythemia, 106
polymorphonuclear cells, 106 (F. 127, p. 106)
pons, 156 (F. 189, p. 157)
portal circulation, 114 (F. 138, p. 113)
portal vein, 111, 119 (F. 133, p. 108)
position, anatomical, 11 (F. 1, p. 10)
positioning in radiography, definition, 6
posterior, definition, 12
posterior, clinoid processes, 76
prefixes, 9
premolar teeth, 81 (F. 97, p. 80)
primary center of ossification, 32
process, definition, 16, 28
processes:
    alveolar, 78, 81
    coracoid, of scapula, 36
    coronoid, of ulna, 40
    ensiform (xiphoid), of sternum, 67
    odontoid, of axis, 61
    olecranon, of ulna, 40
    spinous, of vertebra, 61
    styloid, of radius and ulna, 37, 40
    transverse, of vertebra, 61
    zygomatic, 78
    articular, of vertebra, 61
progesterone, 151
progestin, 151
pronate, definition, 13
pronation, defintion, 13
prone, 13
prostate gland, 147 (F. 179, p. 146)
proteins, 133
protoplasm, 16
proximal, definition, 12
psoas major muscle, 102 (F. 124, p. 101)
pubic bones, 48 (F. 40, p. 47)
pubic arch, 48 (F. 40, p. 47)
pubis, 48 (F. 41, p. 47)
pulmonary arteries, 111 (F. 135, p. 110)
pulmonary circulation, 113 (F. 138, p. 113; F. 149, p. 120)
pulmonary veins, 111 (F. 135, p. 110)
pulse, 114, 117
puncture, lumbar, 159, 162
pupil of eye (F. 198, p. 165)
pyelogram, 141
pyelography, 141
pylorus of stomach, 128 (F. 159, p. 129)
pyloric sphincter, 126
quadrants of abdomen, 125 (F. 151, p. 125)
quadriceps muscle, 103 (F. 126, p. 101)
RADIOGRAPHIC APPLICATIONS:
    circulatory system, 115
    digestive system, 134
    ductless glands, 152
    female reproductive, 145
    growing bones, 32
    joints, 93
    lower extremity, 55
    nervous system, 162
    respiratory system, 124
    skin, 27
    skull, 84, 89
    thorax, 69
    upper extremity, 42

radiographic base line, 86
radiographic centering, 24 (F. 11, p. 23)
radius, 37
ramus, definition, 29
rectum, 130 (F. 162, p. 131)
red blood cells, 105 (F. 127, p. 106)
reference books in anatomy, 8
reflex arc, 154
ren (kidney), 139
renal artery, vein, 139
renal capsule, 139
renal corpuscle, 140
reproductive system, female, 142 (F. 174, F. 175, p. 143)
reproductive system, male, 146 (F. 178, F. 179, p. 146)
respiration, 123
respiratory passages, 121 (F. 145, p. 120)
respiratory system, 121
reticular layer of skin, 25
retina of eyeball, 165 (F. 196, F. 197, p. 165)
retrograde urogram (pyelogram), 141
retrograde urography (pyelography), 141
review questions in anatomy, 177, 178, 179
ribs, 67 (F. 73, p. 66)
right colic flexure, 130 (F. 162, p. 131)
right lymph duct, 112
roots of lungs, 123
roots (pedicles) of vertebrae, 60
rotate, definition, 13
rotation, 13
sacroiliac joints, 53 (F. 51, p. 55)
sacrospinalis muscles, 102 (F. 123, p. 101)
sacrum, 62 (F. 62, F. 63, F. 64, p. 61)
sagittal plane, definition, 12
salivary glands, 127 (F. 157, p. 129)
scaphoid bone (carpal), 41 (F. 31, p. 39)
scaphoid bone (tarsal), 51 (F. 47, p. 52)
scapula, 35 (F. 25, p. 36)
sciatic notch, 48
sclera of eyeball, 165 (F. 196, F. 197, p. 165)
scrotum, 146 (F. 178, p. 146)
sebaceous glands, 27 (F. 15, p. 27)
secondary centers, ossification, 32
section, 12
sella turcica, 76
semen, 146
semilunar cartilages (knee) (F. 111, p. 91)
seminal ducts, 147
seminal vesicles, 146
sensory nerves, 156, 158, 160
sensory neurons, 154
septa of heart, 109 (F. 134, p. 110)
serous membranes, 17
shaft, definition, 29 (F. 17, p. 30)
shin bone (tibia), 50 (F. 43, p. 49)
shoulder blade, 34, 35 (F. 25, p. 36)
shoulder girdle, 34, 35 (F. 24, p. 34)
shoulder joint, 41 (F. 30, p. 38; F. 35, p. 41)
sigmoid (pelvic) colon, 130 (F. 162, p. 131)
sinus, definition, 29
sinuses, paranasal, 84 (F. 104, p. 88)
sinuses, venous of skull (F. 102, F. 103, p. 88)
skeleton, see parts of,
skeletal muscles, 17, 94 (F. 117, F. 118, p. 98)
skin, functions of, 27
skin, 25 (F. 13, F. 14, p. 25)
skull, bones of, 72 (F. 74 to F. 78, p. 70; F. 79, F. 80, p.71)
skull, structure of bones of, 31
skull, summary of, 84, 85, 86, 87
small intestines, 128 (F. 160, F. 161, p. 131)

smell, end organs, 171 (F. 204, p. 170)
smooth muscle, 17
spelling, 13
spermatic cord, 147
sphenoid bone, 72, 76, 87 (F. 87, p. 77)
sphenoidal sinuses, 76, 84 (F. 104, p. 88)
sphincters, 126
spinal column, 60 (F. 55, p. 58)
spinal cord, 156 (F. 190, F. 191, F. 192, p. 157)
spinal nerves, 156, 161 (F. 190, p. 157)
spermatozoa, 146 (F. 9, p. 20)
spine of a bone, definition, 29
spine of scapula, 36 (F. 25, p. 36)
spinous process, definition, 29
spinous process of vertebra, 61 (F. 60, p. 59)
spine of ischium, 48 (F. 41, p. 47)
spleen, 112 (F. 156, p. 129)
spondyloisthesis, 63
squamosal suture, 84
squamous epithelium, 17 (see skin)
squamous part of:
    frontal bone, 75 (F. 81, p. 74)
    occipital bone, 75 (F. 83, p. 74)
    temporal bone, 75 (F. 85, p. 77)
stapes, 81, 169 (F. 202, p. 170)
stenosis, definition, 126
Stenson's duct (parotid), 127
sternomastoid muscle, 100 (F. 119, p. 99)
sternal angle, 68 (F. 71, F. 72, p. 66)
sternum, 67 (F. 70, F. 71, F. 72, p. 66)
stomach, 128 (F. 159, p. 129)
striated muscle, 17
stroma, defintion, 17
student's use of Handbook, 6
styloid process of:
    radius, 40 (F. 27, p. 38)
    ulna, 40 (F. 27, p. 38; F. 33, p. 40)
    temporal bone, 76 (F. 85, p. 77)
subarachnoid space, 158 (F. 189, p. 157)
subcutaneous tissue, 26 (F. 13, p. 25)
sublingual glands, 127 (F. 157, p. 129)
submandibular glands, 127 (F. 157, p. 129)
submaxillary glands, 127 (F. 157, p. 129)
sudoriferous glands, 27 (F. 16, p. 27)
suffixes, definition, 9, list of, 11
suggestions for instructors, 7
sulcus, definition, 29; groove
superior, definition, 12
superior vena cava, 111 (F. 136, p. 110)
supinate, definition, 13
supination, 13
supine, 13
supra-orbital border, 75 (F. 81, p. 74)
suprarenal glands, 151 (F. 168, p. 138)
suprasternal notch, 67 (F. 71, p. 66)
surface markings, value of, 24
sutures of skull, 84 (F. 79, F. 80, p. 71; F. 105, p. 91)
sweat glands, 27 (F. 16, p. 27)
sympathetic ganglia, 159
sympathetic nervous system, 159
sympathetic trunks, 159
symphysis, definition, 30
symphysis pubis, 48 (F. 106, p. 91)
synapse, 154
synovial membrane, 17
systemic arteries, 116 (F. 144, p. 118)
systemic circulation, 113 (F. 138, p. 113)
systemic veins, 117 (F. 144, p. 118)

systems of body, 19
systems - parts of, see parts of systems
talus, 51 (F. 47, p. 52)
tarsal bones, 51 (F. 47, p. 52)
tarsus, 51
taste organ, 171
teaching material for anatomy, 8
tear glands and ducts, 166 (F. 201, p. 167)
teeth, 81 (F. 97, p. 80; F. 99, p. 82)
temporal bone, 72, 75, 85 (F. 85, F. 86, p. 77)
tendons, 95 (F. 115, p. 94)
terminal, definition, 12
testes, 148, 151 (F. 178, p. 146)
testosterone, 151
theelin, 151
thigh bone (femure), 50 (F. 42, p. 49)
third ventricle of brain, 158 (F. 189, p. 157)
thorax, bones of, 67 (F. 70, p. 66)
thoracic cavity, 19, 107
thoracic contents, 107, 172
thoracic duct, 112
thoracico-lumbar nervous system, 159
throat (pharynx), 121, 128
thrombus, 115 (F. 141, p. 116)
thumb, bones of, 41 (F. 38, p. 44)
thymus, 151 (F. 184, p. 150)
thyroid cartilage, 121 (F. 146, p. 120)
thyroid gland, 150 (F. 182, p. 150)
thyroxine, 151
tibia, 50 (F. 43, p. 49; F. 50, p. 53)
tissue, types of, 17 (F. 7, p. 15)
toe, bones of, 53 (F. 54, p. 55)
tongue, 127 (F. 155, p. 129)
tonsils, 121 (F. 145, p. 120)
translucent layer of skin, 25 (F. 13, p. 25)
trachea, 121 (F. 146, p. 120)
trapezium (greater multangular bone), 40 (F. 31, p. 39)
trapezoid (lesser multangular bone), 31 (F. 31, p. 39)
triangular bone, 40 (F. 31, p. 39)
triceps muscle, 102
triquetral (triangular bone), 41
trochanter, definition, 30
trochanters of femur, 50 (F. 42, p. 49)
trochlea of humerus, 37 (F. 26, p. 39)
trochlea of talus, 51
tubercle, definition, 30
tuberosity of a bone, 30
tuberosity of ischium, 48
tuberosity of tibia, 50
turbinate bones, 80
tympanic membrane (ear-drum), 169 (F. 202, p. 170)

ulna, 40 (F. 27, p. 38; F. 33, p. 40)
ulnar styloid process, 40
upper extremity, bones of, 35 (F. 24, p. 34)
ureters, 139 (F. 168, p. 138)
urethra, 139
urinary bladder, 139 (F. 168, p. 138)
urinary system, 139 (F. 168, p. 138)
urogram (pyelogram), 141
uterosalpingogram, 145
uterosalpingography, 145
uterogram, 145
uterography, 145
uterine tubes (Fallopian), 142 (F. 174, p. 143)
uterus, 142 (F. 174, p. 143)
vagina, 143
valves of heart, 109
valves of veins, 110
vascular system, 107
veins, 110
venules, 110
vena cava, inferior, 111 (F. 136, p. 110)
vena cava, superior, 111 (F. 136, p. 110)
venography, 115
ventral, definition, 12
ventricles of brain, 158 (F. 189, p. 157; F. 193, F. 194, p. 163)
ventricles of heart, 109 (F. 130, p. 108)
ventriculogram, 163
ventriculography, 163
vermiform appendix, 130 (F. 163, p. 131)
vertebrae, 60 (F. 55, p. 58; F. 56 to F. 61, p. 59)
vertical, definition, 12
vesicles, seminal, 146
visceral, definition, 12
visceral cranium (facial bones), 73, 78
visceral muscle, 17 (F. 7, p. 15)
visceral nervous system, 159
visceral pericardium, 109 (F. 132, p. 108)
visceral peritoneum, 126
visceral pleura, 123 (F. 146, p. 120)
vocal folds, 121, see larynx (F. 150, p. 121)
volar, definition, 12
voluntary muscles, 17, 94
vomer, 80 (F. 93, p. 79)
white blood cells, 105 (F. 127, p. 106)
white matter of brain, 156
wisdom (third molar) teeth, 82 (F. 97, p. 80)
wrist bones, 34, 40 (F. 32, p. 39)
wrist joint, 42 (F. 32, p. 39; F. 37, p. 41)
xiphoid (ensiform) process, 67
zygoma, 78 (F. 90, p. 79)
zygomatic bones, 78 (F. 90, p. 79)

I think this book is going to make me
Throw up! (gag at least!)

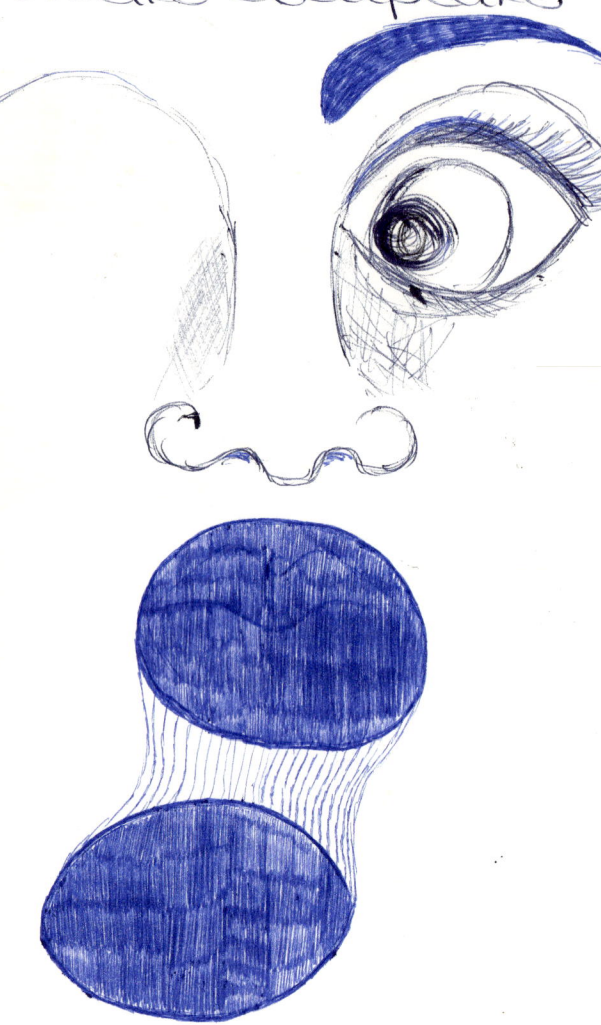

make a cake a cup cake.